COURAGE AFTER THE BATTLE

COURAGE AFTER THE BATTLE

THE STORY OF HOW ARMED FORCES PERSONNEL SURVIVE THEIR MENTAL AND PHYSICAL INJURY AFTER LEAVING THE ARMED FORCES

PETER JACKSON-LEE

BROWN DOG BOOKS

First published 2019

Copyright © Peter Jackson-Lee 2019

The right of Peter Jackson-Lee to be identified as the author of this work has been asserted in accordance with the Copyright, Designs & Patents Act 1988.

All rights reserved. No part of this book may be reproduced, stored in a retrieval system, or transmitted in any form or by any means, electronic, electrostatic, magnetic tape, mechanical, photocopying, recording or otherwise, without the written permission of the copyright holder.

Published under licence by Brown Dog Books and
The Self-Publishing Partnership, 7 Green Park Station, Bath BA1 1JB

www.selfpublishingpartnership.co.uk

ISBN printed book: 978-1-78545-344-1

Cover design by Kevin Rylands
Internal design by Andrew Easton

Printed and bound in the UK

CONTENTS

Acknowledgements	7
Introduction	8
Evacuation from the Battlefield	17
Transporting the Casualty to Hospital from the Battlefield	34
Battlefields Trauma	50
Amputation and Prosthetics	113
Facial Wounds, Face Masks, Deafness and Blindness	147
War Widows	178
Drugs, Alcohol, Prison, Homelessness and Depression	202
How it Affects the Family	221
Armed Forces Covenant and The Third (Charity) Sector	255
Invictus Games	272
List of Charities (August 2018)	284
Bibliography	356

ACKNOWLEDGEMENTS

I would like to thank the following people who have assisted me in putting together the wealth of information that has been used to product this book. I hope the contents will give the public an insight into the problems and hurdles that must be crossed by service personnel who have left the armed services through physical and or mental injury.

Dr Renata Gomes, Head of Research and Innovation at Blind Veterans UK, Surgeon General, Surgeon Vice Admiral Alasdair Walker OBE for pointing me in the direction of further information, Mary Moreland, Chairman of the War Widows Association of Great Britain, Nadine Muller, John Moores University, Liverpool, War Widows Project. Dr Emily Mayhew, Historian in Residence, Department of Bioengineering, Imperial College London who very kindly gave me some sound advice on research.

Not forgetting Elaine, my dearest wife for putting up with me whilst I researched and wrote the book in whatever spare time I had between working and other commitments. I was frequently missing for large periods, only to be found typing or off on further research trips to the various source locations.

Lastly, and by no means least, I would like to dedicate this book to all those men and women who have given their lives in the defence of this country and those who have survived injury to try and rebuild their life through very difficult times for themselves and their families.

INTRODUCTION

"Ever since the days of Agincourt people have had short memories of the war disabled when the fighting is over"

(Lady Apsley, Chairman of the British Legion
Woman's Section 1944)

For many people, a veteran is an old man with medals and a beret, who served in the Second World War and marches on Remembrance Sunday. The truth can sometimes be very different. We are now seeing a generation of men and women leave the services at a youthful age. Some have served their country on the frontline and suffered life-changing injuries. Others have returned to civilian life abruptly because of disciplinary problems or a failure to cope in their chosen career; others have returned to their 9-5 job after doing their bit as a reservist.

In the year to November 2013, 22,530 personnel left the Regular Armed Forces: 14,520 from the Army, 4,010 from the Royal Navy / Royal Marines and 4,000 from the Royal Air Force. On joining, young volunteers adopt an ethos of selfless service, a lifestyle far removed from that of the civilian, ready to go wherever they are ordered, totally committed to the task in hand, and ultimately prepared to give their lives for their brothers in arms and their mission. As a result, the argument goes, society has a duty to ensure that on leaving the military they are integrated successfully back into civilian society and suffer no disadvantage due to having served in the Armed Forces.

Most people have seen the numerous news stories from war torn areas, most recently Afghanistan and Iraq. You will have heard about service personnel being shot or severely injured by an IED (Improvised Explosive Device) or suicide bomber, to name but a few daily situations service personnel find themselves in within the battlefield or theatre of war. You may think theatre is an inappropriate word to use but this is a common reference to a battle or war zone within the military. The definition of a theatre of war can be described as *the entire land, sea, and air area that is or may become involved directly in war operations.*

Did you ever wonder what happens to the service personnel after this traumatic event? How they or their immediate family (husband, wife, children or parents) cope with the event? The following chapters will give you some indication as to how some of these traumatic life-changing events unfold from the initial incident in the battlefield, through to the medical treatment via a casualty evacuation from the battlefield and back to the UK medical centres, and finally rehabilitation in the hope that they can continue their lives.

To understand the trauma and complexity of the battlefield it is sometimes prudent to see how the person got to that stage and the need for a prosthetic arm or leg, and in some instances multiple prosthetics or other form of assistance. So, to understand how everything happens, I have started some chapters with a little bit of what can be described as a history lesson.

I have the opportunity to consider what happens should I be hit. The answer opens up a series of 50/50 possibilities. I will live or die. If I die, I will experience an afterlife or eternal nothingness. If I experience an afterlife, it will be heaven or hell. If I am hit and killed, my best hope is that it will be over in an instant with no pain. If I am hit and survive, a whole load of worrying possibilities arise: immense pain, disability and disfigurement. Whether I live or die, either way a whole lot of shit would be heading towards my wife and family. Processing all of these variables takes only a few seconds. And I do the only thing that will guarantee my sanity – I take these worries and I bury them deep into my subconscious to deal with on another day.
Extract from On Afghans Plains - Barry Alexander

The extract above gives you an insight into the day to day thoughts of a member of the Armed Forces, whether that be regular or reservist, whilst on deployment abroad or on a battlefield. As a civilian, you would not give a second thought about sitting in your garden writing a letter, Facebook comment, Instagram message or email to your loved one, when suddenly, and without warning, incoming mortars or artillery shells are about to seriously ruin your day and the possibility of going home minus a limb or disfigured for life or, worse, losing your life. This, however, is a daily occurrence for the many serving personnel on deployment in a war zone, whether that be in the main base, out on patrol in a hostile area or an observation post in outlying areas.

For a service person this is an all too familiar situation, if you substitute the garden for a tent or other bombed out or derelict building they are occupying, fully dressed and ready, with their weapon at arm's length 24 hours a day, half of them cleaning and maintaining kit whilst the other half are ready to do what they must do to defend the position and their friends at a moment's notice. All this whilst trying to look at a picture of their loves ones, husband, wife, parents, partners, children, no matter what age they are or if they are at university or married with their own children. They are still your flesh and blood, especially if your wife is expecting a child and it is close to the delivery, the service personnel are wondering if they would see them or their newborn again. They may even touch the faces on the photograph to try and imagine them touching that person's face as if in real life.

A tear may well be seen in such a sandy location (service metaphor for shedding a tear as they have sand or grit in their eye) whilst allowing themselves a moment of reflection of being back home with their loved one or family before they go out on patrol or a specified mission. Service personnel naturally have what is commonly called black humour and they make light of bad situations. This is a way of survival and although it seems unnatural or unwarranted and in poor taste, you try and live in their shoes for a while and you will see the rationale behind it. Other times, they may see another person, who may or may not be known to them or in their branch of the services, but the result is the same and normal service rivalry is forgotten. That person may require space whilst looking at his or her photos and they will be given space and understanding to be in his or her private thoughts. Service personnel are a rare breed in that they can be having a laugh one minute and the next either giving someone space for their thoughts or full-on diving into a life or death battle situation. They need this skill to survive and get on with life and the job.

COURAGE AFTER THE BATTLE

A lot of people sit there at home saying 'Oh I would do this and that', and they have had an infinite amount of time to think about that answer in a nice warm house and hot or alcoholic drink in their hand, possibly discussing the situation with friends and family. They may even like playing video games such as Call of Duty and think this is real life. Sorry to burst your bubble but this is a computer graphic, and in real life battles people die or do get blown to pieces; there is no second chance or reboot option in real life. A service person has milliseconds to make a decision that could see them remaining alive for a bit longer, saving another member of their service family or, even worse, taking a life.

Time and time again we see this situation with investigations which have been overseen by people who have no service background, or a basic background knowledge, and they are making these "informed" decisions in what is effectively hindsight and the letter of the law. This is just another version of the above but in more of an official or office 'cover your backside' environment, where people sit around the table discussing the finer points of law and bouncing ideas off each other as to what they would have done in that situation. Ironically, a clear majority of these people have never worn a uniform or held a weapon but there are a very small few who may have spent 'real time' in a real battle situation. Most consider themselves more experienced than the man or woman on the ground being shot at or blown up.

It is these people who try to justify their thoughts in a court of law and put the 'why did you do this?', 'why did you not follow this rule to the letter of the law?' type of arguments, all from the comfort of their armchair. Yes, there is also the Geneva Convention to consider, but not all those fighting, particularly terrorists, adhere to this and at times the service personnel are literally fighting for their lives with their hands tied behind their backs in this era of senior politicians and others covering their own back, not to mention the political correctness brigade.

"The Rules of Engagement brought about by the Geneva Convention are out of date because they only work when the Armies on both sides agree to abide by them, and take prisoners and treat them in a way that is humane. The new danger does neither, which is why the modern-day soldier feels like he is in a boxing match with a blinkered referee who is applying the Queensbury rules completely on him but ignoring the atrocities of the opponent."

COURAGE AFTER THE BATTLE

The above sentiment is from a former Royal Marine and it can be applied to many of the modern soldier's daily problems. He has this along with the IHAT (The Iraq Historic Allegations Team) and Northern Ireland Inquiries (Historic Enquiries Team) which are only looking at British Service Personnel and no other Terrorist Organisations. Some members of the IRA, which is seen as a Terrorist Organisation, or freedom fighters, as they like to call themselves, were given pardons following the 1998 Good Friday peace deal, while others were handed 'letters of comfort' (known as On The Run Letters) by Tony Blair, the then Prime Minister, promising they would never be prosecuted. All of this adds to the pressures service personnel are under and even many years after they have left, they can still be charged with an offence. We are again back to the armchair critics who were not there or have had an inordinate amount of time to think about their answer.

Image the following scenario. You are out on a routine patrol to keep the hearts and minds of the locals assured about you being there and ensuring their safety, when suddenly, all hell breaks loose. There is a loud sound, your hearing is impossible above the whistling inside your ear, you can see people's mouths move but not hear anything. The whole area is covered in dust and bits of debris flying around and you are completely disorientated. What do you do next?

The first thing to do is gather your thoughts quickly; assess where the fire or explosion has come from, is it the only threat or are there enemy shooting / waiting to shoot at you, are you in cover or is there any cover nearby? Is there a possibility that your possible route also contains another larger secondary device yet to explode on your exit route? Is everyone ok or are there injured, and what is the extent of their injuries, do they need a CASEVAC (Casualty Evacuation) and is the area safe for a CASEVAC to be taken to the rear areas for safe extraction to the medical facility?

This plus any number of other things go through a soldier's mind in a matter of seconds and this, along with the rest of the patrol's lives, depends on everyone doing what they should. If the threat or possible threat is known i.e. people shooting at you, can you take it out? You regroup and if the casualties are already being seen to - in most cases they will be looked after by the patrol medic - you can assess the next step. The patrol medic will administer treatment such as the application of tourniquets, dressings to cover the wounds, painkillers and intravenous drip (IV) lines with fluids. The other members of the patrol can also administer basic first aid, but they may be otherwise engaged and leave the medical side to the patrol medic.

If you are the casualty, this is obvious, you are thinking, 'Get me to medical assistance as soon as possible, preferably via a MERT (Medical Emergency Response Teams) Chinook helicopter'. You have come around after the initial attack and thought, 'Have I got all my bits or am I missing some?'. Alternatively, 'Have I got all my bits, but do they work or look the same as I viewed in the mirror this morning before the patrol?' A blast injury from direct or indirect exposure to an explosion can cause traumatic amputations or substantial soft tissue loss and neurovascular damage, which will possibly later result in limb loss due to tissue and other initially unseen damage from the explosives shock wave.

Once the casualty has been evacuated from the battlefield via a quad bike or other means to a safe as it can be location, the MERT team can come in and pick them up. Once inside the helicopter the casualty would get immediate top level medical treatment from an exceptionally dedicated team of doctors and medical staff. On many occasions, this team has been known to literally be the difference between life and death.

Once you arrive at the main camp you are then transferred to the main hospital team and operating theatres. Following on from this you are flown home, where you will be looked after in hospital for as long as it takes. At this point your relatives can come to see you and spend time with you whilst your rehabilitation starts.

Following on from any injuries, Operation Minimise is a Standard Operational Procedure (SoP) for the whole theatre of battle and any outline observation posts or bases. This operation prevents all communication via phone, Facebook, email etc. This is in force until the Emergency Contact (EC) and Next of Kin (NoK) of those who have been wounded, severely injured or unfortunately killed, has been officially informed.

They will inform them of the exact situation rather than a misinformed version via the afore-mentioned social media, TV, press or other communications systems. It is important that the EC or NoK get the news directly and as quickly as possible as this will be a massive shock to them to hear their loved one is injured but not severely, severely injured with the loss of a limb or other injury, or worst, killed.

So starts the long and painful road to rehabilitation and building their life again, which can be very traumatic and stressful. The above situation has happened many times throughout various conflicts and wars and the following chapters could very well be from any number of brave service personnel or their family who have found themselves in this situation.

Eighty-five percent of veterans think that after serving their country, there is not enough support, and some even feel completely forgotten, lost in the system that is civvy street.

In 1892, Rudyard Kipling wrote his famous poem 'Tommy', which includes the following lines:

We aren't no thin red 'eroes, nor we aren't no blackguards too, But single men In barricks, most remarkable like you;

An ' If sometimes our conduck Isn't all your fancy paints, Why; single men In barrIcks don't grow Into plaster saints;

While It's Tommy this, an' Tommy that, an' "Tommy; fall be'Ind",

But it's "Please to walk in front, sir", when there's trouble in the wind, There's trouble in the wind, my boys, there's trouble in the wind,

0 it's "Please to walk in front, sir", when there's trouble in the wind.

You talk o' better food for us, an' schools, an' fires, an' all: We'll wait for extry rations If you treat us rational.

Don't mess about the cook-room slops, but prove It to our face The Widow's Uniform is not the soldier-man's disgrace.

For it's Tommy this, an' Tommy that, an' "Chuck him out, the brute!"

But it's "Saviour of 'is country" when the guns begin to shoot; An' it's Tommy this, an'
Tommy that, an' anything you please; An' Tommy ain't a bloomin' fool -- you bet that Tommy sees!

Among other things a person leaving the services must contend with is the possibility of employment. A 2017 study from Barclays Bank revealed that the UK economy could suffer losses of up to £1.5bn in the next five years if service leavers are unable to find employment or are under-employed upon leaving the Armed Forces. The research calculates the direct and indirect contribution of the up to 85,000 personnel that are estimated to leave the military by 2021; a figure which is equivalent to the number of people currently employed in the UK creative, arts and entertainment sector. While many veterans make a successful transition to civilian employment, the study predicts that 10% will experience long-term unemployment, and that a further 12% will be sub-optimally employed where they are effectively under-utilised by employers.

On 24 November 1918, Prime Minister David Lloyd George gave a speech in Wolverhampton. He was the 'man who won the war' ~~had won~~ and he told the crowd that the work of the nation, the work of the people, the work of those who have sacrificed is not over yet. He said:

"Let us work together, what is our task? To make Britain a fit country for heroes to live in. I am not using the word 'heroes' in any spirit of boastfulness, but in the spirit of humble recognition of fact. I cannot think what these men have gone through. I have been there at the door of the furnace and witnessed it, but that is not being in it, and I saw them march into the furnace. There are millions of men who will come back. Let us make this a land fit for such men to live in. There is no time to lose. I want us to take advantage of this new spirit. Don't let us waste this victory merely in ringing joy bells."

These words were important. Not only because they constituted a promise from the Prime Minister to those who were returning from the horrors of the war and in the memory of those who would not return. But also, because this promise was in many respects the foundation stone of the Lloyd George coalition as it went to the polls, barely a month after the end of the war. A coalition between a radical Liberal PM and the Conservative Party (amongst others) had been understandable during the war. All sides were committed to refocusing the war effort and saw a greater role for the state in doing so. Conscription, for example, Lloyd George and his coalition allies were readier to consider than many Liberals. But what was their common purpose in peacetime?

In speeches such as this, he was laying claim to the notion that this shared spirit was one of reform. As Chancellor of the Exchequer he'd used pensions and National Insurance to commit the British state for the first time to directly addressing the poverty caused by old age and sickness. Now, as Prime Minister, he had no intention of relinquishing his reforming zeal. By the time he left office in 1922, it had amounted to little and does so in many respects to this day.

Veterans' Gateway
In November 2016, the Ministry of Defence announced £2 million of funding from the Covenant Fund for a one-stop service to better support British Armed Forces veterans in need. The service responds to calls from veterans' charities and groups for help in navigating the wide range of services and organisations set up to support those who have served in the Forces. The service will be the first point of contact for veterans and their families to access information, advice and support on a range of issues including healthcare, housing, and employment. It will allow information and services from partners to be accessed from one place and all enquiries will be followed up to ensure that veterans receive the right support.

The Veterans' Gateway will provide website, online chat, phone line and text message services available to any veteran, from anywhere in the world, 24 hours a day. Veterans can access face-to-face support through the Veterans' Gateway network of partners and organisations across the UK and overseas.

Website: www.veteransgateway.org.uk

Phone: 0808 802 1212

Free Military Mental Health Helpline
Funded by the Ministry of Defence and run with the charity Combat Stress, this free telephone line became active in early 2018 following an appeal by the Daily Mail and many former senior officers, and other former and service personnel.
0800 323 4444

EVACUATION FROM THE BATTLEFIELD

In today's battle environment the Tactical Medical Wing (TMW) of the Royal Air Force (RAF) was formed on 1 April 1996 and its role is to provide, support and supply medical services to all deployed personnel worldwide, whether on operations or on exercise. Headquarters (HQ) of the TMW is one of 13 Air Combat Service Support Units (ACSSUs) within 2 Group. It acts as the operational hub for all personnel of the RAF Medical Services (RAFMS).

Acting primarily in an enabling capacity the team provide a number of areas of support, such as:

The provision of Deployable Aeromedical Response Teams (DARTS) at 6 hours' notice to move.

Worldwide Aeromedical Evacuation (AE), including the transportation of highly infectious and/or critically ill patients. The RAF Aeromedical Evacuation team also plan the casualty's eventual movement back to the UK. Sometimes a casualty will be on the way to the UK within 48 hours of injury.

In a combat situation, there is the Medical Emergency Response Team (MERT). Between two teams, eight medics, their RAF Regiment Quick Reaction Force (QRF) team respond to Category A and B emergencies. They are the only medevac service to have doctors on board able to transfuse blood whilst in flight, and they have some of the most innovative techniques in the field at their disposal. The MERT exists to bring the emergency department to the wounded and follows on from the work on the ground by the other members of the patrol or observation post. MERT will be able to provide more advanced medical skills and techniques, administer stronger medication, transfuse blood products, and anaesthetise patients in a clean environment compared to the basic treatment that is available in the cold, wet, dusty, dirty battlefield.

The troops on the ground know that no matter where they are, and what is happening, MERT will fly in and do everything they can to ensure the casualty will get home in the best possible condition to their families. This is a massive morale boost for anyone in the field of battle knowing they will be in good hands should the worst happen.

The crews are initially called out from their main base, following a "Contact" radio call from the patrol, which will also give the number of casualties and their individual medical condition. The crews race to the helicopter, quite often with the basic information from the Contact Report and no information of what they are flying into. As updates come in on this very fluid situation, this will be relayed immediately to the crew as they travel towards the area of battle. As they arrive on scene, the tailgate begins to be lowered as the helicopter descends. This is to reduce the time on the ground and ultimately becoming a target themselves.

The casualties are immediately brought on board, usually in stretchers, when the medical team have a real idea as to what we are dealing with and there could be additional casualties since the *'Contact Report'* initially went out. This could be anything from gunshot wounds to limbs missing, bodies in bits. The teams immediately swing into action as soon as the casualty is onboard despite the dust and debris being kicked up by the downwash from the two enormous rotor blades blowing into the helicopter. The casualty, with open wounds, has had to go through this en-route to the Chinook, being carried on a stretcher or helped along, leaning on his friends for support.

The medical team inside the Chinook have to try to prevent the debris and dust getting into the body of the aircraft, the medical equipment or the patient by leaning over the patient until the Chinook has lifted off and the tailgate fully closed. The patients are sheltered by the medics' bodies as much as possible as others scramble over each other in the confined busy belly of the Chinook to carry out their part of the emergency treatment to save the life of the patient.

In addition to trying to assess the casualty in all the dust and debris as they come on board the helicopter, they will have to cope with the clothing and equipment restricting access to the patient to take vital signs. Communication is difficult between each of the medical team over the sound of the two engines almost right above them creating a large amount of noise. If you have ever been in or close to a Chinook, with its distinctive deep thud of the motor and blades as it is flying overhead at a distance, with that unmistakable distinctive sound, you will know what I mean.

When working in an exceptionally confined, very noisy space and more often working over other people to try and save the patient(s), some of whom may be foreign nationals from their respective armed forces or an innocent civilian, terrorist etc who does not understand English, a simple question such as 'Where is the pain?' becomes an international sign language trial to try to get the patient to understand and give the answer.

The need to take a pulse, assess breathing and even communicate easily with the patient is often impossible in the back of the helicopter. Unfortunately, in a battle situation, some of the injuries are fatal, and like any medical professional, the onboard medics find it difficult to admit they have lost this fight. They take it very personally, but they must concentrate on the other patients whilst in flight to ensure they make it back to the main base and into the operating theatre if needed.

Although the Chinook is effectively a fully equipped medical CASEVAC facility and emergency room with rotors, it would normally be accompanied by 2 Apache attack helicopters for protection. MERT has to (as a rule of thumb) land in a safe place out of contact and its only protection is a small QRF force on board for self-protection. There is always the danger of it being attacked by enemy forces, hence the airborne protection.

In one of many incidents, the Chinook took off as quickly as it had arrived on scene and it then flew right over a hidden machine gun nest. Bullets suddenly raked the helicopter, knocking out its stabiliser. Flying so low to the ground, with medics in the back struggling to sedate the wounded, there was no time to hand over to the co-pilot. Stunned but still conscious the pilot, Flt Lt Fortune, had just seconds to keep control of the aircraft. Fragments of metal and Perspex had ripped into his face, cutting a groove in his cheek. The medical team now have one additional casualty to look after, and he is flying their hospital at the same time. Through sheer skill and determination, he landed back at Camp Bastion with blood streaming down his cheeks. Upon landing, an ambulance was scrambled to meet him but to everyone's amazement he walked off the helicopter to receive his stitches. In October 2010 Flt Lt Fortune was awarded the Distinguished Flying Cross (DFC) along with Flight Lieutenant Timothy Pollard for their actions in Afghanistan. Flt Lt Fortune said:

"Well, for a split second my head was forced back and when my eyes opened again confusion reigned, because I thought, well, I can see cracks, I can see splattered blood, I can smell burning, you know, what's happened? Then I saw the hole in the windscreen and I thought, uh huh, I think I've just been hit in the head! Then came a feeling of elation, of 'I think I've just been shot in the head and I've survived.' Well, good stuff!"

Unfortunately, this incident is not rare and the aircrew, medical staff and accompanying QRF team have been hit on several occasions and a few have been forced to carry out emergency landings whilst carrying their patients who needed immediate hospital treatment. In these cases, another helicopter is despatched and the casualties and crew are taken back to safety. The aircraft may have to be destroyed, which will not only reduce the available aircraft but increase the stress and hours on the existing aircraft until a replacement can be flown out from the UK, usually inside a large transport plane. The Chinook will then be re-assembled and flight checked before it is allowed onto the flight line for operational duties.

The MERT team have been called any number of things, but flying angels seems to fit them the best. I am sure that the many people, both military and civilian, who have come under their excellent care are more than grateful for them being there, and having the skills and professionalism to do what they have done. That is, saving lives time and time again.

COURAGE AFTER THE BATTLE

Royal Anglian Regiment Practicing Casualty Evacuation from the Battlefield (Crown Copyright / MoD)

MERT Extraction with Casualty (Crown Copyright / MoD)

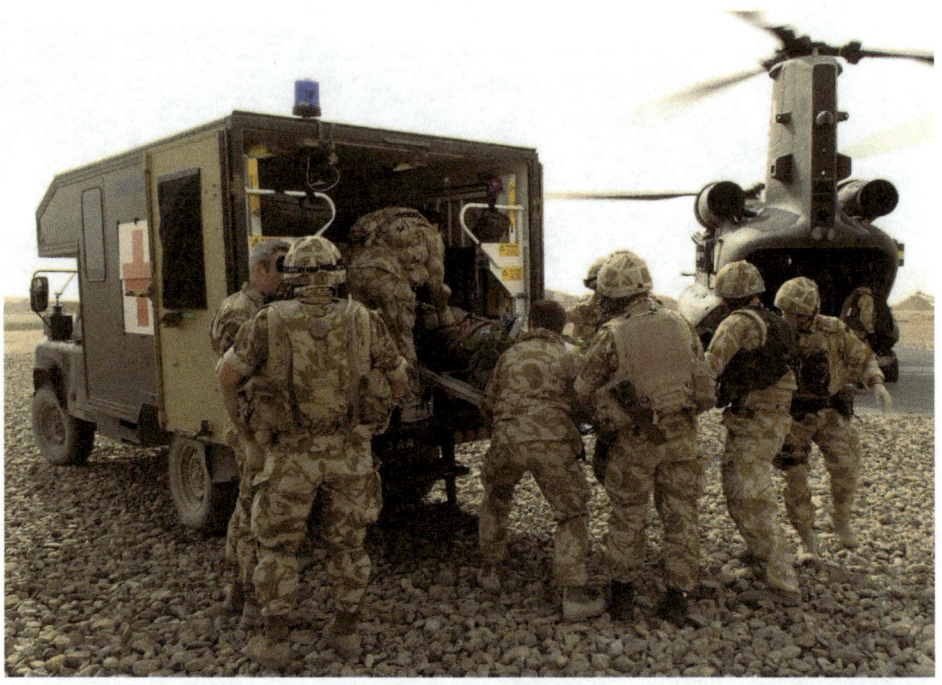

Loading a Casualty into the Field Ambulance from the Chinook (Crown Copyright / MoD)

A Brief History of the Royal Army Medical Corps (RAMC)

The brave men and women who usually go out as a patrol medic or work in other similar fields which require a medic will usually come from the RAMC. The only exception to this is the Royal Navy and Royal Marines, who will normally utilise a Naval Medical Assistant (MA) and, in the case of the Royal Marines, the MA will be commando trained by their successful completion of the All Arms Commando Course, which is a reduced version of the Royal Marines basic six-month course. The All Arms Course is seen as an additional course to the basic training received from the course participant regimental basic training. The successful completion of the All Arms Course allows the participant to wear the coveted Green Beret, which can then be worn with their respective regimental cap badge and become fully integrated with the Royal Marines Commando units.

The Royal Army Medical Corps (RAMC) was created on a regimental basis and continues to do so in the same way today. The family tree, so to speak, was comprised of a medical officer with a warrant officer as his assistant. The regimental basis of appointment for medical officers continued until it was abolished in 1873. It was in Queen Anne's reign that the Duke of Marlborough instituted what were known as "marching hospitals" and "flying hospitals." You may say this was a regiment that was working before its time. It was not until around 1812 in the Duke of Wellington's time that an organised medical service was born.

In 1857 the Medical Staff Corps was reorganised into the Army Hospital Corps, a title it held until 1884. It was in 1898 that all ranks became fused together into a single Corps. On the 23 June 1898, Queen Victoria gave the Royal Warrant to the Royal Army Medical Corps.

The RAMC has a most distinguished record, both in the practice of medicine and in the gallantry displayed by its members. In the 3 major wars (Boer, WW1 & WW2), the RAMC dealt with 14 million casualties, was awarded 14 Victoria Crosses (two with Bars), one George Cross, 630 Distinguished Service Orders, 1,806 Military Crosses, 464 Distinguished Conduct Medals, 2,375 Military Medals and 16 George Medals.

The price was not small as the Roll of Honour contains 1,180 officers and 8,165 soldiers who died in the service of their country.

History of the Cap Badge

RAMC Badge (MoD)

COURAGE AFTER THE BATTLE

'The Rod'
The rod and serpent goes back to ancient Greece and a man called Aesculapius who lived around 1256 BC. He was a doctor of such renown that legend tells that he was able to bring the dead back to life. Pluto, the god of the underworld, was so appalled at not gaining the souls of the dead that he complained to Jupiter, the head of all gods. Jupiter obliged by slaying Aesculapius with a thunderbolt.

'The Serpent'
After his death Aesculapius himself became a god who was worshipped in hundreds of temples. The temples quickly became places of healing for the sick and were used as the first hospitals. Within each one there was a circular pit that contained a species of snake that was harmless, but whose forked tongue was believed to have healing properties, which is where the origins of the snake originate. A somewhat strange symbol until you look into the history and reasons for it being there. Ever since those days the Rod and the Serpent have been used as a symbol of medicine throughout the world.

'In Arduis Fidelis'
The motto underneath the cap badge can be translated from Latin to "Faithful in Adversity". It sums up the character and the ideals of the RAMC and is applicable in both war and peace time. The medical profession will always show a steady nerve during periods of pressure and this can be found in the hospital as much as it can be found on the battlefield.

    A footnote to this is by no means an individual case, as similar situations would have happened in the battlefield, both historically and in the future. Whilst with A company 40 Commando in the Falklands, we found ourselves in the middle of a minefield. Two men were injured by mines in the frozen ground, one lost his foot and the other later lost his lower leg. On both occasions, the Naval Medical Assistant (MA) attended to the casualties, knowing the frozen ground was the only thing protecting them and us from further mines being detonated.

    The mines were in what can only be described as 'very much danger in close proximity', but their patient was the priority. Some may think it was foolish to attend to the casualty whilst we stood there waiting for a CASEVAC. Their patient was the priority and they survived. You also have to consider it was the middle of the night, we were moving to the start line for Mt Harriet as reserve unit to 42 Commando, and we had a timetable to keep on this live operational task.

A Historical Review of the Treatment of War Wounds in the Battlefield

The need for surgical care of wounded in the battlefield over the past 250 years, and particularly during the 20th century, and developments in military trauma care for musculoskeletal injuries have greatly influenced civilian emergency medicine. The history of military trauma care must be understood in terms of the wounding power of weapons causing the injury and how the surgeon understood the healing process. The most basic problem during wartime has been how to transport the wounded to care or in the early years, to transport the medical teams and stretcher bearers to the wounded.

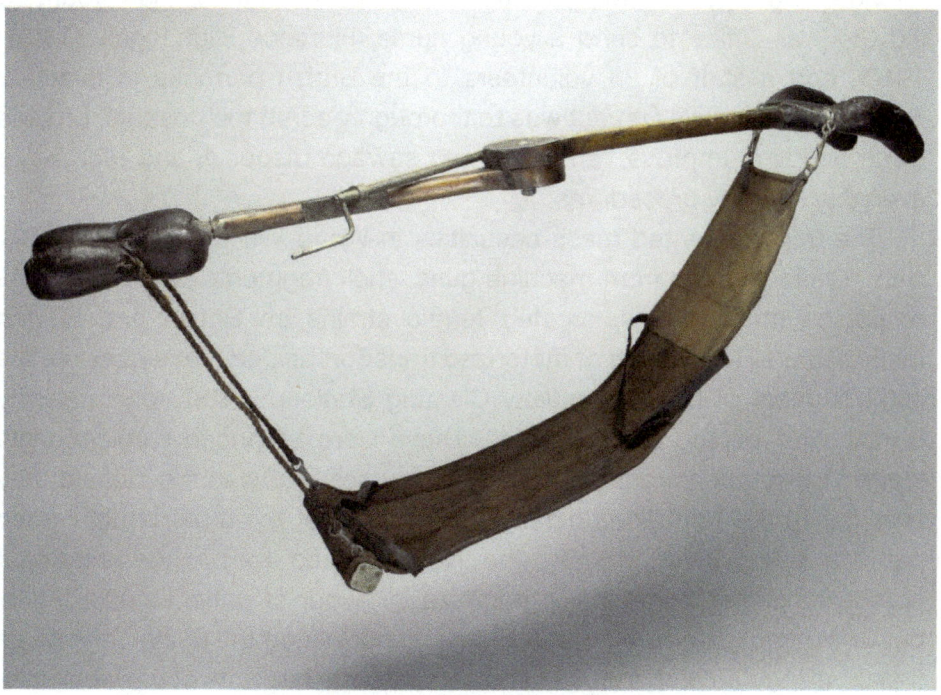

Photo Narrow Trench Stretcher (Science Museum)

During the American Revolutionary War, surgeons from the British and American sides emphasized conservative care. John Hunter (1728–1793), the Surgeon General of the British army, directed physicians to resist aggressive debridement in smaller wounds. Wine was applied typically to minor burns, and hog lard to full-thickness burns. John Jones (1729–1791), a veteran of the French and Indian Wars (1754–1763) and Professor of Surgery in King's College, New York, advised surgeons to delay primary wound closure and apply nothing but dry, soft lint to recent wounds; which is generally the best application through the whole course of the cure. Bullets were removed only if within easy reach of the surgeon. If a wound had to be closed, a piece of onion was placed in the cavity before closure, and the wound reopened in 1 to 2 days. As in the past, colonial physicians saw the development of pus a few days after injury as a sign of proper wound digestion.

The Crimean War (1854–1855) revealed a stark contrast between the battlefield care provided by the French, with their expert organization and system of light ambulances, and the poorly organized British Medical Services. Outrage over the poor treatment offered to the British wounded led the War Office to send a young nurse, Florence Nightingale (1820–1910), and a staff of 38 volunteers to the British barracks in Istanbul, Turkey. Nightingale's first act was to thoroughly scrub the hospital, provide clean bedding, improve ventilation and sewage disposal, and reorganize everyday sanitary procedures.

The unprecedented mass casualties in World War One (1914–1919), with horrific wounds from machine guns, shell fragments, and the effects of poison mustard gas, created terrific strains on British and French medical units. The advent of motorized transport helped make possible the establishment of British Casualty Clearing Stations (CCS) approximately 6 to 9 miles behind the front lines. These were advanced surgical units, staffed by surgeons, anaesthetists, and nurses and was the closest they ever got to the front line. Increasingly, instead of the most badly injured patients being given priority, the time required to provide treatment compelled British surgeons to prioritize in favour of patients with critical but less complicated wounds. A British manual listed the goals of triage as first conservation of manpower and secondly the interests of the wounded.

I realise that most people say 1914-1918 but the 1919 date refers to the year when the Treaty of Versailles was signed. This was the peace treaty drawn up by the nations who attended the Paris Peace Conference and officially ended the state of war between Germany and the Allied Powers when it was signed on 28th June 1919. Some war memorials also feature the dates 1914-1921, although this is less common. On 25th August 1921, the United States of America signed a separate peace treaty with Germany, the Treaty of Berlin.

Of all the severe injuries recorded in battle, none are of more frequent occurrence or of more serious consequence than compound fractures. During World War One the death rate from battlefield fractures of the femur was approximately 80%. Medics and stretcher bearers were blindfolded during training sessions so that they would be ready to apply the splint in total darkness. By 1915, better immediate management of femur fractures had reduced the mortality rate to approximately 20%. The major change in the evaluation of wounds during the Second World War involved the timing of closure. In World War One, surgeons learned the value of delayed primary closure in aiding recovery and fighting infection. Cultures would be the main determinant of whether a wound was ready for closure.

However, it has not always been that efficient to get a wounded soldier from the battlefield and onwards to the medical assistance they urgently need. During World War One, many types of stretcher were tried, pre-supposing the injured man was able to crawl back to his trench, or through the sheer bravery of his men and the stretcher bearers, be brought back to the trenches under cover of darkness or enemy fire.

One such stretcher was the Miller Stretcher, which was a collapsible system with pneumatic tyres which were a twin wheeled support for the stretcher itself. This system was enhanced by Lt Colonel O.W.A. Elsner in 1917. Another was the chair stretcher, which is exactly as you imagine, a stretcher which has a portion at one end in an upright position.

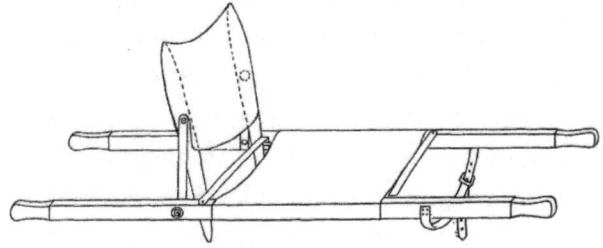

Chair Stretcher (Journal Royal Army Medical Corp 1915 25: 350-351)

The US Army Medical Department was in the process of reorganizing based on experiences of World War Two when the Korean War (1950–

1953) began. New Mobile Army Surgical Hospital (MASH) units were developed rapidly to provide resuscitative surgical care within 10 miles of the front lines. Helicopter ambulance companies supported the MASH, allowing treatment of patients within 3 to 12 hours of wounding. Mortality from all wounds decreased to a low of 2.4%, with mortality from abdominal wounds decreasing to 8.8%.

In Korea, combat medics worked effectively to resuscitate wounded before they were transported by helicopter or truck. Pressure dressings were applied as a first resort to control bleeding; guidelines stated tourniquets should be used only if pressure dressings were not sufficient. Fractures were splinted and wounded extremities immobilized. The medic may have begun antibiotic therapy if the casualty could not be transported for 4 to 5 hours. Wounds with massive soft tissue damage were covered with occlusive dressings or a mesh graft. Innovations included increasingly sophisticated vascular repair and treatment of hypovolemic shock.

Improvements in medical evacuation technology and organization, particularly the use of helicopters, again played a major role for US forces in Vietnam (1962–1974). Medics splinted and bandaged the wounded patient, frequently radioing the hospital and warning of his arrival and diagnosis. Helicopter evacuation minimized the use of morphine, eliminating an additional complication of the morphine masking the pain when the doctor wanted to know where the pain was and delaying the overall treatment and diagnosis. Mortality from abdominal wounds declined to 4.5%. Most soldiers wounded in Vietnam were delivered from the battlefield to fixed hospitals with the capacity to provide definitive treatment, eliminating the need for multiple transfers and levels of care.

The nature of wounds sustained by service members in Iraq and Afghanistan was transformed by suicide bombers and Improvised Explosive Devices (IEDs) which have contributed to limb amputations as a result of massive tissue damage from explosives. In Iraq and Afghanistan, resuscitation begins on the battlefield (Level I) and continues during transport. Tourniquets and advanced hemostatic dressings, such as HemCon®(HemCon Medical Technologies, Inc, Portland, OR) and QuikClot™ (Z-Medica, Newington, CT), are also used in the field. Depending on battle conditions, the wounded may reach a Level II or Level III facility in 30 to 90 minutes. Care at Level II facilities is limited to damage control, such as the placement of vascular shunts and stabilization, whereas Level

III facilities can provide definitive repair of arterial and venous injuries using autologous vein, with a goal of definite repair of vascular injury before evacuation from Iraq. Once at the Level IV or V facilities, wounds are evaluated and definitive treatment of injuries occurs.

Surgical Techniques and Technology
In both World Wars and Korea, artillery was the deadliest threat to soldiers. In Vietnam, because the enemy had relatively little heavy weaponry, most injuries were caused by machine gun fire, mines, and booby traps. As a consequence, the rate of major amputations as a percentage of all battle injuries actually increased to 3.4% from 1.4% in Korea and 1.2% in World War One. Blast injuries, often from beneath the injured soldier, caused deep penetration of foreign material into the thigh and often hips and knees. After battlefield evacuation, usually by helicopter, surgeons evaluated the wound, and the decision to amputate was made by an orthopaedic specialist. The open-flap amputation was the preferred procedure, with delayed closure, although the circular method also was allowed. Amputation was performed at the most distal point, with all nonviable tissue debrided. Although experience from previous wars and official recommendations called for continuous skin traction, a 1970 study of 300 amputees indicated only 44% had been treated with some form of skin traction.

In today's military, enhanced body armour and modern resuscitation have increased survival rates for soldiers with blast wounds that would previously have been fatal. This positive development poses a challenge for surgeons treating the wounded from Afghanistan and Iraq, particularly in the realm of limb salvage. The care of patients who have sustained IED wounds is complex; trauma, burns, blood loss, devitalized tissue, and embedded fragments of the explosive along with rocks, dirt, glass, and debris can be present. Damage control resuscitation performed by military surgeons recognizes that a successful outcome depends on more than merely treating the wound. Blood chemistry needs to be stabilized and hypothermia must be prevented, in addition to controlling bleeding, removing foreign bodies, debridement, and fracture fixation.

Current guidelines emphasize the need to preserve maximum length of limb and tissue for later preservation. The patient undergoes thorough surgical debridement within 2 hours of injury and re-debridement every 48 to 72 hours through evacuation. No viable tissues are removed, and the level of soft tissue injury determines the amputation level. Wounds are left open through transport; no skin traction is used because of the relatively short evacuation time, although negative pressure dressings have been used at sites along evacuation routes. Once in hospital, the patient is evaluated, and debridement is continued until the wound is ready for delayed closure. A now greatly expanded rehabilitation program, with the aid of prosthetic devices using digital technology, assists amputees in their return to civilian life as far as possible.

Blood Transfusion

The British Army began routine use of blood transfusion for treatment of combat casualties in 1916, when surgeons performed direct transfusions on patients whose conditions were considered desperate. Of the 19 casualties it was tried on, 15 died. Despite the inauspicious start, surgeons with the British Second Army routinely performed direct transfusions on patients using a syringe cannula technique. Despite the lessons of World War One, many surgeons still believed shock was caused by inadequate arterial pressure rather than inadequate capillary perfusion. Although the British had entered the war with large quantities of blood and plasma, and Charles Drew (1904–1950) of the American Red Cross had developed an international blood collection and distribution system for the Blood for Britain campaign of 1940, the US Army had no blood banks, and when blood was given, it was only in small amounts (100–150 millilitres). After heavy losses in North Africa, military surgeons recommended a blood bank be instituted. The system was implemented rapidly, and doubtless saved thousands of lives but was completely dismantled by the onset of the Korean War.

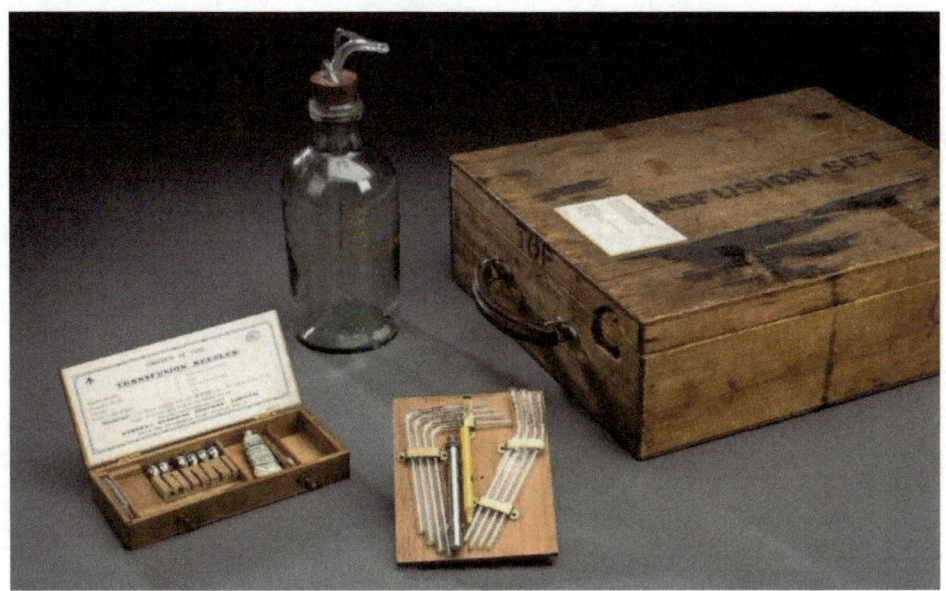

WW1 Blood Transfusion Equipment (Science Museum)

Chinook on Approach on UK Exercise in NW England (Author)

Battlefield Tourniquet Dr Timothy Hodges

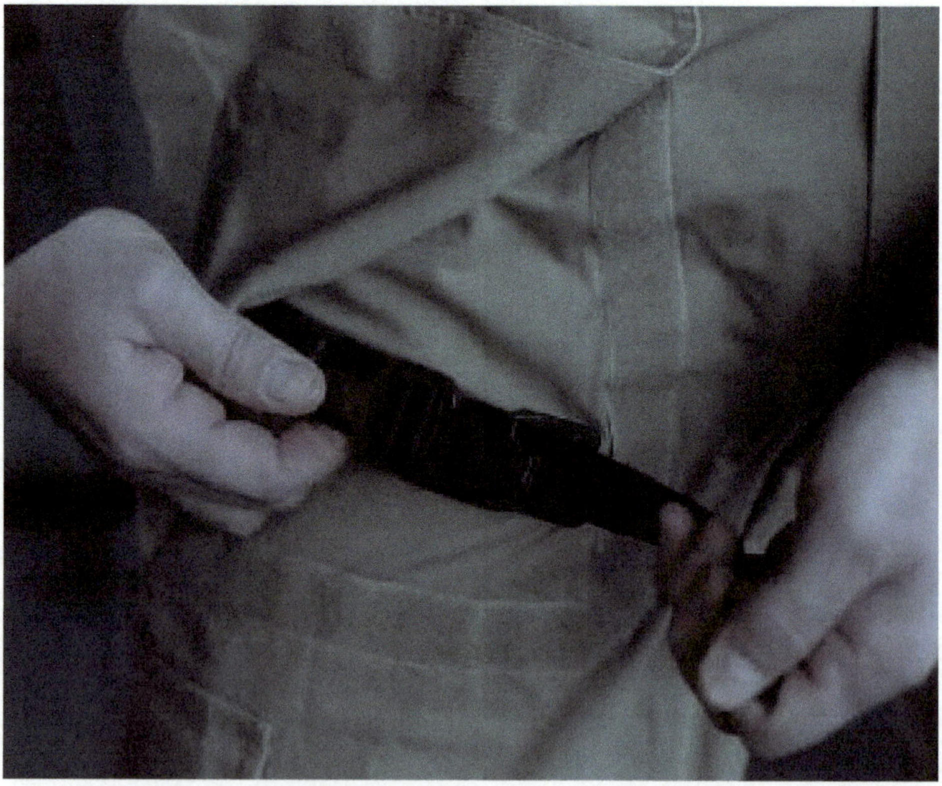

Battlefield Tourniquet in use Dr Timothy Hodges

COURAGE AFTER THE BATTLE

Battlefield Quick Clot in use Dr Timothy Hodges

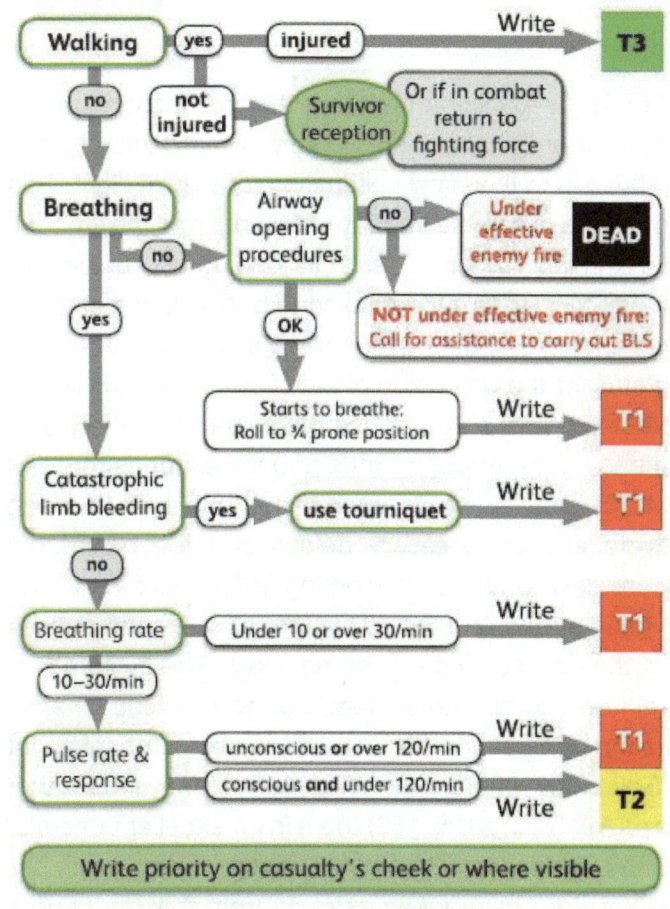

Casualty Aide Memoire Dr Timothy Hodges / MoD

TRANSPORTING CASUALTY TO HOSPITAL FROM THE BATTLEFIELD

During World War One, injured personnel were transported back to Britain on trains, fleets of ambulances and lorries to the docks, then in ships and then onward by train to their final destination, usually at night. This was so the public were not able to see the tragedy unfolding from the amount of men and their injuries returning home. To assist in loading and unloading the injured personnel and allowing them to be taken to hospital, one of these systems is described in the journal of the Royal Army Medical Corps (1915 24: 280-281) as an "Apparatus for the Unloading of Sick from Hospital Ships".

The system is designed to reduce the suffering of the wounded soldier as he has already gone through battle and the arduous route home. It was thought that the system would enable the ship to be unloaded quickly and thus avoid any unnecessary delays and the minimum amount of stretcher-bearers, who would be working in far less strenuous conditions. The system used a tried and tested system of wires and pulleys which had been used in the naval service for some years. The system is designed so that any strain or slack in the system, due to the vessel rising and falling with the tide and general harbour conditions, would be taken into account.

In the Bradshaw Lecture on Wounds in War (Journal Royal Army Medical Corps 1916 26; p125-152) there is an excellent description of how a casualty finally arrives at a treatment centre, having been shot or blown up in the battlefield. I have taken extracts from this long and explanatory detailed lecture, which are shown below:

COURAGE AFTER THE BATTLE

Still, the fact remains that, owing to their partially subterranean life, men are usually covered thickly with either mud or dust at the time when they are wounded, and that their comrades who help them are in a similar condition. When a man in one of the advanced trenches is hit and falls, he lies in mud or dust, or else, as during last winter, in muddy water a foot or more in depth. Close at hand, or else perhaps some hundred yards distant, the regimental medical officer has prepared a larger and deeper excavation commonly known as a " dug-out," and to this the wounded man will walk if he is able. If unable to walk he must be carried, but be cannot be carried on the usual stretcher, because it is too long to pass along the narrow trench, which is rendered tortuous by the many "traverses." Under these circumstances he may be carried sitting on sacking slung from a pole, if he is well enough to help himself, or else he may be taken on a "trench stretcher", which is much shorter than the usual stretcher and is a very simple and ingenious invention which has been of great service. His wound is not infrequently dressed by his muddy and dusty comrades if it is accessible to them, and in any case, it is dressed in the dug-out if not before. From here the patient has now to be transferred to the first-aid post, which is established by a section of a field ambulance at some place which is as much sheltered from fire as may be, half a mile or more in the rear. Access to this is generally obtained by passing along a "communication trench", which may be six or eight feet deep, and more or less muddy or wet. The first-aid post is usually above ground, but may be ·in a "dug-out" or in a cellar. The patient is not detained here longer than absolutely necessary, but is transferred by a horse drawn vehicle or on a wheeled stretcher to the main field ambulance, a ·mile or two further back. Here are either tents or buildings which have been adapted for use, and here fresh dressings and food and much-needed rest on stretchers are all provided. The wounded man is now in comparative safety, and if his injury is slight and there is no crowd of wounded, he may remain here for some hours. If, however, his wound is serious or dangerous, or if a battle is in progress, he is taken in a motor ambulance to the "casualty clearing station", a very few miles further back, and usually placed so as to be just out of the range of ordinary shell-fire.

On many other occasions, after a fight in the open, badly wounded men have been left lying between the opposing trenches, because any attempt to rescue them at once drew the fire of the enemy, and might easily have resulted in the death of the patient as well as of his would-be rescuers. In such circumstances, after nightfall, men will crawl in even with badly smashed limbs, and in other cases they are brought in by stretcher-bearers at very great risk.

In addition to bullets, an immense number of other forms of missiles have been employed, so that wounds have presented the utmost variety. It is not possible or necessary to describe in detail all the forms of shells, but in order to understand the nature of wounds it must be realized that shells differ immensely in their structure and in the way in which they produce injury.

   (1) Shrapnel shells of all kinds and sizes are characterized by the fact that they contain some two hundred and fifty to four hundred round bullets of lead, which is in some shells soft, but in others is hardened by various agents.

   (2) "High explosive" shells vary in weight from a few pounds to about a ton, and they consist of a thick iron case containing in a central cavity a violent explosive charge.

   (3) Bombs, hand grenades, rifle grenades, trench mortars, etc., are all characterized by a shell case of iron or other metal containing a relatively large charge of a high explosive. In the German projectiles this is always tri-nitro-toluene.

Nothing is more striking than the immense amount of destruction wrought by even quite small pieces of a shell burst by a large charge of a high explosive, for the wound in the tissues may be ten times as large as the missile. Thus, I have seen a man in whom a piece of shell not so big as the end of the little finger tore a large wound in the liver and then rent completely away the whole of the hepatic flexure of the colon, while in the limbs I have seen wounds as large as a clenched fist caused by quite small fragments, *which evidently mainly owed· their power of destruction to the extraordinary velocity with which they travelled, as well as to their jagged edges*

The truth of this may be demonstrated on any limb shattered by a bullet, or a fragment of a high velocity shell perforating it, for it will be found on examination that the missile has not only shattered the tissues in the line of its flight, but that the divulsive force has separated the fascia from the skin and split the muscles from each other along their intermuscular planes. The effect of the injury may, indeed, spread up and down a great part of the length of the limb, and vessels may ·be burst and extravasation of blood may be found far from the obvious track of the missile.

Below is a series of illustrations showing the system for Transferring Wounded from Ship to Shore once they had reached home waters and started their route to hospitals.

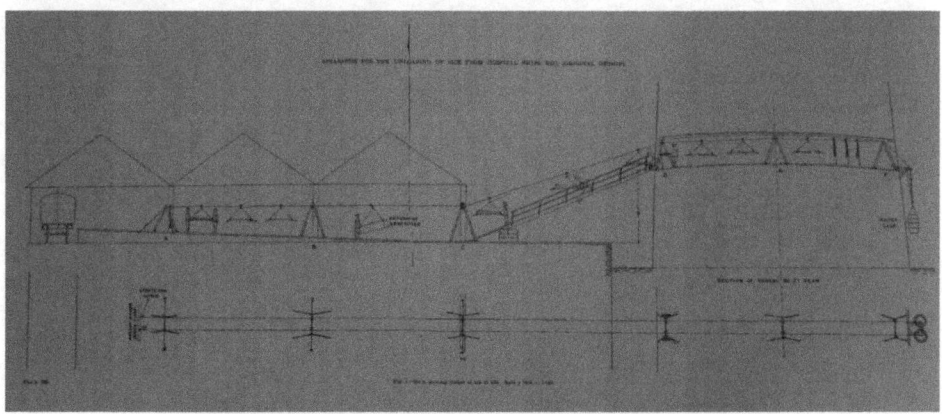

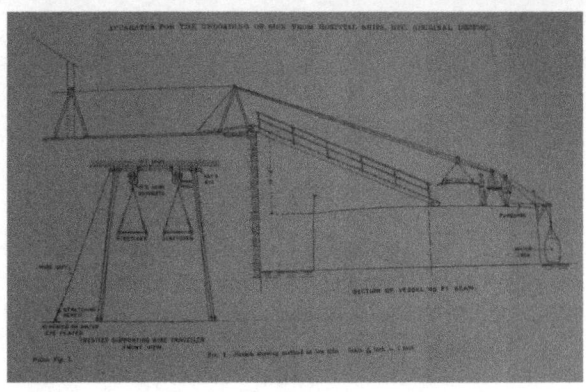

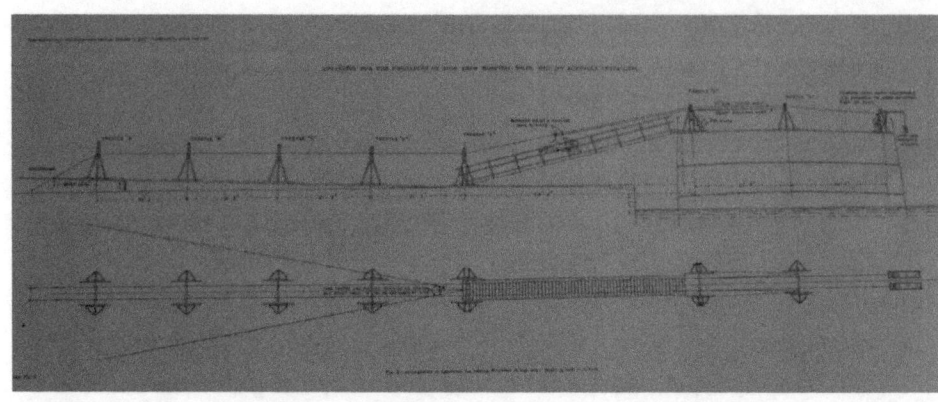

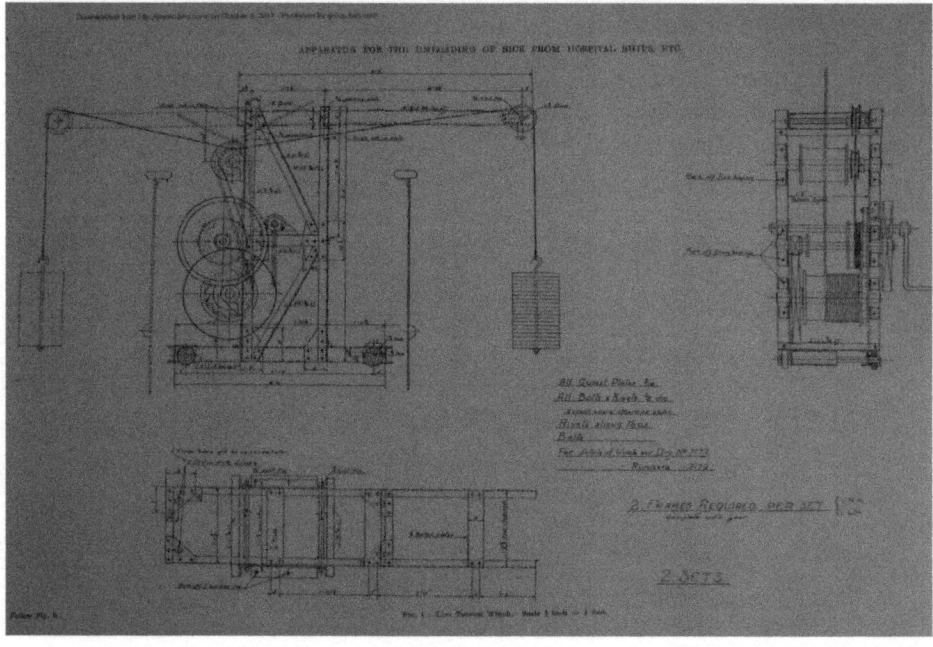

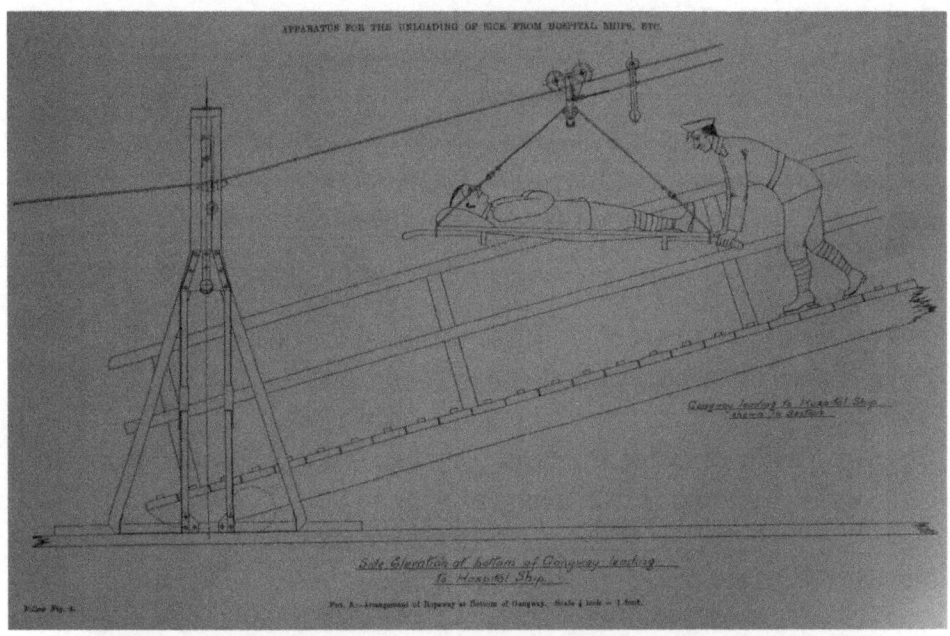

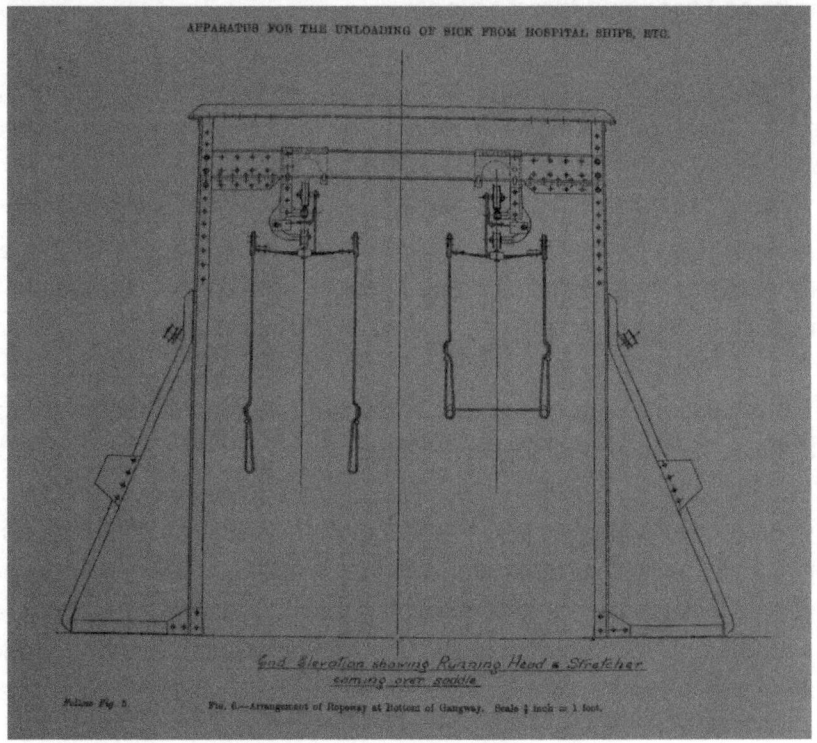

Transferring Wounded from Ship to Shore
(Journal Royal Army Medical Corps 1915 24; 280-281)

During World War Two, the methods of transportation of the wounded had changed dramatically and there was more likelihood that the casualty would not die from their injuries or sustained time to get the right assistance. Given the vast expanse of the war, compared to World War One, let alone the addition of aircraft to the world stage, many aircraft and helicopters were used and the system of evacuation was still in its infancy.

Light Aircraft
L5 - Flying jeep or Stinson - A single-seater mono plane with a low speed and requirement for 350 yards to take off and land

Tiger Moth - Two-seater Bi-Plane with the rear cockpit converted to a coffin-like compartment with a hinged back lid

Medium Aircraft
Anson – A low wing two engine monoplane with a capacity to have four sitting or one lying and three sitting

C64 Norseman – A high winged single engine aircraft with a capacity of three stretchers on the right-hand side of the cockpit in tiers, plus two sitting

C47 Dakota – An aircraft that will be familiar to most people for this era. A twin-engine monoplane with a capacity for 18 stretchers in three tiers (9 on each side) plus 5 sitting

C36 Commando – Larger than the Dakota with a capacity of 24 stretchers in four tiers, 12 on each side, plus 10 sitting.

In the interim between the two World Wars, the concept of the basic field medical unit, the field ambulance, was that of a cumbersome organization, inadequately mechanized and heavily laden with medical equipment which was suitable only for trench warfare, and therefore incapable of completing its role in the current crisis. The first campaign in Flanders drove this fact home, and in the deserts and battlefields of following wars, this fact was emphasized in the need for mobility. To this aim, it was found that the main field ambulance should have the ability to split into smaller units and move forward with the advancing forces. It is with this they also required the additional casualty evacuation process. The managing senior officers of the day also found it necessary to have a progressive modification of medical establishments, until finally the optimum· compromise between compactness and utility was realized in the organization of the parachute medical units.

In 1943 the first trials of penicillin were made in North Africa during the Sicilian landings. As supplies became plentiful, penicillin was used increasingly in the forward treatment of wounds. When the time came for the invasion of Normandy in 1944, the medical personnel were more than happy with this new treatment and had an abundance of knowledge on it being administered to the casualty. Even in the grim weeks of the D-Day beachhead, the majority of casualties had their first injection of penicillin within a few hours of being wounded and had maintenance doses during treatment and on the way to England. Later, when the Army broke out, penicillin administration was carried out during the whole phase of advance across Europe, regardless of movement and distance, with the same regularity as in a civilian hospital.

The Royal Centre for Defence Medicine (RCDM) Clinical Unit is based at the Queen Elizabeth Hospital Birmingham (QEHB) and is the primary receiving unit for all military patients from overseas. In addition to operational casualties the hospital also accepts non-operational casualties from around the world and routine military referral. The hospital works in partnership with the University Hospitals Birmingham NHS Foundation Trust (UHBFT) and a number of other NHS hospitals in the Birmingham area, and the focus is on the needs of the patient and their immediate family. The multi-disciplinary team, both military and civilian, combine the skills, experience, and training of a wide variety of professionals to individually tailor the care needed.

The Royal Centre for Defence Medicine
(Formerly Defence Medical Rehabilitation Centre – Headley Court)
Defence Medical Rehabilitation Centre (DMRC) had been located on the site of Headley Court, Epsom, Surrey for over 60 years and has seen many changes in its time. Originally founded as RAF Headley Court after the Second World War, for the treatment of injured RAF Aircrew, it became part of the Joint Medical Command (JMC). With a staff of over 360 service

and civilian personnel, it provided a range of rehabilitation services from outpatients through residential courses for those with sports, exercise and industrial injuries up to those with complex life-changing trauma injuries including amputation and brain injury.

DMRC is the Services rehabilitation facility and the wide skill base of its personnel allows for the treatment of the most complex of rehabilitation cases, offering support to the Regional Rehabilitation Units and forming an integral part of the Defence Medical Rehabilitation Programme. DMRC has access to all manner of specialists in rehabilitation with on-site consultants, physiotherapists, remedial instructors, occupational therapists, speech and language therapists, social workers, prosthetics, podiatrists, a psychologist and a cognitive therapist. It has 5 gymnasiums, a large hydrotherapy pool to support the clinical departments and the new H4H swimming pool. The medical records department, workshops, supply and administration staff all support DMRC's clinical role. In addition to this it also contains the Joint Services School for Exercise Remedial Instructors.

In April 2001 it was decided that Birmingham would accept the worldwide aero medical evacuation of military patients requiring acute hospital admission or urgent out-patient review. This partnership between the Ministry of Defence and the Queen Elizabeth Hospital Birmingham (QEHB) which is a NHS, Royal Army Medical Corps, Royal Navy Medical Service and RAF Medical Services hospital in the Edgbaston area of Birmingham, situated very close to the University of Birmingham. The hospital, which cost £545 million to construct, and was opened in June 2010. replaces the Queen Elizabeth Hospital and Selly Oak Hospital. The NHS Trust has quickly established itself as one of the best polytrauma medicine centres in the UK.

Birmingham was chosen by the Department of Health not only because of its reputation as a world renowned medical university, its innovative research and practices but also because of the diversity of treatment and expertise available. Amongst the five hospitals in and around Birmingham that military personnel may use, it has the added convenience of good road and rail links and Birmingham Airport on the door step.

In 2001, when Birmingham was chosen for the receipt and treatment of military patients, the contract was set up for 30-40 aero meds per month. In 2006/07, the numbers arriving monthly at QEHB exceeded this figure with 170 patients arriving in the month of July 2007 alone. It soon became clear that more support resources and a higher visual military presence should be put in place to increase the administration, practical and welfare support to the military casualties.

Improved military staffing at RCDM in support of the NHS staff was the answer. This included bringing military nurses onto the main trauma ward. The majority of military patients are admitted to this ward (because of the nature of their injuries) and the NHS Trust tries to keep military personnel together so long as it is clinically safe to do so. These extra staff produce the visible military effect ensuring patients feel more comfortable to talk and, of course, use military black humour to assist in the healing process.

One unique additional resource placed at RCDM are the Military Liaison Officers (MLO). These are Warrant Officers from the deployed brigades who are deployed to Birmingham for the duration of the operational tour. They provide the vital links between family, rear parties, (those left at the main UK camp carrying out day to day duties and not on deployment) and deployed commanders in the field. The commanders will relay any information to the casualty's troop or section on the health of the casualty. This to a degree aids morale as they will know their "brother" or "sister" is doing well and being looked after.

The medical care provided at QEHB is second to none, and few places in Europe have built up the same level of experience in dealing with military casualties. But total care is more than just medical care and in the last few years, the administrative and welfare support provided to military patients and their families has become just as good. For many families, being told that a loved one has been wounded and is being brought back to QEHB, can seem like the world has suddenly changed. It is the military bubble which QEHB endeavour to put in place that helps the patient group to cope with that initial stress and trauma.

The former Chief of General Staff (CGS), Gen Sir Richard Dannatt, (now Lord Dannatt) when asked about the hospital said:

"There is nowhere better in the country, nowhere more expert at polytrauma medicine than that hospital in Selly Oak, that's why our people are there."

Patients aeromedically evacuated from the battlefield or theatre of operation and also from expeditionary operations and exercises around the world are transported by the RAF Aeromed team operating from Brize Norton.

COURAGE AFTER THE BATTLE

Only about 20% of aero med patients actually come to Birmingham; the others will progress from the UK arrival airport into the Primary Health Care pathway which best suits their clinical and geographical needs.

The Aeromed Cell based at QEHB provides the expertise and co-ordination of the arrival of military patients who need to be admitted to hospital. Generally, the Aeromed Cell liaises directly with the NHS Trust to determine the best clinical pathway for each patient within Birmingham. Those who arrive at Birmingham tend to be those with multiple trauma and listed patients (listed means a patient is categorised as Very Seriously Injured (VSI), Seriously Injured (SI) or Incapacitating Illness or Injury (III)).

Listed patients are entitled to DILFOR (Dangerously Ill Forwarding of Relatives), which means accommodation, travel and subsistence are provided at public expense for the immediate family. Patient Support Services (PSS) provide a number of roles which include: daily visits to patients, practical support, signposting for non-clinical matters and provision of accommodation and transport. There is always a Military Liaison Officer (MLO) and Defence Medical Welfare Service (DMWS) Welfare Worker on call 24 hours a day. The Patient Support Services Team, particularly the DMWS, are pivotal in the arrival of the patient group to QEHB.

Once the hospital knows a casualty is inbound, contact is made with the Visiting Officer, Unit Escorting Officer or unit, to assist in the co-ordination of arrival, accommodation, briefing and then escorting the patient group to the bedside at the appropriate time. One essential element of the military bubble is a daily meeting of all agencies and departments who have a responsibility for the patient and patient group. They meet to ensure all needs, concerns and issues are known by the relevant experts and the appropriate action is taken during the patient's time at Birmingham. Furthermore, where a long-term welfare requirement is identified, referral is made to the appropriate single service Welfare Agency.

Casualties injured in theatre do not receive the usual decompression package received by those returning from Operational Deployment. For many, they are coming to terms with life-changing injuries, and in some cases disfigurement. To help manage this, QEHB has its own dedicated military Mental Health Team, which consists of two highly experienced Army Psychiatric Nurses who help patients to understand the normal feelings they will be experiencing.

Hospital staff go out in uniform with the patients, which takes the focus away a little. This decompression really helps the injured troops through the normalisation process, coming to terms with their injuries and being in the public eye. One particular example of the need for the normalisation process came about around the initial phases of Afghanistan, when a group of injured personnel were using a local pool on a training session from Headley Court and there were elements of the civilian community jeering at them. Two women demanded they be removed from the pool and claimed that the soldiers "hadn't paid" and might scare the children. The incident sparked widespread condemnation. Admiral Lord Boyce, a former head of the Armed Forces, said:

"The women should be 'named and shamed'. These people are beneath contempt and everything should be done to get their names and publish them in the press. It is contemptible that people who have given up their limbs for their country should be so abused when they are trying to get fit again."

The unpleasant scenes were witnessed at the Leatherhead Leisure Centre in Surrey when wounded veterans had to use the 25-metre public pool because the hydro-pool at the Headley Court defence rehabilitation centre was not big enough for swimming. The servicemen were about to begin their weekly swimming therapy in closed-off lanes when they were verbally abused by some of the swimmers. One woman in her 30s was said to be infuriated by the lane closures, saying the soldiers did not deserve to be there when she had paid.
    Charles Murrin, 79, a Navy veteran who saw the incident, said:

"The atmosphere was understandably tense, given that the soldiers were trying to get their lives back together after giving up so much for this type of person to have her free speech, and then to say such a thing. The instructors removed the service personnel from the pool and the session was cancelled. The woman said the men do not deserve to be in there and that she pays to come in the pool and they don't. I spoke to the instructor in the changing room afterwards and he was livid."

At the time a Ministry of Defence spokesman said:

"We are disappointed that a small number of people objected to the closure of

swimming lanes so that patients of Headley Court could use them."

It is not the first time that Headley Court neighbours have been accused of poor behaviour. Earlier the same year, residents objected to planning permission to convert a home into a six-suite hostel for injured soldiers' families to stay in. The local council later approved the building work.

Defence Medical Rehabilitation Centre at Headley Court is being transferred from its current location of Headley Court in Surrey to the new site at Stanford Hall in the East Midlands. A formal celebration spanning the previous 2 years of Headley Court and the first year at Stanford Hall was in October 2016. Over the last 10-15 years, Headley Court has made significant advances in the specialist care of severe and complex casualties, which have resulted in many more people surviving their injuries who would have died even a few years ago. Leading on from this, a tremendous amount has been learned about best practice in trauma care.

Battle Back Programme
Battle back is an MOD initiative in partnership with Help for Heroes and The Royal British Legion. It is a sport and training programme for wounded, injured and sick personnel across the Armed Forces. The programme is designed to promote confidence and independence and help accelerate physical, psychological and social recovery throughout the duration of recovery, and it is formed to inspire the personnel taking part to focus on what they can do rather than what they cannot.

Physical development is a key component in recovery and the Battle Back programme and regular participation in adaptive sport, adventure training and other activities can help the individual. In support of the programme, there are a number of Battle Back Centres which have been established by The Royal British Legion at the National Sports' Centre, Lilleshall. Battle Back programmes and activities can be delivered from the Battle Back Centre, Lilleshall, the Defence Medical Centre, the personnel recovery centres (PRCs) at Tidworth, Catterick and Colchester, the Naval Service Recovery Centre (which also delivers a bespoke Fortitude programme) as well as at specialist centres both in the UK and abroad. In addition adaptive sports and adventure training will be delivered from the PRCs at Edinburgh and in Germany.

Participants can expect to attend one of the Personnel Recovery

Centres during the recovery period and it is here they can participate in activities under the guidance of military staff working closely with staff employed by Help for Heroes. External activities such as fishing, canoeing, sailing, golf, swimming, riding, sub aqua diving, parachuting, archery, cycling, sledge hockey, shooting and even flying are available to both serving and veteran personnel who were wounded in service from the Recovery Centres.

Many recovering service personnel and veterans wish to take their activities to a higher level and can do so with some rising to a competitive, even Paralympic level. Men and women who first enjoyed standing on a water-ski in the early days at Headley Court are now competing in cycling, skiing, athletics and sledge hockey, while others have gone on to gain their pilot's licences.

The Recovery Career Service are focused on delivering an individualised and inspirational careers service that empowers wounded, injured and sick service personnel. The Recovery Career Services deliver an individual careers service to wounded, injured and sick soldiers leaving the Armed Services to help them find a fulfilling and long-term second career.

21st Century Treatments
BURNS VICTIMS – STEM CELL SPRAY TREATMENT

Burns victims are making incredible recoveries thanks to a revolutionary treatment that sprays stem cells on to their wounds, enabling them to rapidly grow new skin. People who suffer extensive burns usually have to endure weeks or even months of treatment, with surgeons taking large sheets of skin from elsewhere on the body, usually the legs, and grafting them to the area affected by the burns. The process is painful, and patients are often left with permanent, unsightly scars. Now researchers in the United States are using a new technique that allows patients to regrow a new layer of healthy skin in as little as four days. Patients who have benefited say their new skin is virtually indistinguishable from that on the rest of the body and the actual procedure is gentler and the skin that regrows looks, feels and functions like the original skin.

First, a small patch of healthy skin the size of a postage stamp is removed and the stem cells are separated out and put into a solution that is sprayed on to the wound. The whole process takes just 90 minutes. In one case, a 43-year-old man sustained an extensive hot-water scald to his left shoulder and upper arm. This was sprayed with 17 million stem cells and within six days, new skin had formed over the whole wound and he was discharged from hospital. Within six weeks he had recovered a full range of motion.

In another case, a 35-year-old man suffered electrical burns to more than a third of his body. Doctors harvested nearly 24 million stem cells from an area smaller than an iPhone, and sprayed them back on to his body. After four days, a thin layer of skin had regrown over his arms and chest, areas which had suffered the least severe burns. After 20 days, 'all of the areas treated with cell spray grafting were noted as completely healed'.

In normal circumstances, wounds heal from the outside in, with healthy skin on the edges supplying the stem cells needed for the repair process. Plastic surgeons assist this by taking skin grafts and puncturing them with many holes. This is then laid on the wound. The holes cover over with skin, creating a new layer. Wounds up to six times the area of the donor skin can be healed, but the process is slow and prone to scarring. By contrast, the new skin could form evenly across the whole wound from day one.

Regenerative Medicine
Looking further ahead, the field of regenerative medicine, potentially in conjunction with nanotechnology and stem cell therapy, could in time have a game-changing impact on both the nature and the practice of clinical rehabilitation.

A simple definition of regenerative medicine is that it replaces or regenerates human cells, tissue or organs, to restore or establish normal function. A great deal of research in this area is being carried out around the world and, whilst clinical applications are still limited today, the prospects for translational research increasing the number of applications are good. We are still a long way from being able to regenerate limbs, but a recent strategic partnership between Imperial College London and Georgia Institute of Technology (Georgia Tech) in the USA is leading to the creation of a bold new initiative aimed at researching and developing regenerative medicine treatments for landmine injuries. Funded by the 'Find a Better Way' charity established by Sir Bobby Charlton, the REgenerative medicine SOLutions for the Victims of landmine Explosions (RESOLVE) initiative will unite academic and clinical experts at these two leading universities to focus on the fundamental goal of engineering biological replacement limbs created from an individual's own cells.

BATTLEFIELDS TRAUMA

Vince Bramley was a machine-gunner with 1 Parachute Regiment at the night-time battle of Mount Longdon in the Falklands War. He describes it as 'combat at very close quarters, hand to hand, eye to eye, very bloody stuff' and recalls the scene at the top of the mountain after the battle in the early hours of the morning:

"It wasn't until daylight, when I ran into the bowl on the summit and saw the number of dead people there, including my own friends and colleagues, that the shock hit me. Nobody touched me, but it was as if somebody had punched me in the stomach. And I just went into a state of shock. I remember looking around at some of my friends who had survived as well and were in this bowl, and I hadn't realised until then that I wasn't the only one crying. There were Argentines who had been taken prisoner, and they were crying as well. I think all of us were shocked at the extent of what we'd done to each other. And then you begin to realise you're not the rough, tough British paratrooper that the programme of training had made you out to be. You realise you're human, and you have human feelings, and that the men beside you are no different."

The current stance of the UK Ministry of Defence (MoD) is that psychological welfare of troops is primarily a chain of command responsibility, aided by medical advice when necessary, and to this end uses third location decompression, stress briefings, and Trauma Risk Management (TRiM) approaches. Outpatient treatment is provided by Field Mental Health Teams and Military Departments of Community Mental Health, whilst inpatient care is given in specific NHS hospitals. In the long and short of it, no one wants to admit that a clear majority of service personnel are left to fend for themselves or seek assistance from the many charities and goodwill of the people who volunteer their own time and money to help service personnel.

The overall reputation of the Armed Forces is extremely positive, and rightly so, but with one troubling feature. Research published in 2012 found that 91% of the British public thought it was common for former members of the Armed Forces to have some kind of physical, emotional or mental health problem as a result of their service. Not only is this untrue, it is damaging, and creates an extra hurdle for service leavers looking for a job.

Given this mass misconception, employers have the impression that they will be employing a person who has a short temper, will be off for extended periods with drink, take drugs and more than likely have mental health issues. Is there no wonder that this is a barrier which can be impossible to break down? In reality, service personnel will be amongst your best employees, and people who are willing to take decisions and, more importantly, responsibility. If they find a problem, they will not look the other way, it in their genes to solve that problem immediately if not sooner, and move onto the next task. They are not the type of person to have a meeting to have a meeting about the problem. In the middle of nowhere, when something crops up, they can't say 'Oh that is not my job', 'Oh this and that', they sort it and move on to the task or mission at hand – Next!

Employers - 10 Reasons Veterans Make Great Employees

- We have shared an independent list put together highlighting the credibility and skill sets that our armed forces veterans bring to the workplace. UK employers are already realising the benefits of supporting returning veterans to civvy street.
- Leadership and teamwork skills: Veterans typically have led colleagues, accepted direction from others and operated successfully as part of a small team.
- Character: Veterans are perceived as being trustworthy, accountable and possess a strong work ethic.
- Structure and discipline: Companies appreciate veterans' experience in following established procedures.
- Expertise: Companies value veterans' occupational skills and job-specific experiences.

- Dynamic environment: Veterans are accustomed to performing and making decisions in dynamic, rapidly changing circumstances.
- Effectiveness: Company representatives report that veterans 'get it done'.
- Proven success: Some organizations hire veterans largely because other vets already in their organization have been successful.
- Resiliency: Veterans are accustomed to working in difficult environments, traveling and relocating.
- Loyalty: Veterans are committed to the organizations they work for, which can translate into longer tenure.

Source: Civvy Futures.org

The current interest in comparing and attempting to explain differences between different nations' military health is by no means a new phenomenon. Both the United Kingdom and the United States have a history of military research collaboration dating back to the World War One, when the American National Research Council and British Medical Research Committee jointly published a medical bulletin focusing on the health problems of war. This research alliance was strengthened during World War Two, though became fraught when American doctors accused the British of "minimizing the problem" of civilian neuroses in the British population caused by air raids.

Members of 42 Commando Royal Marines on Patrol in Afghanistan (Crown Copyright / MoD)

COURAGE AFTER THE BATTLE

On Patrol in Afghanistan (Crown Copyright / MoD)

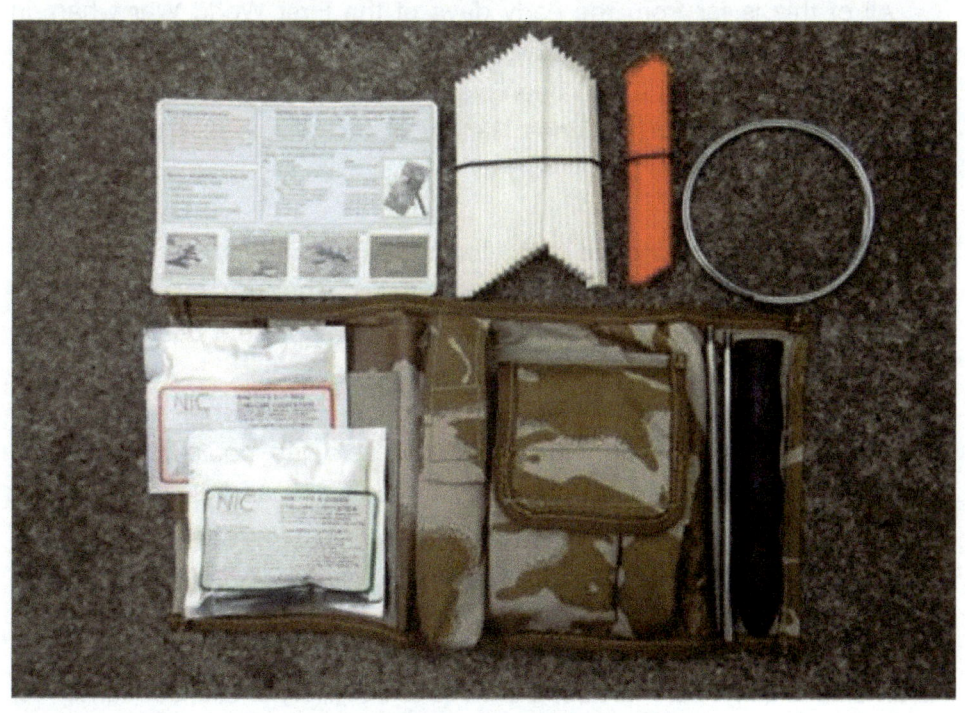

Personal IED Mine Extraction Kit (MoD)
(It is not always possible to have a team with you, so it is DIY time to find and disable the IED)

COURAGE AFTER THE BATTLE

Research into the mental health of serving members or veterans of the UK Armed Forces was undertaken between 1945 and 1995. However, the emergence of the "Gulf War Syndrome" amongst personnel who took part in the 1991 Gulf War was a stimulus for change and led to the commissioning of research into the health and well-being of UK Gulf War veterans. The Americans referred to this as "Desert Storm Syndrome".

A second stimulus was the large class action brought in 2002/3 by veterans claiming that the Ministry of Defence had failed to address the issue of post-traumatic stress disorder (PTSD). The class action failed, but the combination of this and memories of the Gulf War Syndrome saga encouraged the planning of a new study into the physical and mental health of military personnel taking part in the 2003 invasion of Iraq. This study had to be extended with increased UK operations in Afghanistan.

In recent years, the UK has been working closely with the US, and is even currently undertaking specific research projects funded by the US Department of Defence, such as studying the effectiveness of post-operational screening for mental health problems.

All of this is far from the early days of the First World War when, in September 1914, it was rumoured that at the Battle of the Marne, dead soldiers on the front line had been discovered standing at their posts but seeming to be alive. The Times History of the War, published in 1916, stated:

The illusion was so complete that often the living would speak to the dead before they realized the true state of affairs. Asphyxia, caused by the powerful new high-explosive shells, was the cause for the phenomenon— or so it was claimed.

This new artillery type of powerful and destructive firepower had never been seen before. A battery of mobile 75mm field gun, could cover an area of ten acres at a depth of around 435 yards in less than 50 seconds. Over a period of approximately five days, 432,000 shells had been fired. Could such a machine as this destroy a man mentally and physically without wounds and seem to destroy men's brains?

Ordnance of all types, mortars, grenades and artillery shells, accounted for an estimated 60 percent of the 9.7 million military fatalities of World War One. Many of the soldiers arriving at the casualty clearing stations who had been exposed to exploding shells, although clearly damaged, bore no visible wounds. They appeared to be suffering from a form of shock caused by blast force from the ordnance. A medical report concluded that this new injury appeared to be the result of the actual explosion itself, and not merely of the projectiles set in motion by it. In other words, it appeared that some dark, invisible force had in fact passed through the air and was inflicting novel and peculiar damage to men's brains.

The primary blast from an explosion is the shock wave which is rapidly expanding air pressure advancing outward from the detonation, faster than the speed of sound. This shock wave passes so rapidly that it has gone before the person knows about it. Just how a shock wave enters the brain is still not understood and various theories have been cast, including entry is through the natural openings in the skull such as the eye sockets, ears, nostrils, and mouth. Another theory is that since shock wave pressure hits the entire body, not just the head, it's transmitted into the chest or abdominal cavities and surges to the brain by way of the body's vasculature system. Once inside the skull, the wave advances through the brain at the speed of sound, passing through both fluids and brain matter, which respond differently to the wave's properties. A distinctive pattern of scarring occurs precisely in those places where different compositions of brain tissue intersect. An example of an explosive shock wave can clearly be seen in aircraft film of the bombing raids of World War Two. You can see the circular wave disseminating out from the explosive ordnance impact site.

In modern conflicts, service personnel travel around in personnel carriers, tanks and all manner of other equipment. If one of these is hit, say by a Rocket Propelled Grenade (RPG), the resulting explosion may well reverberate around the inside of the vehicle and the resulting explosion would have less room for the blast wave to go. It would therefore be more intense inside the vehicle than outside the vehicle, with fatal consequences for the occupants.

Mental illness, especially for those who have been captured during a war or conflict, has been observed as far back as the First World War, and possibly beyond that. Initially, psychiatrists and doctors saw this as an extension of some of the ideas surrounding war neuroses, so it was questioned how a person who was in the security of a POW camp, and away from the battlefield, could possibly suffer from this condition? In German

COURAGE AFTER THE BATTLE

PoW camps in the UK, phrases such as *"camp disease"* and *"barbed-wire disease"* began to circulate. Red Cross officials became concerned and persuaded governments to act. At an Anglo–German conference held at The Hague in July 1917, *"barbed-wire disease"* was added to the list of categories determining prisoners' eligibility for internment in neutral Switzerland and their eventual repatriation. In 1919, a comprehensive study on *"barbed-wire disease"* was undertaken by surgeon and Swiss embassy official Adolf Lukas Vischer, who had visited POW camps. Vischer had also published a book on the subject, along with an article in The Lancet.

Vischer classified *"barbed-wire disease"* as a *"psychoneurosis"* that arose in the *"abnormal"* conditions of captivity, such as POWs being crowded together and uncertain of the duration of their internment. Its effects were described as barbed wire winding like a thread through the mental processes of the prisoner. Symptoms included irritability, difficulty concentrating, restlessness, failure of memory, moodiness, depression and unpleasant dreams. 10 years later, the 1929 Geneva Convention acknowledged *"nervous troubles"* in captivity. The term to which it referred, however, was different and the convention stated that those suffering from *"psychasthenia"* should be accommodated in a neutral country. Psychasthenia was a mental condition coined by French psychologist Pierre Janet at the end of the 19th century. Psychasthenia resulted from a disturbance of the mind's "function of reality" and a tendency not to concentrate on the present. This theory lent itself well to POWs. To mentally escape their incarcerated world, they tended to drift into their past and future lives.

According to many of the diaries from prisoners of the Second World War, it was suggested that mental afflictions caused by captivity were common in the camps. They used various names, including *"barbed-wire fever"*, *"depression"*, *"stalag happy"*, *"the blues"*, *"temporary lapses"*, *"kriegy weariness"*, and *"round the bend"*. The symptoms were quite broad in that they covered such areas as feelings of depression, irritability, lethargy, poor concentration, fits of temper, and memory loss.

First came the *"adaptation"*, or *"breaking-in period"*. It was a time of confusion, when the prisoner realised the extent of his loss. Then came the *"stage of recovery"* or "convalescence" when POWs tried to reconstruct their way of living. After this, all agreed the prisoner began to mentally decline. Boredom and the fear of being forgotten at home took their toll.

COURAGE AFTER THE BATTLE

The War Cabinet was informed that 40,000 British and Commonwealth POWs in captivity since July 1940 were suffering from the *"increasingly harmful effects, both mental and physical, of this prolonged captivity"*. The War Office and Foreign Office argued there were *strong grounds* for proceeding with an exchange of 3,000 Germans captured before July 1943, with British and Commonwealth prisoners captured before July 1940. But, in the event, no action was taken.

Almost one in five POWs who returned to the UK in the summer of 1945 were referred for interview by army psychiatrists, yet few required long-term treatments. When the UK Government and army psychiatrists showed concern about the mental states of POWs, any problems were generally attributed not to what had happened in the camps, but to an individual's predisposition to mental illness and his long absence from home. The POWs' experience while in captivity remained without recognition and without a definitive name. Even though this malady existed outside the diagnostic framework, these wartime writings reveal it was still experienced as something very real by servicemen in captivity.

Shell Shock

The term 'shell shock' first appeared in the British Medical Journal, The Lancet, in February 1915, only six months after the start of World War One. It is also known as "war neurosis", "combat stress" and "Post Traumatic Stress Disorder" (PTSD). Capt. Charles Myers of the Royal Army Medical Corps noted the remarkable similarity of symptoms in three soldiers who had been exposed to exploding shells in the battlefield. All three men exhibited symptoms of reduced visual fields, loss of smell and taste, and some loss of memory. Captain Myers concluded that they appear to constitute a definite class among others suffering from the effects of shell-shock.

THE THREE SAMPLES IN QUESTION WERE:

- A man who had endured six or seven shells exploding around him

- A man who had been buried alive (possibly following the ground impact explosion of the shell) under earth for 18 hours after a shell collapsed his trench

COURAGE AFTER THE BATTLE

- A man who had been blown off a pile of bricks 15 feet high.

It is not known if he was thrown 15 feet into the air or the bricks were 15 feet high, but it is more likely that it was the brick height being referred to.

All three men would have suffered from the blast wave from the exploding shell as the initial cause of the unseen injuries.

One notable case of shell shock is of a man who spent 118 days in the hospital being treated for loss of speech, inability to sleep, and loss of memory and concentration before being returned to active duty as fit to fight. This was despite him complaining about weak hands, and weakness in his body in general, with a weak if not poor understanding of questions given to him, where he answered in a vague and contradictory way. It is not known who this man was or what happened to him once he returned to the front, but suffice to say it is very likely he did not survive for long or was possibly shot by his own side for cowardice. This is something that would not be of his making but would be down to his mental state of mind. The men were routinely shot for desertion, mutiny, cowardice (even if it was caused by shell shock or other mental affections), and other breaches of discipline.

In another case, a First World War soldier who was shot for cowardice refused a blindfold, so he could face his 12 British comrades in the firing squad as they aimed their guns at him. Private Harry Farr, who was shot at dawn in October 1916 at the age of 25, was never recognised alongside men who died in battle during the Great War because he was considered a deserter. His act of bravery and defiance in his decisive moments stood in stark contrast to the alleged cowardice his superiors had him shot for. In 1915 he spent more than five months in hospital before reporting sick for a nervous condition in September 1916, during the Battle of the Somme. He again reported sick in 1916 and again later in the war. This third time he was refused treatment by Royal Army Medical Corps soldiers because he had no physical injury.

He then refused to re-join his battalion, telling his commanders: 'I cannot stand it' and was then arrested, charged with 'misbehaving before the enemy in such a manner as to show cowardice' and had his death sentence confirmed by Field Marshal Earl Haig, the British Army's commander-in-chief.

COURAGE AFTER THE BATTLE

Private Farr's descendants made all efforts to have his name cleared, and this made Pte Farr a test case. In 2006 the Government finally caved in to demands and gave a formal posthumous pardon to all 306 British soldiers executed by firing squad for desertion between 1914 and 1918. Some academic historians voiced unease over the move, pointing out that some of those included in the blanket pardon were probably genuine deserters who let down their comrades and were not suffering from mental breakdown.

Shell shock was initially deemed to be a physical injury, and the shell-shocked soldier was entitled to a distinguishing wound stripe for his uniform, and to possible discharge and a war pension. By 1916, military and medical authorities were convinced that many soldiers were exhibiting the characteristic symptoms: trembling much like a jelly, headache, tinnitus, dizziness, poor concentration, confusion, loss of memory, and sleep disorders. Some men were showing the symptoms, but had been nowhere near exploding shells, so they were classed as neurasthenia, or weakness of the nerves. This is a nervous breakdown brought on by the stresses of war.

Medical opinion used recent advances in psychiatry, and most of shell shock cases were now thought to be seen more as emotional collapse in the face of the unprecedented and hardly imaginable horrors of trench warfare. There was a convenient outcome from the officers and military's point of view, which was that if the disorder was nervous and not physical, the shell-shocked soldier did not warrant a wound stripe, and if unwounded, was fit to fight and could be returned to the front.

In the Journal of the Royal Army Medical Corps (JR Army Med Corps 1925 24: p343-352) William Aldren Turner M.D, F.R.C.P. Physician to King's College Hospital and the National Hospital for the Paralysed and Epileptic, Queen Square; Temporary Lieutenant-Colonel, R.A.M.C noted the following in his observations of Shell Shock, some of which you may not have even considered before:

From time to time cases are sent down from the casualty clearing stations in a state of mental stupor. Some of these cases are unaccompanied by any history or statement which would throw light upon the cause or method of onset of the symptoms. Other cases of a similar, though less profound type of stupor, on recovery from the acuter phases, are able to give some account of the nature of the psychical shock through which they have passed.

The symptoms exhibited by these cases of stupor are interesting and create a clinical picture of a striking character. In the more severe class of case, the patient is entirely unconscious of his surroundings. All the usual tests applied with the object of arresting attention, such as throwing a bright light on to the eyes, pinching the skin, or clapping the hands close to the ears, fail to provoke a response. The deep reflexes, however, are normal or brisk, and the plantar response is of the flexor type. The pupillary light reflexes frequently impaired or lost. Urine is passed normally; swallowing is carried out usually without difficulty.

In some cases, the patient would appear to be living again through an experience of the past, probably associated with the time of onset of the symptoms. In a very striking instance, the patient lay curled up under the bedclothes. From time to time he would look out, as if peering over the parapet of a trench, stare wildly around him, and then hide under the clothes. These actions were often repeated and lasted for several days with gradually diminishing frequency. In another case of a somewhat similar character, the patient would suddenly start and sit up in bed and look around him, crying out, "He's gone, he's gone." It was subsequently ascertained that this patient's brother had been killed when fighting beside him in the trench. Many of these cases present a scared or startled appearance. When approached they shrink and hide under the bedclothes. Others are dull, lethargic, and apathetic, taking no interest in what is going on around them. A closer examination reveals a marked degree of rigidity of the limbs in most of the cases. As a rule, all the extremities are affected; the thighs are tightly flexed upon the abdomen and the fingers clenched in the hands.

Comparable in many ways to the cases of stupor just described are those cases of loss of memory, or transitory amnesia, which are admitted to the base hospitals for further observation. Prolonged fatigue and exhaustion, coupled with continuous shelling, seem to be the primary causes of these mental breakdowns. The history furnishes evidence that the patient had been found wandering and was unable to give a satisfactory account of his movements. On inquiry of the patient himself as to what had happened to him, one is told that he had been under heavy shelling for a time just previous to his 'losing consciousness', as he says. One such patient said that in the stress of the engagement he had 'lost his head' and became unconscious. The loss of memory may extend over a period of several days. The patient has no knowledge or recollection of what had happened to him during this interval. Attempts to bring back the memory by suggesting possible events or circumstances have not met with success. In one patient, however, the memory was partly restored by a striking association. When lying in hospital he saw a number of men being prepared for inoculation against enteric fever. This recalled to his mind that he himself had been inoculated a few days before the loss of memory came on. From this clue he was able to give some account of himself, although his memory for a period of three or four days had not returned by the time he was sent home. Attempts to recall the memory by the use of "word associations " were not tried.

In addition to the loss of memory the patients complain of headache, and sometimes of a feeling of strangeness and discomfort in the head; the head, they say, is muddled. Sleep is disturbed at first. The reflexes are normal, although the pupillary light reflex may be impaired. Recovery takes place satisfactorily with rest in bed and ample feeding.

Deafness of a transient character is not an uncommon symptom resulting from the explosion of big shells in close proximity to the patient. In addition to the deafness the effects of the explosion are a stunning or dazing of the mental faculties and sometimes temporary loss of consciousness. In other cases, the patient is 'blown away' or forcibly precipitated on to the ground by the violence of the explosion. On recovery from these immediate effects the patient discovers that he is deaf in either one or both ears.

Deaf-mutism is another effect of the explosion of big shells and provides one of the clinical surprises of the war. In all the cases observed this cause was given by the patient in explanation of his symptoms, although in one case the patient appears to have been buried as well. As the patient is able to write an account of the *incidents which led to the onset of his symptoms, the following statements are given as characteristic of all the cases.*

In comparison with the cases of deaf-mutism just described, blindness, or impairment of vision, following the explosion of shells is relatively infrequent. There would appear to be two types of case in which blindness is complained of in consequence of shell explosions. In the first class, quite a number of soldiers suffering from the symptoms of a general mild neurasthenia following prolonged fatigue complain of being blind. An examination of these cases shows that they are not really blind, but are suffering from photophobia and tonic spasm of the eyelids (blepharospasm). Further investigation into the origin of the symptoms reveals that at the time of the explosion sand, dust, or mud was blown into the eyes and has given rise to conjunctivitis, hypersensitiveness to light, and spasm of the eyelids. Recovery takes place quickly under suitable local applications and rest. In the second class, the patients suffer from a temporary blindness or impairment of vision. In the cases of this character which were examined, consciousness was stated to have been abolished temporarily at the outset. In addition to the loss of vision, the eyeballs are tender to pressure in the early stages. The pupillary light reflex is normal. An ophthalmoscopic examination shows no structural change in the media, retina, or optic discs. In one case in which the blindness was unilateral, an associated partial ptosis of the upper lid on the same side was present. In another case the examination revealed a large patch of opaque nerve fibres. In a third case Colonel Lister found a slight peripheral contraction of the visual fields. Most cases show some error of refraction. Recovery is said to be complete eventually, although I have myself not been able to observe a case sufficiently long to ascertain the duration of visual impairment.

Hesitation of speech has been observed in several cases in consequence of shell explosions. As in the previous cases of shock, the impediment may or may not be preceded by a temporary loss of consciousness. The outstanding symptom of spinal shock is loss of power in the legs. This is brought about by shell or mine explosion in the immediate vicinity of the patient, with or without an accompanying burial of the patient in the trench or resulting debris. It has been found also as a result of a fall, the patient being knocked over and striking his pack against the wall or parapet of the trench and injuring his back indirectly in this way.

Following on from this Journal of the Royal Army Medical Corps (JR Army Med Corps 1916 26: p782-797) Contributions to the Study of Shell Shock (iii): Being an Account of Certain Disorders of Cutaneous Sensibility , Temporary Lieutenant-Colonel Charles S. Myers, M.D., Sc.D., F.R.S.

Royal Army Medical Corps noted the initial communication he had come across with three cases of severe shell shock. The first of these was a 19-year-old stretcher bearer, with 18 months service, six of which had been in France:

Four days before admission he had been '' blown up three times by aerotorpedo trench mortars" while attending to the wounded in the trenches during an enemy attack. He said that one had blown him in the air, that another had blown him into a dug-out, and that the third had knocked him down, but that nevertheless he continued his work of carrying away the wounded to the dressing station. Two or three hours later, after he had finished, he was resting in a dug-out when 'everything seemed to go black' (probably he had a hysterical 'fit') and he became "shaky', and had remained so ever since. He said that he had hardly slept for seven days before he 'gave in'.

He appeared an honest, courageous lad, but was obviously in a very "nervous' condition, making irregular spasmodic movements of the head, arms (especially the right) and legs (especially the left). There were well-marked coarse tremors and incoordination during voluntary movements of the arms. He touched his nose with far greater uncertainty when his eyes were closed. The lightest touch of cotton wool on the limbs or head provoked very lively movements; obviously he dreaded the next touch. '' I was always ticklish," he explained, '' but never like this. I can't stand it, sir." A pin-prick produced a series of most violent spasms, almost amounting to a convulsion. He sweated considerably during examination. There was much rigidity in the legs, and so much spasm that a knee-jerk was unobtainable until my second visit, the sixth day after admission. Plantar stimulation gave a flexor response. He suffered from visual hallucinations of bursting shells; he also heard them when dozing. He improved considerably with rest and treatment; but seventeen days after admission, lying asleep in bed outside his tent in the sunshine, he woke to find himself being carried back in his bed owing to a sudden shower of rain. This brought about a recurrence of such terror that a special nurse was considered necessary that night. The next day he was still very "jumpy" and alarmed, even at the sound of a footstep; he complained of severe headache. Three days later he had again improved and was transferred to England.

The official report of the War Office Committee of Enquiry Into shell shock made at the end of the war concluded that shell shock resolves itself into concussion / commotional shock, or emotional shock. The evidence about damage from concussion shock was largely based on the observations of senior officers in the field, many of whom were clearly sceptical of any attempt to explain what was simple loss of nerve or cowardice.

A consultant in neuropsychiatry with the American Expeditionary Force reported a percentage of concussion shock at around 50 - 60 percent of this as shell shock cases. He reported that patients had lost consciousness or memory after having been blown over by a shell. Information about the circumstances of such injuries was very hit and miss and depended upon the doctor's own interpretation of his findings. To process the large numbers of casualties on a daily basis, it was not unusual for this important detail to be omitted as part of the daily administration to get the wounded registered and treated.

By 1917, medical officers were instructed to avoid the term shell shock and to designate probable cases as

- Not Yet Diagnosed (Nervous)

- Shell shock (wound)

- Shell shock (sick)

Both shell shock (wound) and shell shock (sick) were sent to a psychiatric unit, where the soldier was assessed by a specialist. Shell shock (sick) was given if the soldier had not been close to an explosion. The wounded would then be transferred to a treatment centre in Britain or France, and the invalided soldier was placed under the care of neurology specialists until discharged or returned to the front. Officers might enjoy a final period of convalescence before being sent back into the war. Quite often they convalesced at a private treatment centre.

Shot at Dawn Memorial at the National Arboretum (Author) Note the individual name plaque on each post and the hands tied behind the back of the figure.

Many treatments at the time are now seen as barbaric, even useless, and were given to neurasthenic soldiers. The most notorious was Dr Lewis Yealland's electric shock therapies. These were conducted at the National Hospital for Paralysed and Epileptic, at Queen Square, London, where he claimed his cure had been applied to upwards of 250 cases (an unknown number of which were civilian). Yealland was among the first doctors in Britain to incorporate electricity in the systematic treatment of shell shock. Yealland's treatment approach used peripheral and central electrical stimulation with a variety of other psychological and physical interventions.

An electrical stimulation of the affected muscles with suggestion of imminent improvement was the hallmark of his approach but he never followed up his patients later, so we have no record of his success or failures, not to mention the patients and how they fared in later life.

The sudden rise in reports of shell shock along with symptoms of hysteria and functional nervous disease after the outbreak of the First World War posed a major threat to the war effort. Some military casualties were transferred to the National Hospital for the Paralysed and Epileptic, which was at the time the National Hospital for Neurology and Neurosurgery in Queen Square, London. The hospital, which had gained an early reputation for its expertise in electrotherapy, suddenly found itself at the centre for the development and implementation of new treatments for functional neurological disorders.

The first patient treated by Yealland with faradism was Solomon ('Solly') W, a 35-year-old private from the 9th Oxfordshire and Buckinghamshire Light Infantry who had mainly worked as a waiter in an officer's mess in France. He was admitted to Queen Square Hospital on 14 December 1915 complaining of shooting pains in the right shoulder and running up to the neck. He had no objective sensory loss but, on examination, Yealland found weakness of the right arm, particularly in the shoulder. Muscular power in other muscle groups was normal, and there was no muscular wasting so Yealland applied faradism to the right arm and leg combined with massage, radiant heat to the right shoulder and analgesia. The patient was discharged improved, but nothing is said about cured or fit to fight after 2.5 months of treatment.

Yealland wanted to create a permanent neurological record of some of his cases of war neurosis and document the treatment process from the beginning to the end. To this aim, he managed to secure a grant from the Medical Research Committee to record cases on film, and in July and August 1917, Yealland's treatment of at least two soldiers with functional disorders was filmed by a Pathé cameraman on the roof of the hospital. The patients in question were Mark Edward M, 44-year-old private from the Northampton Regiment and 33-year-old private James C from the 12th Royal Sussex Regiment. It is thought that no actual recordings or copies of this film exist today, so we are unable to see the results. However, there are other films in existence which show the terrible effect shell shock and its treatment has on soldiers.

You may like to look at the following to get a visual image of the trauma that was shell shock

Verdun Shell Shock (includes images of men on crutches and artificial limbs) (1 Minute 32 Seconds)
https://www.youtube.com/watch?v=SS1dO0JC2EE

5 Disturbing Photos and Description of WW1 (7 minutes 41 seconds)
https://www.youtube.com/watch?v=OK6ZTXrEUfc

Shell Shock WW1 Documentary (50 minutes 21 seconds)
https://www.youtube.com/watch?v=YPJW3A-e6jo

Yealland's approach was generally in line with medical practice of the time and Yealland played on the soldier's greatest fear of being accused of malingering, by explaining to the patient:

"If you recover quickly, then it is due to a disease, if you recover slowly, then I shall decide that your condition is due to malingering"

He also appealed to the soldier's sense of honour, responsibility towards his family, pride and self-respect. Much like today's service personnel, they will always retain self-respect and pride, even after leaving. The way he addressed the patient was authoritative, sometimes patronizing, denying the patient compassion and moral support. Treatment could be extremely painful, when strong electrical currents were used, or supra-orbital pressure was applied for extended periods to patients with hysterical fits and hysterical blindness.

Yealland asserted that his treatment cured all the most common hysterical disorders of warfare, sometimes in a single half-hour session: electric heat baths, milk diets, hypnotism, clamps and machines that mechanically forced stubborn limbs out of their frozen position. As the war went on, and shell shock became recognized as one of its primary afflictions, treatment became more sympathetic. These included rest and rehabilitative activities, sometimes accompanied by psychotherapy sessions. There was an element of difference depending on your location, as there was no real recognised national system for treatment or rehabilitation.

In 2009, the United States Defence Department undertook a two-year $10 million-dollar study on the effects of blast force on the human brain. This study not only advanced the prospect of modern treatment but cast new light on the old shell shock condition.

The study revealed that limited Traumatic Brain Injury (TBI) (this covers conditions that range from penetrating head wounds to blunt-force trauma, which are typical of concussions) shows that patients may not be aware an injury has been sustained but they have difficulty concentrating, sleep disturbances, altered moods. These are conditions shared with Post-Traumatic Stress Disorder (PTSD), which is a psychiatric syndrome caused by exposure to traumatic events.

According to Col. Geoffrey Ling, the director of the study

"Someone could have a brain injury and be looking like it was PTSD."

It was shown in the study that at low levels the blast-exposed brain remains structurally intact but is injured by swelling. This was presaged by the observation in World War One that spinal fluid drawn from men who had been blown up revealed changes in protein cells.

During the study, one area was to study autopsied brains of eight military service members who had served in the Middle East. All the patients had suffered trauma after exposure to blast force on the battlefield, mostly from Improvised Explosive Devices (IEDs). The study demonstrated the pattern of damage caused by exposure to blast force is distinct from that commonly observed in the brains of football players or boxers. The implications of the findings are profound, pointing to the possibility that symptoms long thought to be psychological and attributed to PTSD may be direct results of physical damage to the brain.

At the end of World War One shell shocked veterans dispersed into the mists of history. Officially the Ministry of Pensions had been left with the care of 63,296 neurological cases. By 1929 there were 74,867 such cases, and the ministry was still paying for such rehabilitative pursuits as basket making and boot repairing. An estimated 10 percent of the 1,663,435 military wounded of the war would be attributed to shell shock. Many were confined in Mental War Hospitals under Martial Law - with the risk of being sent on, without appeal, to asylums.

Today, we have a wealth of information and help available to those who want it, but the critical point in most cases is that they must initially ask for it. Whether that be from the GP or veteran's groups, it is up to the individual. As stated previously, service and ex-service people are a proud and honourable people who are unwilling to ask for help, but the time will come when they must swallow that pride to get the help.

Many former service personnel have complex physical and mental health issues, including psychological injuries such as depression, anxiety, panic attacks and, for a significant minority, PTSD. There is also an element of substance misuse with some veterans' using drugs or alcohol in ways that are harmful to their health. For many, this substance misuse can hide the symptoms of other disorders and make it difficult for them to ask for, or find, effective help and treatment.

Recognising the Symptoms of PTSD

The term Post-Traumatic Stress Disorder (PTSD) was first used by veterans of the Vietnam War, but the problem has existed a lot longer and been known as shell shock, battle fatigue and soldier's heart, to name but a few. In civilian life, a traumatic event such as being involved in an accident or assault can lead to PTSD. A key difference with war veterans is that they usually present with multiple traumatic experiences. Many also have a feeling of guilt or shame based on survivors guilt - they have seen colleagues maimed and killed and there is a sense of 'I should have done more', 'I've let the side down', or even feelings that it 'should have been me'.

Veterans' present with cluster symptoms, the first involving re-experiencing. They have one or more memories in which they feared for their life and those memories haven't been processed and stored properly.

Consequently, random triggers can make them pop out unpredictably. Examples of common triggers are fireworks -a reminder of explosions and gunfire - and barbecues- the smell of burning flesh. When a veteran has a trigger moment, he or she may suddenly zone out, glaze over, stop talking mid-sentence or lose track of a conversation. They may also start breathing rapidly and even adopt a body position, such as crouching down, that is part of the re-experiencing process.

The second symptom is connected to mood swings. Veterans with PTSD may be more irritable, snappy or critical. Disturbed sleep caused by nightmares and flashbacks can exacerbate black moods. They may be hyper-vigilant and unable to cope with crowds, confined spaces and loud noises.

The third symptom is connected to avoidance. If you are having flashbacks triggered by random experiences, it makes sense that you will withdraw to avoid the triggers. Veterans may become reclusive, avoiding shopping trips or meals out for fear of something unpredictable happening. If they do go to a restaurant, they may want to sit close to the door in case they need to get out in a hurry, or even sit with their backs to the wall so they can see who is entering and leaving the premises. Veterans with PTSD may become emotionally withdrawn as their minds and bodies go into a state of numbness. They appear to be cold and cut off, which can be particularly hard for partners and children to understand.

Self-medication is common, particularly with alcohol or drugs such as cannabis and cocaine, and eating disorders and self-harm. Veterans with PTSD may use alcohol to shut off emotionally and numb painful memories. Seeking prompt treatment is key to maximising the chances of recovery from PTSD. If the sufferer receives the right treatment in the right environment, rates of recovery are very positive. Veterans can live normal, fulfilling lives, and are able to work with the condition and generally become symptom-free for extended periods.

Any of us can, without warning, be caught up in a traumatic event that is frightening, life-threatening (to ourselves or others) and beyond our control. Examples of such events could be what may at the time seem rather a benign event, but later realisation and shock tells a different story, or a major event where it would immediately become apparent how stressful the situation is.

For the layperson on the street some examples may be:

getting a diagnosis of a serious illness
being involved in or seeing a serious road accident
an unexpected death of someone close
being the victim of a violent assault

As is with human nature, everyone will react differently, and some quicker than others. There is no right or wrong way to realise you have had a traumatic event or how you will cope with this. It is common to feel anxious, angry, emotional, and to have difficulty putting the event out of your mind. This is called Acute Stress Reaction, which will fade over the coming days or weeks, depending on the incident and your reaction. However, this may then see a more severe condition developing into PTSD.

The symptoms usually start within a few weeks of the trauma, but they can start up to 6 months later and, in a few cases, much later than that. In PTSD you may have flashbacks and nightmares where you relive the event in your mind again and again, can't relax, feel anxious and can't sleep, get physical symptoms - aches and pains, diarrhoea, irregular heartbeats, headaches - feelings of panic and fear, depression, start drinking too much alcohol or using drugs (including painkillers).

Some of the treatments that can help are as simple as talking to someone or taking medical assistance for:

Cognitive Behavioural Therapy (CBT) which helps you to think differently about your memories, so that they become less distressing and more manageable. This is usually undertaken by relaxation to help you tolerate the discomfort of recalling the traumatic events.

Eye Movement Desensitisation & Reprocessing (EMDR): this method uses eye movements to help the brain to process flashbacks and to make sense of the traumatic experience.

Medication. Antidepressant tablets can help. If you are so distressed that you can't sleep or think clearly, you may need sedative medication which should be prescribed by your doctor and reviewed regularly by your doctor or specialist.

There are several myths about PTSD / Battlefield Trauma which I have taken from the Combat Stress website. The following may alleviate your fears and answer some questions you or a worried loved one may have:

Post-Traumatic Stress Disorder (PTSD) is the only mental illness caused by military service.
PTSD is one of the mental illnesses most associated with military service but there are a range of other more common mental illnesses which might affect service and ex-service personnel. These include depression, feelings of anxiety, panic attacks and substance misuse, most commonly alcohol misuse.

Mental illnesses only occur amongst junior ranks; senior ranks don't get them.
This is incorrect. Mental illness as a result of the traumatic experiences witnessed during Armed Forces service can affect any member of the Armed Forces, regardless of rank. We have treated Veterans of various ranks suffering from PTSD and other mental ill-health - from Privates up to Brigadiers.

You can only get mental illness if you have seen combat.
Far from it. There are many traumatic experiences that sailors, soldiers and airmen could witness during their military careers which take place outside of live combat situations. Whether it is training incidents, administering medical treatment, or other activities in war zones, these traumatic experiences can stay with personnel and lead to mental ill-health in later life.

PTSD is the biggest mental health problem facing the UK veteran community.
PTSD is a problem for a minority of veterans. Around 1 in 25 veterans of the Iraq and Afghanistan wars are likely to develop PTSD, similar to that in the general public. However, while the rate of occurrence is similar, the complexity of the disorder tends to be much greater in veterans. Furthermore, it often occurs alongside other medical problems such as pain, disability and substance misuse, particularly alcohol misuse.

You cannot cure PTSD.
PTSD that has been left untreated for a number of years or decades will require more intensive treatment. There are still positive health outcomes for sufferers, and the potential for a life beyond symptoms, but seeking

suitable, timely treatment is key to maximising the chances of recovery. If PTSD is diagnosed early and the sufferer receives the right treatment in the right environment, rates of recovery are very positive. Veterans can live normal fulfilling lives, able to work with the condition and generally become symptom free for long periods.

There is a risk of delayed-onset of PTSD, where symptoms do not occur for years or decades after the traumatic event. Veterans who present with delayed-onset PTSD have often been exposed to the effects of multiple traumas over a longer period of time. This suggests that those who serve multiple tours are more at risk of developing PTSD several years after leaving the Military.

Most UK Armed Forces personnel who have served in Iraq and Afghanistan return with psychological injuries.
The majority of Armed Forces personnel deployed do not experience lasting mental wounds as a result of their service. However, around 1 in 25 Regulars and 1 in 20 Reservists will report symptoms of PTSD following deployment in Iraq or Afghanistan. This is very similar to the rate in the general population.

Furthermore, 1 in 5 veterans are likely to suffer from a common mental illness - such as depression, anxiety or substance (generally alcohol) misuse - which has been caused or aggravated by their Armed Forces experiences.

There is a bow wave of veterans' mental health problems building up.
Combat Stress is UK's leading veterans' mental health charity. Combat Stress has experienced an increase in the number of referrals year on year. However, recent studies suggest this is due to an increased awareness of the symptoms and where to seek help.

PTSD Symptoms Fabricated by Veterans
An article in the Guardian newspaper in 2016 by a former military psychiatrist stated military veterans' PTSD claims were being fabricated and exaggerated. It was also claimed that some could be classed as 'Walter Mitty' characters. This is a service phrase for someone who is making out that he is something he most definitely is not, such as those who parade on Remembrance Sunday with vast amounts of medals or wearing a beret and cap badge they have no right to. 42% had no link to military service

and were therefore diverting resources from those with a genuine need.

Mr Ian Palmer, a former senior military psychiatrist who ran the government's medical assessment programme (MAP), a veterans' mental health service, found that in 42% of cases there was no definite link to military service and at least 10% appeared to be making up or significantly exaggerating their service history. He stated:

"Fabrications are intriguing because they range from outright fraud through to the fantastic and even delusional. I reckon about 10%, which may be an underestimate, of those coming for assessment may have either exaggerated or fabricated. Within society there seems to be an almost reflex desire to link health problems in veterans with their military service. Just because someone has served, it does not mean that their mental health problem is related to their service."

Palmer's comments coincided with a study published in the Defence and Security Analysis Journal that claims some veterans embellish their military service because of media scrutiny of PTSD associated with Iraq and Afghanistan, which has consequently led the British public to expect that most veterans had been traumatised by their tours of duty.

A Falklands veteran, 'Iddy' Iddon, a former member of the Royal Army Medical Corps, was like most lads, including myself, a teenager when he 'went down south'. Iddy treated the Welsh Guards after the Sir Galahad attack and in 2012 he took part in the Army's *'Don't Bottle it up Campaign'*. He was found to be suffering from PTSD and is haunted by the memories of that day.

Iddy, in true military terms, states:

"Thirty years ago, sufferers got swept under the carpet and vanished out the back door, but that doesn't happen now. Army mental health has changed a huge amount. Post-traumatic stress is only like any other medical condition and it's treated as an illness. To be honest, it's just like catching the clap. If you address it now, it won't become deep-rooted."

For years, Iddy spent years being too terrified of water to drink it and living out of a trench in his parents' back garden for fear of going indoors. The

COURAGE AFTER THE BATTLE

Army said he had an inability to communicate with people. Thanks to the charity Combat Stress and the support of friends at The Royal British Legion's Riders Branch, Iddy's life is improving. His advice to anyone would be to act now, not later, and the sooner you get treatment, the lower the chance that you will end up a basket case.

Iddy spent most of his life avoiding psychiatric units, but things have altered enormously since 1982 and he would ask anyone with problems to follow what may seem simple advice - but taking that first step is the hardest.

In an article in the Daily Mail in June 2017, Staff Sergeant Kim Hughes, a bomb disposal expert who received the George Cross for his actions, stated the following:

Staff Sgt Kim Hughes was awarded the George Cross for his efforts in disarming an entire Taliban minefield using a pair of pliers. Injured men lay close by, screaming in pain and wanting assistance, but until a safe route could be found they had to stay. In his words noted below, the story is unveiled along with the trauma and pressures of getting a clear path to the casualties as quickly as possible:

"A good example of the day to day work, if I can word it that way so it is comprehensible to those who have not been in the armed service:. My bomb disposal team and I arrived in 2009 when British troops were getting badly smashed. Choppers were coming under fire, and every day our boys were being killed or maimed as the Taliban routinely sneaked in under cover of darkness and laid bomb after bomb just yards from our base.

Improvised explosive devices (IEDs) were hidden in walls and trees, in rubbish dumps, abandoned buildings, even in dead animals. The place was a minefield where every road, every street, every step had to be cleared, otherwise, we all knew the consequences. A large device, say 20 kilos or more, will blow you into so many pieces that a mop will be needed to deal with what's left. But at least that's quick and painless. If you're unlucky, the blast will cut you in half, take away your legs and leave you disembowelled. You might survive, but not for long.

The only real defence against them was the small band of bomb disposal operators, front-line experts like my team who dodged death every day as we lay face down on the ground to sweep away the sand from a buried *pressure plate, and our most important piece of equipment was a paint brush.*

Heavyweight protective bomb suits made from woven Kevlar and armoured plate were too hot in the 37c heat and would weigh you down if you had to beat a retreat under enemy fire. Chin down and face-to-face with an IED, I was in the zone, pitching my wits against the Taliban's, even though the sun was beating down on my head and large flies feasted on the dried salt on my face. My back ached, and my knees were sore, but the sense of achievement was often overwhelming.

All the time you're aware that it's all too easy to screw up, in which case what's left of me gets flown home in a box and I become just another sorry statistic on an ever-growing casualty list. In fact, the best you can hope for at the end of a six-month tour is to be alive, preferably with arms, legs and your b***s intact. Anything beyond that is a bonus.

When you have just watched your mate being blown up, you have to bury it deep inside and let the job take over. Get the help you need and if it means sending you to Combat Stress for six weeks or to the Army psychiatrist, it's nothing to be ashamed of. Seeing things at war will change you, but it shouldn't change who you are. So, if you get offered some sort of treatment, don't sit there and brush it off, bloody do it!"

One story from Staff Sgt Hughes is that of Lance-Corporal Fullerton who stepped on an IED, and he then reported that both his own legs have gone above the knee. Staff Sgt Hughes and his team tied tourniquets around what was left and got him onto a stretcher. As they started the evacuation, the two stretcher-bearers triggered another IED. He goes on to say that following the explosion, they think they are dead. He sends out one of his team to search for a safe path to Lance Cpl Fullerton and mark this with spray paint.

This is a slow but much needed process, as the unfortunate stretcher-bearers had shown that it was not known how many more IED's there were, or where they were located. But it was the only way to ensure that everyone stayed inside a safe area. Staff Sgt Hughes continues:

"We had reached the injured woman medic, to discover that the bottom half of her leg was barely attached, and she was going into shock and beginning to slip away. We were trying to lift her out when suddenly an

anxious cry went up: 'Kim, we've got another IED!' It was in the gravelly bottom of the dried riverbed, barely an arm's length away from where the casualties lay waiting to be rescued.

Normally I would have thrown up a cordon around the entire area and evacuated everyone before getting to work on the IED. That's what the training manual said. But this was real life, and there were simply too many injured and dead people on the ground. I realised that there were no batteries to power the individual IEDs, as you would normally expect. Instead, everything was wired up to a central power line, which the Taliban could connect or disconnect as they saw fit.

The two dead soldiers remained undisturbed, one in some reeds, the other in the open, almost as if they were peacefully sleeping. I dropped down on my knees next to one of them and reached for his identity tags, which were required for the records to confirm that he was killed in action (KIA). The bomb had caused appalling injuries. What was left of his body was battered and torn beyond recognition and stripped of all dignity. I hoped his death had been quick and painless. I patted him on the shoulder as if to say: 'Rest now. Your job is done.'

As his comrades stepped forward, their eyes full of tears, to carry him in a body bag to a waiting helicopter, I knew that somewhere in the UK, an officer dressed in his best military uniform was going to make that dreadful journey to the next of kin. There would be that knock on the door, a moment of confusion, then disbelief and anger followed by unimaginable sorrow and pain.

The suddenness with which death came in Afghanistan was always shocking. An hour ago, the dead soldiers had been vibrant and carefree, full of life, smiles and fun. Now those same sons, husbands and brothers were dead and everything they were and everything they were going to be was gone. We returned to base just 90 minutes after we had left it. In the time it takes to play a game of football three soldiers had been killed, more were wounded, one seriously, and God only knows how many traumatised."

Extract from a Daily Mail Article of June 2017:

In October 2017 it was reported that soldiers at risk of shell shock can be spotted, before they are even sent to the battlefield, with a simple questionnaire. The pre-deployment psychological tests identify those most at risk of developing post-traumatic stress disorder or depression before they have been in combat. A study of tens of thousands of veterans found those who scored worst in the tests were much more prone to mental illness triggered by experiences of war. The screening tool in combination with other personnel information could help pick out individuals vulnerable to depression and PTSD.

The researchers at the Naval Postgraduate School and Research Facilitation Laboratory in Monterey, California, also generated a composite risk score for each individual. This was based on psychological attributes along with gender, age, race, ethnicity, marital status, education and military occupation group. Out of those whose score classified them as being at the highest risk for mental health disorders, 31 per cent screened positive for depression and 27 per cent for PTSD after return from deployment.

In an article in the Lancet in May 2010 entitled, '*What are the consequences of deployment to Iraq and Afghanistan on the mental health of the UK Armed Forces? A cohort Study,*' it was noted in the Introduction that it had been previously shown that deployment to Iraq has not adversely affected the mental health of regular UK military personnel; however, deployment did affect the mental health of reservists (individuals paid by the military only when they are undertaking military duties; reservists typically have civilian jobs when not working for the military). The results contrasted with data from the USA that show increased prevalence of probable mental disorders, particularly post-traumatic stress disorder, in military personnel returning from deployment.

Much has changed since the publication of our initial report in 2006. The war in Iraq continued and UK armed forces experienced an increase in hostilities in the south of Iraq. At the same time, the campaign in Afghanistan intensified, with UK armed forces deployed in large numbers to Helmand Province in southern Afghanistan, close to the Pakistan border (at present there are 9500 UK armed forces personnel in Afghanistan). Fighting continues to be intense, and casualties, often resulting from improvised explosive devices, have been frequent.

Further, as the military operations in Iraq and Afghanistan continued, rates of post-traumatic stress disorder in the USA have increased with time since return from deployment. If replicated in the UK, this increase in prevalence over time would have implications for the long-term effect of deployment, with some predicting a so-called tidal wave of mental disorders in years to come. Additionally, some speculate that experiencing multiple deployments will lead to an increase in the frequency of mental disorders. To address these issues, we assessed the effect of deployment to Iraq and Afghanistan from 2003 to the end of data collection (September 2009). We have re-assessed the mental health of those who participated in phase 1 of our cohort study and included two additional groups of UK armed forces personnel to represent the present military structure (those who have joined the military since 2003) and present operational deployments (those deployed to Afghanistan, between April 2006 and April 2007). We examined: (1) the effect of deployment to Iraq and Afghanistan from 2003 to the end of data collection (September 2009); (2) the effect of multiple deployments of UK personnel to both Iraq and Afghanistan; and (3) whether any effects of deployment on mental disorders increase or decrease with time since return from deployment.

The study recorded a significant interaction between deployment status and engagement type for probable post-traumatic stress disorder which was anticipated from phase 1, thus implying that the effect of deployment on the reporting of probable post-traumatic stress disorder differs between regulars and reservists. We also examined whether stage of deployment to Iraq or Afghanistan had an effect on probable mental disorders. For those with deployment experience to Iraq and Afghanistan, the number of times they had been deployed to Iraq and Afghanistan was explored in relation to mental disorders. These analyses were restricted to regular army personnel who were still in service at the time of questionnaire completion, because this group generally deploy for periods of 6 months, whereas the pattern of deployments differs for the other services and for reservists. For example, RAF personnel (eg, aircrew) deploy more often but for shorter periods of time than do other military personnel. Further, these analyses were restricted to still serving personnel, because there was a significant interaction between number of deployments and current serving status for probable post-traumatic stress disorder.

For regulars, unadjusted analyses showed evidence of a positive effect of time since return from deployment on reporting both symptoms of common mental disorder and probable post-traumatic stress disorder. The odds ratio peaked at up to 3 years since return from deployment for symptoms of common mental disorder and at up to 4 years since return from deployment for the reporting of probable post-traumatic stress disorder. The report recorded the opposite for alcohol misuse-time since return had a negative effect on the reporting of alcohol misuse, with the lowest odds ratio reported at up to 5 years since return from deployment. After adjustment, we recorded no association with symptoms of common mental disorders and alcohol misuse. These associations were mainly accounted for by educational status (symptoms of common mental disorder) and age.

For regulars, unadjusted analyses showed evidence of a positive effect of time since return from deployment on reporting both symptoms of common mental disorder and probable post-traumatic stress disorder. The odds ratio peaked at up to 3 years since return from deployment for symptoms of common mental disorder and at up to 4 years since return from deployment for the reporting of probable post-traumatic stress disorder. We recorded the opposite for alcohol misuse-time since return had a negative effect on the reporting of alcohol misuse, with the lowest odds ratio reported at up to 5 years since return from deployment. After adjustment, we recorded no association with symptoms of common mental disorders and alcohol misuse. These associations were mainly accounted for by educational status (symptoms of common mental disorder) and age. After adjustment, there remained a small but significant trend for the reporting of probable stress disorder for reservists. Adjustment for sociodemographic characteristics, military factors, and deployment status at phase 1 had a small effect on the odds ratios. In regulars, examination of the characteristics of those deployed between phase 1 and phase 2 of the study again showed that they were more likely than were those not deployed to be younger, male, be a non-commissioned officer, remain in service, and have been deployed at phase 1 and be in the army. In reservists, being younger, remaining in service, and having been deployed at phase 1 were predictive of being deployed between phase 1 and phase 2 of the study.

Living with the Ghosts of Your Past
A comprehensive 2009 study cross-referenced the 233,803 individuals who left the Armed Forces between 1996 and 2005 with the database held by the UK National Inquiry into Suicide and Homicide. The investigation identified 224 suicides and observed that the rate of suicide was no greater in veterans than for the general population. The risk for men aged 30–49 was lower than for the equivalent group in the general population. The

rate of suicide was higher for young males (19–24 years) who had left the Forces than among the equivalent group in the population. However, the researchers concluded that this may reflect pre-Service vulnerabilities rather than factors related to Service experience or discharge.

Despite the evidence, the review team encountered several assertions regarding suicide among service personnel and veterans. The most frequently quoted statistic was that the number of suicides among Falklands veterans is greater than the number of Servicemen killed in action during the 1982 conflict. This story first appeared in the Daily Mail in 2002 and continues to resurface, though it is not true. A recent study by Defence Statistics found that applying a UK general population mortality profile to personnel who had served in the Falklands campaign would produce an expected 2,079 deaths. The study found that as of 31st December 2012 only 1,335 Falklands veterans had died. In comparing the expected with the actual death rate, the Falklands cohort has a 36% decreased risk of dying compared with the UK population. For those who survived the conflict, the Defence Statistics study identified a total of 95 suicide and open-verdict deaths (7% of all deaths); this represents a 35% decreased risk compared to the age-matched general population and is considerably less than the number killed in action.

Matthew Green's book Aftershock: The Untold Story of Surviving Peace, sharply exposes the faults in the current system whereby the NHS and veterans' charities are responsible for discharged soldiers and reads like an urgent manifesto for change to cope with the growing number of cases of PTSD; the legacy of the 220,000 who served in the brutal wars in Iraq and Afghanistan stated.

"Nobody at the top is trying to make sure the most vulnerable don't fall through the cracks."

The stories Green has collected are so powerful, in part because they are some of the only means we have of measuring the true scale of PTSD in Britain. He also questions the efficiency of the UK's bewildering array of military charities. In 2015 there were approximately 2,000, with an estimated 350 relating to welfare and mental health, a group with an annual income of some £400 million. Many of the veterans criticise Combat Stress (the largest) for neglecting difficult cases, but Green says:

"It is unfair to lay the blame solely at its door. It's not reasonable to expect a charity to provide the whole range of services that we need. The problem is the government has abdicated responsibility to the charity sector."

Many veterans insist more work should be done on preparing people for the transition from conflict to peace. In the words of one former Royal Marine, they are let out *'with the safety catch off.'* (This is a service phrase that indicates the weapon is live and ready to use as and when required, and only needs the trigger to be pulled. You may know this better as *'light the blue touch paper and run'*.

Matthew Green goes on to comment that:

"It's not enough for the army to recruit from a pool of young men who have few other prospects, then let them leave the army and stand back and watch them implode. Even if, for others, the symptoms take years to materialise, we can no longer afford to ignore the ghosts in our midst."

Below are two personal stories giving you an insight into the ups and downs of military life and PTSD. Both stories have been taken from a Daily Telegraph Article in September 2015.

Former Royal Engineer, Dean Upson, 35:

"I served with the Royal Engineers for 14 years before my medical discharge in 2011. When I came back from Iraq in 2003 my mum told me I wasn't behaving like myself: I was really aggressive and just felt negative about everything. I went in secret to the medical centre. I thought if anybody found out it would be the end of my career, and worried even more what the lads would think. I should have been red-flagged but instead they told me I had depression and could leave the Army if I wanted. I just bottled it all up instead. In Afghanistan I was working on the Chinooks with the Medical Emergency Response Teams, bringing casualties back. We picked up children, soldiers who had been blown up; what pushed me over the edge was a young artillery officer who had been shot going out for a run. I was diagnosed with PTSD in 2009. I was lucky in a way to be recognised while still serving. I have had various suicide attempts and can count on two

hands the number of lads I know that have killed themselves because of PTSD. You feel like you are getting palmed off by everyone and treatment is a postcode lottery."

The wife: Susan McInally, 44:

I've been married to Joe for 23 years; five years ago, he had his first breakdown and was diagnosed with PTSD. When he suffers flashbacks, he is transported straight back to Northern Ireland. He has attacked me and other people but only ever out of fear, because he perceives himself to be under attack. The past five years have been horrific. It's a day in, day out fight, every inch of the way, to get help from the NHS and charities. Not just for your other half but for yourself. There are a lot of people in the same boat. I set up the PTSD Angels as a support group and it currently has about 230 members.

Long-Term Responses to Treatment with Military-Related PTSD

The number of service personnel diagnosed with post-traumatic stress disorder rose by nearly a fifth in 2013 amid concern about the enduring psychological toll of the Iraq and Afghan campaigns. This was part of a warning by Combat Stress that it had seen a 57 per cent increase in former soldiers, sailors and airmen needing treatment after serving in Afghanistan, and this was a matter of concern. The Ministry of Defence's own figures were showing an additional increase of around 12 per cent for cases of mental disorders, including depression and anxiety.

The MoD pointed out that the rate of mental illness in the military is the same as among the wider population and the clear majority of returning troops have no mental health problems. However, Andrew Cameron, Chief Executive of Combat Stress, stated:

"The figures should be a matter of concern for everyone who cares passionately about the welfare of our brave Armed Forces, particularly the substantial increase in PTSD. It is also not a one-off. Government reports this year have shown similar substantial increases. The Government has made significant progress in supporting the mental wellbeing of our troops. Yet, we should not assume that these figures can simply be explained as the *result of a heightened awareness of the support available. Across the board, military mental health support services are witnessing an unprecedented increase in demand for support. There is an underlying cause at work which we must work together to address."*

In 2012, 2,550 armed forces personnel were treated for mental health issues, taking the total diagnosed since 2007 to 11,000. Of these, 176 were treated for psychoactive substance abuse including alcohol abuse; there were 1,662 cases of neurotic disorders, including 273 reports of PTSD; 547 cases of mood disorders, including depression and 167 cases of other mental and behavioural disorders.

The MoD has worked to improve care for personnel with mental illness and introduced a programme of decompression in Cyprus for up to two weeks after returning from tours of Afghanistan. This is to allow the service personnel to try and normalise their lives before being thrown back into life in the UK. It is, however, accepted that all those who experience combat will suffer from some form of stress and every military unit (regular or reservist) will have taken this and trained personnel to recognise the signs of trauma and stress. One problem with this learning curve is that it takes no account of what happens to the person or their family after they leave.

Once a person has left military service, if that be via redundancy - and yes, there are many cases of people returning from combat to then be told 'Thanks but no thanks, off you go to Civvy Street as you are SNLR (Services No Longer Required), - this can be traumatic, no matter how they are mentally after returning home from the battlefield. The lives of these people are falling apart at the seams and there is no one there to help apart from the established military charities. If it was not for them, these people would quite likely have an unimaginable ending to life.

From 2003 to 2013, 123 serving personnel have died of suspected or confirmed suicide while serving in the Armed Forces, compared with 619 recorded as dying in Iraq and Afghanistan from all causes, including combat, accidents, suicide and natural causes. The MoD have stated that every year around 24,000 personnel leave the Armed Forces. Most people do this successfully but for some this can be daunting, so we have worked hard to ensure our services personnel get the support and mental health care they need, including those going through the redundancy process.

A report in the Lancet in 2013 put together the experiences of almost

COURAGE AFTER THE BATTLE

14,000 serving and former military personnel with information from the police national computer for the first time. Within this research, links were found between active combat and post-traumatic stress disorder, alcohol abuse and depression. The research was part funded by the MoD who wanted to improve the care of military personnel. The report found that there's room for improvement and it does not allow for such things as domestic violence; if it did, the figures would be considerably worse.

Overall the armed forces are normally more self-controlling and mindful of the ramifications of being charged with offences than their civilian counterparts. That said, those who served in combat in Iraq or Afghanistan were 53% more likely to offend violently than those not on the frontline. Those with multiple experiences of combat had a 70%-80% greater risk of being convicted for acts of violence. It was found that there was a likelihood of having some participants who would have offended before they joined up, which again made it more likely for them to be selected for combat.

It seems from this that disadvantaged, poorly educated young men who had committed criminal offences before joining up are more likely to be sent into combat and are then more likely to be both traumatised and criminalised by their experiences. Isn't this just a modern take on WW1 cannon fodder? The meaning of *cannon fodder* is 'soldiers regarded merely as material to be expended in war'. It's supposed to be an archaic term, but, for too many, it probably doesn't seem that way.

Just because someone commits violence when they are very young - and we all have our wild periods, which we later regret - it doesn't mean that they're going to be violent for ever. The main aim for most young men and women who join the armed forces would be learning a trade, travel and start a new life, and not learning how to be better at how best to injure someone in a fight. Look at the recent glossy adverts for the Royal Navy, showing a person in a civvy job, then on board a naval vessel. They state that they were born in the north east but made in the Royal Navy.

For some, being repeatedly thrown into combat situations might prolong and enhance violent tendencies they might otherwise have grown out of. Others, those who are part of the PlayStation generation, realise the reality of life and war. This comes as a shock to see that when you are killed you are killed, and there is no reset button. The irony is that when the service personnel leave active duty, the same single-minded aggression is swiftly denounced as wrong by society. Is it any wonder they don't know which way to turn when they are being pulled from pillar to post by people telling them different things and they have seen the horrors of the battlefield?

You only have to see how physically disabled soldiers are treated in this country (some are forced to rely on charities for help and assistance) to imagine how all these good intentions are going to pan out in this era of savage cuts and savings. You would have thought that the sacrifice they have made would have seen them treated and cared for in a more appropriate manner.

A study undertaken in 2016 looked at the long-term responses to treatment of veterans with PTSD. This study tried to evaluate longer-term treatment and identify which individuals may need added support within a clinical practice. The intervention was offered by Combat Stress and included 401 veterans who completed a standardised 6-week residential treatment. Of these, 268 (67%) were successfully followed up a year after the end of treatment.

Significant reductions in PTSD severity were observed a year after treatment and reductions in the secondary outcomes were also reported. The study, although an uncontrolled study, suggests the longer-term benefits of a structured programme to treat UK veterans with PTSD were possible.

The number of serving and ex-forces personnel being awarded compensation for mental disorders hit record levels in 2016, which has seen fears that we are now starting to see the slippery slope of the actual cost of the Afghanistan and Iraq wars in the form of the mental scars left on those who had to fight them.

Analysis of the Armed Forces Compensation Scheme statistics showed that the annual number of mental disorder pay-outs has increased by 379 per cent, from 121 in 2009-2010 to 580 in 2015-16, to reach the highest total in the 11 years the scheme has been running.

The details are not broken down by type of mental disorder or whether a claimant saw combat, but mental health professionals say the timing of the increase mirrors the expected time lag before Afghanistan and Iraq veterans start to experience symptoms and seek help.

It was reported that unlike those with visible injuries, the men and women left with the hidden wounds of mental trauma are being left to struggle against an Armed Forces Compensation Scheme determined to give them as little as possible.

Dean Upson, 36, a former Corporal in the Royal Engineers and both an

Iraq and Afghanistan veteran, left the Army in June 2011. He was initially awarded just £3,000 for complex PTSD that was so severe it has left him suicidal and unable to do a full-time job. After four years, and with his lawyer's involvement, he eventually received a maximum award of more than £160,000. Mr Upson stated:

"After 14 years' service, tours of Iraq and Afghanistan and an entire life messed up by PTSD, it was a joke. They will fight and question everything, they will even try everything they can to discharge you before you get your diagnosis of PTSD. I've known guys discharged on the grounds of personality defect or burnout. Because they didn't get their diagnosis of PTSD before they were discharged, they got nothing. They don't care. The fact that you have fought for your country, done three combat tours, that counts for nothing. The visible injuries that they can't argue with, the lost limbs, they will pay straight away. But the non-visible injuries, they don't want to give you a thing. Given that many soldiers tried to crack on, seeking help only when they were at breaking point, I would expect a tidal wave of traumatised veterans to come forward in the coming decade."

Dr Walter Busuttil, Director of Medical Services at the charity Combat Stress, and a consultant psychiatrist who served for 16 years in the RAF, stated:

"Given that mental symptoms can take years to surface and many veterans only start experiencing them after leaving the forces, it was highly likely the increase in compensation claims was driven by Afghanistan and Iraq veterans. It's the tip of the iceberg. We just don't know how big the iceberg is. If it's a small iceberg, we are going to be really, really busy. If it is a big iceberg, we are going to be overwhelmed. This is not going to go away for some years. The indications are people will keep coming forward. I am not predicting for how long and how many. I am not saying it's out of control, but it has increased every year, so I am worried. We need funds, we need help, from any direction as either veterans don't know compensation is available, or they are too ashamed to apply. Stigma is a big thing in the military.

Both the armed forces and NHS were working increasingly hard to help minimise the trauma experienced by veterans, and treatments were proving *ever more effective, especially for those seeking help early. However, the services are good but there aren't enough of them. There is a lack of expertise all round. Many doctors have never served in the military. There is a lack of understanding of military culture. Training is really important. The NHS needs to ring-fence funds for veterans' mental health."*

The Ministry of Defence has consistently argued that the rates of PTSD among forces personnel generally is low. However, there are many forces personnel who were deployed to Iraq and Afghanistan but did not directly experience combat or were in non-combat roles. Not wishing to be disingenuous to personnel who were not in forward observation bases on daily patrols, those who were out on patrol and in forward observation bases were 7% more likely to suffer PTSD later. The MoD line has been confirmed by a 2014 study by the King's Centre for Military Health at King's College London, which found that PTSD rates among UK regulars returning from Iraq or Afghanistan ranged between 1.3 per cent and 4.8 per cent – comparable to the 3 per cent rate found in the general civilian population.

Given the above, why do politicians and others in high places still refuse to acknowledge that service personnel are not to be used and then thrown on the scrap heap, or used to make points against an opponent in another party? They are human beings who have defended you in your time of need and now need your help. You can plaster over the cracks all you like and make the punch lines and half-truths sound as if you are doing something. You can ask the GPs and hospitals to ask, "are you a veteran?" and put this on the records and tick a box; but don't sit on the information - use it! I know we have the war pension and this gives certain rights to advance up the medical treatment ladder. This is a scheme whose benefits are rarely used given the state of the NHS. We only ask one thing; help me when I need it.

Percentages and statistics are a wonderful way to hide information and figures. 10% of a figure cannot be the same as 10% of another figure. To get a true representation, you must take a like-for-like approach to the information and figures used. If this is not done, then the figures being given by either party are completely meaningless. It is like comparing an apple to an orange and saying they are the same when they clearly are not. The only similarity is they are both round and edible.

Combat Stress's own figures show a 26 per cent increase in the number of veterans seeking the charity's help for mental health problems between 2014 and 2015, followed by a further six per cent increase to 2,472 referrals in the fiscal year 2015-16.

Source - http://www.independent.co.uk/news/uk/home-news/ptsd-iraq-afghanistan-british-army-mental-health-depression-wars-combat-stress-veterans-uk-armed-a7199461.html

In 2015, we had 16 Departments of Community Mental Health (DCMHs) specialist units, run by the Ministry of Defence's Defence Medical Services. By January 2018, there were 11 with the closures announced by the Ministry of Defence, which included the busiest DCMH at Catterick, North Yorkshire, which supports 13,000 troops. More than 400 serving personnel have committed suicide between 1995 and 2015 with the number diagnosed with PTSD almost doubling to around 2,500. The doors of the DCMH at Leuchars were closed even though the base is intended to become the Army's main centre in Scotland.

In January 2018 the MoD conceded that the number of DCMH centres had been cut to 11 as part of a restructuring of provision and stated that mental health services had been added at nine other places, making a total of 20 sites around the UK. A spokesman added:

"We are investing millions of pounds to improve those services for personnel and veterans to ensure they get the help they need and deserve."

The MoD admitted it had also been forced to fund treatment externally after its mental health waiting times for service personnel seeking help fell behind those of the NHS. Defence sources added that the average waiting time for service personnel to be treated for PTSD and other conditions based on figures up to September 2017 was now 46 calendar days.

To add insult to injury the MoD deemed an estimated cost of £2 million too costly to install and run a helpline for serving personnel and veterans. However, in their non-service understanding of service personnel needs, the minions at the MoD decreed that they would spend £1.5 million on specialist consultants to advise them how to cut costs.

MoD chiefs wrestling with a £20 billion budget black hole are now so concerned about balancing the books that they plan to spend the much-needed cash on expert advice about slashing the Armed Forces' budget.

Despite the numerous versions of rhetoric and political speak, they think more of the accounts than the personnel which they are supposed to be looking after. According to plans for an MoD Efficiency Assurance Review, the MoD has undertaken significant assurance work internally over the summer of 2017 over its efficiency savings.

As part of the contract, an external company will have to answer questions including: How credible is the revised efficiency plan within the MoD financial forecast? and: Do the planning assumptions currently used stack up? Tory MP Leo Docherty, who sits on the Commons Defence Committee, branded the plans 'obscene' and urged the MoD to spend the money on key military services. An MoD spokesman said:

"We are making good progress towards our challenging efficiency targets but are not complacent, and this is just an example of how we are ensuring we remain on track."

On 25th February 2015, Defence Secretary Gavin Williamson announced that the crucial helpline service will be launched from midday. An extra £20 million will be found to fund the helpline over the next ten years, along with other new mental health initiatives to stem the shocking level of suicides among the Armed Forces. This is only £2 million a year, and there is no mention of what the other mental health issues are. When the cost for helplines such as the *Childline and Schools service for 2017 was £20.3 million* (source Childline web site), £20 million over ten years is insufficient if the MoD are honest about their intentions in helping service personnel, former and current, in their hour of need.

CASUALTIES IN NUMBERS
400 troops are estimated to have killed themselves since 1995
393 troops medically discharged from UK Armed Forces in 2016/17 due to mental disorders
6,137 troops assessed by MoD for mental health issues last year
317 new cases of post-traumatic stress disorder in the Armed Forces in 2016/17
1,630 new cases of adjustment disorders among UK troops last year
1,672 new cases of mood disorders among UK troops last year
96% rise in Royal Marines diagnosed with mental disorders since 2007

COURAGE AFTER THE BATTLE

129% rise in officers across Armed Forces seeking mental healthcare since 2007

The free Military Mental Health Helpline 0800 323 4444 will be funded by the Ministry of Defence and run with the charity Combat Stress. The new helpline will, however, be integrated with the MoD's existing mental health services.

The campaign to have the helpline installed was fully supported by Lord Dannatt, General Sir Mike Jackson; Field Marshal Lord Guthrie; former Gulf War pilot John Nichol; Chantelle Taylor, the first British woman to kill in combat; and soldiers who won the Military Cross for bravery, and many more.

In February 2018, around the same time as the MoD finally caved in to pressure on the helpline, it emerged that around 40 per cent of the money from the LIBOR fund released so far has been used for worthy causes within government departments. Ministers had taken £326 million from a pot meant for military charities and worthy causes for their own cash-strapped departments. Former chancellor George Osborne set up the fund in 2012 to support veterans and emergency services charities and used the fines from banks who manipulated the inter-bank interest rates.

The money was spent on projects such as improving Army barracks, installing sports facilities on military bases and funding wounded vets' rehab centres. Treasury sources stressed the money was not going to the department's budgets and was instead being used for extra projects deemed worthy enough. Some cash was also spent on buying air ambulances and even maintaining cadet troops. The MoD was handed around £126m for projects deemed as worthy causes. A further £200m was also claimed by education ministers to spend on creating 50,000 apprenticeships.

Is this not the case that they were using the funds to assist the departments in their financial commitments in undertaking these tasks, rather than the budget allocated to them for the tasks? Therefore, they were using the monies incorrectly and not what they were intended for or, to put it bluntly, misappropriating funds intended to assist veterans but instead using them for their own departmental aims.

Examples of some of the projects ministers spent the LIBOR cash on are:
£200m was also claimed by education ministers to spend on creating 50,000 apprenticeships

COURAGE AFTER THE BATTLE

£20m to build the Defence and National Rehabilitation Centre
£2.5m to replace Sea Cadets' sailing dinghies
£300k to erect an Outdoor Centre for Royal Navy
£250k to renovate welfare facilities at RAF Brize Norton
Unveiling the £973 million fund in 2012, George Osborne announced: The proceeds from LIBOR fines would be used to support Armed Forces and Emergency Services charities.

On the flip side of this, one of the worthy causes to which the monies were intended was Help For Heroes, who were given just £7.1m in grants, which is just a paltry 1 per cent of the whole LIBOR pot.
Help for Heroes Chief Executive Mel Waters said:

"Every month over 200 men and women are medically discharged from our Armed Forces, but it's getting harder to raise money to help them rebuild their lives and become a force for good once more. It is extraordinary that this money has been used to top-up Government departments and other budgets when it could have done so much for our wounded Servicemen and Servicewomen."

Tory MP Johnny Mercer stated that the amount wasted here is almost criminal, and he was going to ask the Defence Committee if we can conduct a full inquiry.
Only £773 million in grants from the LIBOR pot has been publicly declared so far, so the final figure given to departments could be higher. A total of £40million has not yet been committed through any scheme. A total of £141 million is the amount committed to the Covenant Fund from the LIBOR fines that is yet to be spent.
A HM Treasury Spokesperson said:

"'Armed Forces, emergency services charities and other related good causes benefit from hundreds of millions of funds from LIBOR banking fines. Money given to Departments since 2012 from these fines is ring-fenced to be spent on these worthy causes. Funding for centres and facilities is consistent with supporting good causes and is making a difference to the Armed Forces community."

In March 2018, it was announced that NHS chiefs had withdrawn £3.2

million from Combat Stress. This equates to around 20% of their budget and will drastically affect the work Combat Stress will be able to undertake. Combat Stress was forced to make 40 staff redundant just before Christmas as part of a £2.5 million cost-cutting programme, which was a massive blow to the charity and the people they help. Combat Stress provides mental healthcare for up to 3,000 veterans a year, including 324 who took part in the charity's six-week residential treatment programmes in 2016-17.

Chief executive Sue Freeth described the situation as an 'SOS moment' for the charity. She stated:

"Patients with complex cases of PTSD need to be in a caring environment and to be surrounded by people similar to themselves. Yet now NHS England is going to treat them as outpatients. We will continue to offer residential care for as long as we can. But we can no longer use our reserve funds to subsidise the service. We will struggle. This is an SOS moment."

A short while after the announcement, NHS England announced a new mental health initiative for veterans, costing the same amount as it has pulled from the charity. Dr Jonathan Leach, from NHS England, said:

"We are investing £3.2 million in a national complex treatment service, launching next month, which will treat more patients over a longer period. "

While Combat Stress offers residential care to former troops, they will now be treated as outpatients and the care and support they desperately need will no longer be there. This service would not help the country's most vulnerable veterans but can be seen as a cost-cutting exercise which on paper sounds great to those looking after the budget, but in reality is a death sentence to many others who would actually benefit from the likes of Combat Stress.

If successive governments, and I will include some senior management at the NHS in this, really and truly cared about service personnel it would not have to be the national press, public and others to shame them into getting real assistance to those who have served and are now suffering. Why do they, time upon time, say what they think people want to hear, and dodge questions which have factual issues? Why do they say one thing, not only on mental health care but also on equipment and services, then fail to deliver? They had no intention of purchasing the equipment or services, some of which can be lifesaving - see the Snatch Land Rover fiasco as one of many examples. Do they honestly care or, as suspected, just use this as a ploy to feather their own nest and climb the political ladder, and nothing else?

Equine Therapy

Equine therapy is a recent innovation into the UK and there are two distinct approaches, one based on an hourly introduction and progression into the therapy and the other a military format. The initial style is undertaken by a group called Horse Thinking in Derbyshire, and the person undertaking that course will expect to have around 6-8 hours, once or twice a week. The other style is based in Scotland and is run by a former Royal Marine from 45 Commando. Within this course the participant works with other ex-military people, some of whom have also been injured in combat. Almost immediately there is the inter service camaraderie and what can only be described as a military mindset in other areas including map reading, fishing, falconry and bush craft, as well as an introduction to the environment.

Both schemes have a different approach to the use of the horse but the end result is that they want the participant to gain confidence and find their inner self to assist themselves in coping with life in general.

HORSE THINKING

Horse Thinking is spread over a 6.75 acre site with Pennine scenery and forestry, adjacent to a lake and nature reserve in northern England, which has been carefully designed around the needs of clients, their work and the horses. The horses are encouraged to live totally naturally outside and as a family herd. There are no stables or permanent buildings on the site except for a temporary office building. Clients normally attend either as an individual or in groups, depending on the circumstances, and would typically experience 6 to 8 one-hour sessions, perhaps once or twice a week.

One method of aiding the road to recovery is the horseback therapy system. Equine-Assisted Psychotherapy (EAP) is a highly effective, credible method used to help people address a wide variety of problems, from combat-PTSD to alcohol dependency and the effects of abuse. Far from the initial thoughts, EAP does not involve riding a horse but the person is brought near to the horse. They do not even have to touch the horse, as the trainer will observe the reactions of both the horse and person being treated.

From this observation, the trainer can gain a crucial insight into the client's own emotions, attitudes and behaviours, which will provide vital clues as to the person's feelings. One bonus to this is that the person can also get an insight into understanding for themselves. Horses don't naturally trust easily as their survival depends on a good relationship and communication to those close to and around them.

As a result, horses are remarkably intuitive, and can read human moods and intentions very accurately, particularly through body language. This process enables soldiers and veterans to identify potential changes they need to make in themselves to alleviate their symptoms and improve their lives.

HORSEBACK UK

In November 2008 Jock and Emma Hutchison moved with their young family to Ferrar, just outside Aboyne in Aberdeenshire. Their plan was to set up a business using American Quarter Horses and western riding to explore the beautiful scenery of Royal Deeside. That Christmas several friends, many of whom were either serving or ex-military, came to the farm to celebrate New Year. Having played around with the horses during the day and whilst sitting around the bonfire a comment was made.

"This is what the guys should do when they come back from War." So, the seeds of HorseBack UK were sown.

As an Ex-Marine, Jock had served at 45 Commando in Arbroath. Jock approached the current Commanding Officer. 2008 had been a particularly traumatic year for 45 Commando as in their recent tour of Afghanistan they had lost 9 of their own in combat with a further 16 suffering life-changing injury. Jock and Emma offered the farm as somewhere that the injured marines could come to as a break, away from clinical recovery, and over the next 12 months had several groups come and visit the farm.

In 2009 HorseBack UK gained charitable status with the aim of taking wounded servicemen and women and introducing them to horses. Through working with the horses amongst a like-minded group, service personnel who had been mentally and physically scarred could regain their confidence, dignity and, especially in the case of amputees, mobility.

COURAGE AFTER THE BATTLE

HorseBack UK uses horsemanship to inspire recovery, regain self-esteem and provide a sense of purpose and community to the wounded, injured and sick of the military community. Using horsemanship and exposure to the natural environment, participants gain self-confidence and self-esteem amongst people who have experienced similar trauma.

PHASE 1 – DISCOVERY
The discovery week is aimed at finding out about the individual, the horses and the environment. Attendees will be introduced to like-minded people with similar experiences. They will work with the horses on the ground as well as riding them in the latter part of the week. Other activities will include fishing, falconry and bush craft as well as an introduction to the environment.

PHASE 2 – CONSERVE
The conserve week aims to improve horsemanship skills, both on the ground and in the saddle, as well as an introduction to conservation of the local environment. Participants will recap skills such as map reading as well as learning possible new skills such as dry-stone walling.

PHASE 3 – EXPLORE AND SHARE
The final week is about planning and preparation for the overnight expedition. Participants will plan the route and pack all necessary equipment. They will then ride the horses to the pre-planned destination where they will set up camp for the night. The horses will be ridden back to base the following day, where preparation will then be made to give a five-minute presentation on their experience of the course. This presentation can take any number of formats from audio recordings, art, poetry, photography or by using more traditional methods. An award ceremony will follow these presentations.

On completion of the three phases the participants have improved confidence and self-esteem and a feeling of self-worth. They will have become part of a team once again and had to work within that team to achieve set goals. Through working with the horses, they will have re-established leadership skills, addressed body language and possibly other issues such as anger. They will have made new friends who have experienced similar issues, with whom they are encouraged to keep in contact, and set realistic goals and short and long-term targets.

COURAGE AFTER THE BATTLE

The Fight for a Helpline

In February 2018, a Mail on Sunday article had a story on the first female soldier to kill in combat. Extracts of this are highlighted below, along with other articles on how the MoD are throwing away service personnel with PTSD, and the personal stories and pleas from senior officers and service personnel for a 24-hour helpline and assistance.

Former Army medic Chantelle Taylor urged MoD chiefs to give traumatised troops a round-the-clock helpline. This plea was following the announcement that the number of troops diagnosed with PTSD has almost doubled in the past 10 years, with more than 400 serving soldiers having taken their own lives since 1995. There are growing calls for a 24/7 helpline for troops suffering with mental ill health.

Chantelle said:

"As a female soldier, I was never supposed to get involved in close-quarter combat until the day I shot dead a Taliban fighter at close range. While serving as a senior medic, I treated dozens of horrifically wounded soldiers from the battlefields of Helmand.

Today, the anguished expressions of those injured troops remain etched in my memory and I still feel guilty about those we couldn't save. Yet for all of that, I don't suffer from any mental or emotional disorder. I am one of the lucky ones.

Enough is enough, I say. What more evidence does one need that the current provision of mental healthcare is lacking than the suicide of yet another respected and experienced soldier, Afghanistan veteran, Warrant Officer Nathan Hunt, of the Royal Engineers?

The Ministry of Defence expects an extremely high level of professionalism from its military so it's time for them to meet like with like and care for those who selflessly serve their country.

So today I'm backing The Mail on Sunday's campaign for round-the clock care, including a 24/7 helpline. Serving sailors, soldiers and airmen suffering from PTSD should not have to rely on charities or the already overburdened NHS to provide lifesaving treatment at night and at weekends. Simple measures like this will save lives.

As a medic, it concerns me deeply that so many troops are being failed by the mental healthcare system, or the lack of it. That is why I've previously driven through the night to be there for suicidal friends.

It is the norm for people in close-knit military communities to go the extra mile to support their comrades. Yet I can't help thinking the MoD should be keeping a caring eye on our troops too.

So in addition to a helpline, we should introduce routine testing for psychological problems. We test our people's physical fitness, so why not their mental health, as the Americans already do?

Across the Armed Forces, tens of thousands of troops who served in Northern Ireland, Iraq and Afghanistan are still in service. For as long as they remain in uniform, their welfare is the MoD's responsibility. These men and women deserve a dedicated 24/7 helpline, staffed by military experts who are vetted, cleared and supported by a nationwide network of first-responders.

The existing helplines run by military charities are not designed to support serving personnel, yet serving members still reach out because they have nowhere else to go. These helplines are not integrated into the MoD's mental healthcare system, so soldiers cannot speak to their allocated care team if they are already receiving treatment."

The Ministry of Defence stated:
'We take the mental health of our Armed Forces very seriously and are committed to providing the best care possible. We are spending £20 million this year on mental health provisions."
In relation to this statement, former Army medic Chantelle Taylor said:
"This isn't good enough. It smacks of a half-hearted attempt to tackle a problem, a money-saving measure which exploits the voluntary sector. As does suggesting traumatised troops should visit their nearest A&E. I couldn't think of anything worse. The MoD is better placed to provide carers with the necessary experience and affinity with combat troops than the NHS.

The officials who baulked at spending £2 million to fund the helpline, which is backed by former Army chief Lord Dannatt, should have considered that sum a worthy investment. Having invested so much money in training soldiers, why are they so flippant about losing them to mental health issues?

I was never assessed for mental health problems when I left the military so any warning signs that I might later suffer were lost. We cannot leave to chance whether members of our Armed Forces develop such conditions.

COURAGE AFTER THE BATTLE

Waiting for a fatality is not acceptable. Our military has spent the last 20 years at war. We will all need to talk at some point. That's normal, so a 24/7 helpline is the absolute minimum.

Medics like me didn't do our damnedest to save soldiers' lives on the front line to then stand aside when they need help back home. We are all relying heavily on Gavin Williamson, who has made a promising start as Defence Secretary.

Soldiers don't need or want special treatment. They deserve the right treatment.

Colour Sergeant Jones, of 1st Battalion The Princess of Wales's Regiment, was awarded the Military Cross in 2012 for leading a bayonet charge against the Taliban in Afghanistan. He was later diagnosed with severe PTSD and has recently spent time in residential care due to his illness.

He stated that: *"In my case, as in many others, early warning signs about my mental health problems were missed, hence why annual tests should be introduced. Initially medical staff thought I was just suffering from stress. By the time I was diagnosed with PTSD, my health was a lot worse. The Army has spent a fortune training me. Leaving now is a waste of resources given my level of experience and seniority."*

A British Army War Hero and Military Cross winner Sean Jones, 31, has accused the Army of giving up on traumatised troops. 'Defence chiefs fix tanks but ignore us.' He has accused top brass of giving up on traumatized troops as it was announced that Sean was being medically discharged due to 'mental illness.'

Military Cross winner Sean Jones, 31, who suffers from PTSD, said:

"The provision of mental healthcare isn't good enough. I'd liken it to putting a plaster on a catastrophic bleed. We need a 24/7 helpline run by the Armed Forces, round-the-clock care and annual mental health testing for all personnel. Testing would prevent a lot of people developing full-blown PTSD. You've got to wonder why these provisions don't exist.

'Defence chiefs are basically showing the door to anyone who dares admit they've got mental health issues. They fix tanks but they don't bother fixing soldiers. The Army insists it has a 'retention positive' approach towards soldiers diagnosed with PTSD and other issues. But since 2012, the number of soldiers medically discharged for mental or behavioural problems has more than doubled – to 393 in 2016-17. Figures for mental health discharges have also increased in the Royal Air Force and Royal Navy.

Last year, an Armed Forces report into medical discharges claimed there was *difficulty returning personnel with severe or enduring mental ill-health, given the nature of their role and access to weapons."*

Given the £20 million being spent by the MoD on Mental Health for the armed services, and to see this in comparison to the NHS, you will see what a pitiful sum this is, considering that the armed personnel have given everything and the MoD have spent a large amount of money training these people to effectively throw them away along with the investment it has made in their careers and skills.

The Chief Executive of NHS England says it is also spending more on mental health, so if he can see the increase, why can the MoD not see the need - or is this just a civilian problem? Notwithstanding that a large proportion of homeless people are former military personnel, who have many issues, would this not give you a clue as to one of the root causes for this additional NHS spending?

In November 2017 the Health Secretary, Mr Jeremy Hunt, stated:

"Extra staff cost money so this is what the data shows: last year alone spending on mental health went up by £575m"

"with CCGs increasing spend by 6.3% vs an overall increase of 3.7% in their funding - in other words, spending up both in absolute terms and as a proportion of NHS spend"

Jeremy Hunt, 20 November 2017

The biggest spenders in NHS England are the Clinical Commissioning Groups (CCGs). Mr Hunt's point here is that mental health is now getting a bigger slice of the pie from CCGs. That is correct, although the figures used in his examples don't account for inflation, so the real increase in spending on mental health isn't £575 million, it's about £368 million in the last year.

That's also not all the money spent by NHS England on mental health, as some is spent on specialised mental health services. We don't have good figures on this extra money, but the Chief Executive of NHS England says it is also spending more on mental health.

Mental health spending by CCGs in England totalled £9.15 billion in 2015/16, according to figures published by NHS England. This had gone up to £9.72 billion in 2016/17. That's an increase of around £575 million or 6.3%. But these figures don't account for inflation. Once this is factored in, the increase in spending is actually less: £368 million and a percentage increase of 3.9%

Source https://fullfact.org/health/nhs-spending-mental-health/

Former RAF Officer John Nichol, whose Raf Tornado was shot down in the 1991 Gulf War, initially dismissed claims his interrogation and subsequent appearance on TV whilst in captivity would leave mental scars. He admits how wrong he was and thanked Dr Turnbull, who took the time to explain what could happen and how any symptoms of PTSD might present themselves. John explained that:

"every member of today's Armed Forces deserves the same expert care I received. It is heart-breaking to think there could be so many combat-hardened serving military personnel, including air crews, who suffer in silence due to a lack of round-the-clock care and the stigma that still surrounds mental health issues. I was recently phoned by a serviceman who was in tears talking about his struggles with his demons after seeing so much horror on the battlefields of Iraq and Afghanistan.
He had been affected by his combat experiences but did not feel he could seek help inside the military system. He spoke to me in confidence, so I cannot disclose his identity. But I know there are many other men and women across the Forces who have been similarly affected because of the courage they showed serving the country they love.

A 24/7 helpline, connecting these people to mental health experts, would apparently cost £2 million.

That is a bargain, given the thousands of troops suffering from PTSD and other related conditions.

The British public and the Armed Forces need to get to the same point of understanding and acceptance of troops with mental illness as they are *with physically injured personnel.*

There is a long way to go. It is indicative of the lack of emphasis placed on mental healthcare that at night and at weekends, troops suffering from any of these issues are forced to rely on A&E departments.

When, in the case of personnel in Northern Ireland, this could put them in danger, it is an absolute disgrace. It is cruelty. That soldiers have waited longer for mental health treatment than civilians, a situation that the Ministry of Defence was forced to admit, is also indefensible. Plainly, when it comes to how the MoD allocates its budget, mental healthcare is very low on the priorities list. Our serving men and women deserve much better care than they get now.

The defence chiefs can buy as many rocket systems, jets and aircraft carriers as they like, but without the highly skilled people to operate them, such equipment is useless. We have a fine tradition in the British military of not leaving anyone on the battlefield. We should not be leaving them to rot in a pit of despair if they suffer a mental illness."

A Facebook page set up by former serving personnel to help soldiers and veterans with post traumatic stress disorder has been closed by Facebook for having violent content. However, there are still other sites on there which promote various acts and groups of terrorism. It seems service personnel now have another wall to climb to get help when it is needed, or just someone to talk to.

The social media giant closed Fill Your Boots UK (FYB UK) in July 2018 without warning after claiming its content, which included discussions with mentally ill soldiers who were considering ending their lives, breached 'community' guidelines. Soldiers suffering from combat-induced traumas after serving in Iraq and Afghanistan would post 'cries for help' on the page on an almost daily basis according to its founder, ex-paratrooper Alfie Usher. FYB UK would then issue SOS messages, asking other veterans to rush to their aid.

Mr Usher informed moderators in a series of phone calls and emails that the page provided a lifeline for troops with mental and emotional disorders, but they still refused to unblock it. Mr Usher, 30, said:

"Facebook's actions have put soldiers' lives at risk. Guys use the page to express feelings which are really troubling them. They're desperate for help. It is very hard for them to discuss issues relating to their experiences in Iraq and Afghanistan with their families. They'd rather talk to people they meet on FYB UK who have probably experienced the same thing. I tried explaining this to Facebook but they just ignored me. I don't think they realise the consequences this could have. The closure of FYB UK also coincides with an unprecedented spike in the numbers of veterans taking their lives"

Facebook's stance is even more astonishing as it is still possible to find jihadi propaganda on the site, including pictures of terrorists brandishing ISIS flags and links to an online suicide game which is thought to have claimed the lives of up to 130 youngsters in Russia.
Over the course of this year UK troops who served in Iraq and Afghanistan have killed themselves at a rate of one every 13 days. A week before the closure of the site, a distressed soldier wrote to FYB UK saying he could no longer cope with feeling responsible for the deaths of two comrades in Afghanistan. He wrote:
"Two of the lads in my section got blown up, my lads, mate, my section, my responsibility. How do you deal with the guilt, mate?"

Another distressed soldier wrote to FYB UK saying he could no longer cope with feeling responsible for the deaths of two comrades in Afghanistan.
'I can't any more, please talk to me. I can't sleep because of it. I'm done with feeling bad mate, I want out, I can't deal with this.'

At the veteran's request Mr Usher posted a public message asking followers to meet the desperate man. This message received more than 50 likes and 18 shares on Facebook. That evening, however, Mr Usher realised his access to FYB UK had been blocked, which meant he could not reply to messages. Fresh cries for help from other ex-troops went unanswered, including the request: 'Hi Alfie, looking for help, I'm a vet with PTSD.
"I have lost everyone and struggling, feeling suicidal. Obviously talking about it means I'm not going to run off and top myself!"

Mr Usher told Facebook:
"The page is a lifeline for so many. It mainly deals with guys that suffer from major PTSD from conflicts in Afghanistan and Iraq. This ban leaves these

messages unanswered. It is vital to get the page up and running."
However, despite the plea, a Facebook spokesperson said:
"The page Fill Your Boots UK was deleted because its content violates our Community Standards. The standards set out limits for acceptable behaviour and content."

Former paratrooper Corporal Rob Fisher, 46 joined the Army in 1994 and served six operational tours, including two of Afghanistan, with the Parachute Regiment. While he emerged unscathed from deployments to Northern Ireland and Iraq, he felt traumatised after a series of terrifying close-quarter battles against the Taliban in 2006. He stated that he would volunteer for his unit's most dangerous patrols deep into Taliban territory, hoping he would be killed in action. He said:
"The enemy were just 20 yards from my position. In combat, you go into a state of hyper-awareness. Afterwards, I found myself slipping into the same state of mind even when I wasn't in danger.

I felt so worthless due to post-traumatic stress disorder, which was not diagnosed until late in my Army career. If someone was going to die, I wanted it to be me, because I didn't see myself as important, so I put my hand up for everything, challenging my luck."

Corporal Rob Fisher was so suicidal that he hoped Taliban forces would kill him, but his condition was initially downplayed as anxiety attacks. He stated:
"These feelings came out in the UK too. I almost killed myself on the M40. I checked nobody was around me and I was ready to accelerate into the crash barriers. But at the last second, I pulled out of it. No soldier should go through what I did, that's why I'm speaking out. We need better mental healthcare for serving troops, including around-the-clock care and a 24/7 helpline. I really hope this campaign succeeds. It could help a lot of people."

That's the essence of PTSD, it makes you go back to when you felt most at risk and it is really difficult to balance that as part of living a normal life. I suffered from PTSD after coming home from Afghanistan in 2006, the incident on the motorway happened in 2008 and I finally started getting treatment in 2009. Then I went back to Afghanistan in 2010. But by then I was in a really bad way. Part of me wanted to go back to the war zone just because it was an opportunity to die.

COURAGE AFTER THE BATTLE

I still need help and so do a lot of serving soldiers. The suicide rate for service personnel is too high.

Mental healthcare should be a funding priority and £2 million for a 24/7 helpline and outreach service is hardly a king's ransom. It could save lives and stop troops injuring themselves and others."

On his second tour of Afghanistan, Cpl Fisher raised thousands of pounds for PTSD charities by running a marathon around his base in full body armour. His mental health problems continued back in the UK and he says the collapse of his 16-year marriage was partly due to his PTSD. He left the Army in 2013 and now works as a fitness instructor.

For RAF sniper Luke Huskisson, months after deployment and safely back at base in Suffolk, the battlefield almost claimed him as another victim. He was alone in his room with the memory of his best mate Ryan, who was killed during an insurgent attack in Helmand. It was the anniversary of Ryan's death that triggered the breakdown. In a race against time his partner, Charlotte McKenna, drove 200 miles to RAF Honington to save him. She stated

"I have no doubt in my mind that if I hadn't gone to get Luke he wouldn't be here today."

Six months earlier Luke, now 31, was diagnosed with chronic PTSD. Back in 2011 and 2012, he witnessed unimaginable horror in his role rescuing badly wounded frontline soldiers.

He also picked up the dead and brought them back to Camp Bastion by helicopter - among them his best friend.

What happened that night in February 2013, when Luke suffered a breakdown, brings into relief why round-the-clock care to prevent suicides is vital. Luke says the nurses assigned to him and others were based in another county and went home at 5pm, and he suffered his breakdown at 2am. There was no out-of-hours provision. For months previously his care was patchy. Mostly he saw a nurse just once a week and he feels like he was effectively left to rot, despite the words from politicians and failed empty promises.

When Luke tries to speak of how he returned to Camp Bastion with Ryan's body in a MERT helicopter, he offers an apologetic half-smile while slowly shaking his head. Twelve months later he visited Ryan's grave in

COURAGE AFTER THE BATTLE

Hertfordshire. Luke stated:
"That night I was pacing the room, unable to focus on anything but the images replaying in my head. I was going to end my life."

With the vague notion of saying goodbye, he called Charlotte and his parents in Cheshire.

Charlotte, 32, says:
"He was an absolute wreck, barely coherent. He kept saying that he was giving up, that it was the end. I was in a state of blind panic. I drove to Honington with Luke's father, Phil. On the way we kept trying to ring Luke but he didn't answer. We didn't know what we'd face when we got there. Luke was in a terrible state. We took him home and he was placed under the care of an NHS crisis team, who were fantastic. The base said he should have taken himself to A&E. Yet he was in no state to take himself anywhere."

The couple have never stopped campaigning for a 24-hour helpline, with Luke even invading the pitch at Liverpool's Anfield stadium during a match in 2015 in protest at the MoD's treatment of its soldiers:
"Mostly we would protect paramedics but often it was too dangerous for them and we'd have to go on our own, administer first aid and get soldiers back to the Chinook,' he says. 'There was a klaxon that went off at the camp when a call came in. At first, it was exhilarating but then particularly after Ryan died I came to dread that noise. On one mission, I was called out to a helicopter crash that killed six American airmen. We tried to save them from the burning wreckage."

Luke was later commended for his courage when faced with an extraordinarily dangerous situation.

Since his breakdown Luke and Charlotte, who live on the west coast of Scotland with their two children, have fought with the RAF and Ministry of Defence. A planned investigation into his treatment before his breakdown kept stalling and the RAF failed, despite requests, to give Luke his full medical records. Eventually a Medical Board dealt with his case in his absence and a decision was made to discharge him. He left the RAF without a pension - a decision he is appealing in that this is yet another case of 'give him an MD (Medical Discharge) and the problem will go away'.

Charlotte gave up a well-paid job with British Airways to care for her partner, who still suffers, often vomiting in his sleep because of nightmares. She has written hundreds of letters and tirelessly lobbied politicians. Some offered words of encouragement but little else. Only Lord Dannatt, she says, took up their case with any gusto.

"I wouldn't have fought for as long as I have if I didn't believe the military are putting people's lives at risk. We are not fighting for ourselves any longer; it's too late for Luke, his career has gone, they have taken it from him. We are fighting for serving soldiers."

Going out on patrol night after night, soldiers Kevin Williams and John Paul Finnigan became brothers in arms, always looking out for each other amid the horrors of combat in Iraq. After leaving the Army, they both struggled to recover from the traumas of war.

In March of 2018, Kevin took his own life at the age of 29. John Paul, already tormented by the suicides of seven other soldiers he knew, was devastated. A brief time after John Paul, a 39-year-old father-of-three, was found hanging in the garden of his home.

Kevin joined the Army aged 16 and flew out to Iraq the day he turned 18, just months after being introduced to the Queen. He was homeless for a time after leaving the Army at the age of 22 and was later diagnosed with PTSD.

In a documentary, Kevin had said:

"Returning to civilian life was a big shock. The skills I learnt, especially being in the infantry regiment were all combat-based, so as civilian life doesn't have any combat, I was pretty much useless. Not too long after coming back from Iraq I just felt sad all the time, I lost a friend out there and I didn't really grieve till I got back."

Their deaths highlight the plight of veterans struggling to adjust to civilian life. Former soldiers are now dying through suicide at a faster rate than those who fell in combat during the wars in Iraq and Afghanistan. At least 12 veterans have killed themselves in the early part of 2018, which equates to one every 13 days. Troops in Iraq and Afghanistan were killed in action at a rate of one every 14 days between 2001 and 2014.

John Paul's sister Nicky Finnigan, 38, said:

"He and Kevin were really good friends. They were in the same platoon and living together in Basra palace, going out in the combat fields day and night.

They were very, very close. He told me there were eight former soldiers who had taken their lives within eight months. The last one was Kevin. It started to eat away at him. John Paul didn't feel he had any problems when he was in Iraq because he was just running on adrenaline like a robot, or a piece of equipment, doing what he was told. But there were times when he had to kill. He was trained in first aid and had to help a soldier who was hit in a rocket attack, by literally holding his face together.

John Paul, who joined the Army in 2005, was also left partly deaf by being close to explosions. He was posted to the family office of his regiment which had become 2 Rifles, and had to deal with injured servicemen and their families, and attend 25 funerals of comrades. He was medically discharged in 2009.

John Paul's PTSD just got worse and worse and contributed to the breakdown of his marriage in 2012. He tried to deal with his PTSD by seeing two psychiatrists, having counselling, undergoing behaviour therapy and taking medication. He had a job in a factory making car seats and lived with fiancée Danielle Miller. But every time another soldier took his own life, it took its toll on him. If anything positive comes from this, I hope those suffering from PTSD get to cut the chains of this illness with the biggest bolt cutters they have and live a full and happy life."

In June of 2018, it was announced that Afghan interpreters will now be given visas, so they can come to UK. Defence Secretary Gavin Williamson tore up a failed policy that meant the translators, who had assisted troops, were abandoned to the Taliban. Around 50 who served on the frontline in Helmand alongside UK soldiers will now be granted visas to Britain under new qualifying measures.

Interpreters had previously been left behind in Afghanistan and were shot at, issued with death threats and even executed on their doorsteps if they were unlucky enough to fall foul of the failed policy and not be given a visa for the UK.

Under the relocation scheme, interpreters had to be serving on an arbitrary date in December 2012 to qualify. They also had to have served in Helmand, the scene of some of the fiercest fighting, for at least a year.

So far, several hundred former translators have started new lives here, but the policy has also excluded those who worked with British troops during some of the worst fighting in Helmand in the years before 2012.

The qualifying period to include those who spent at least a year with British forces it to reset to 2006, to allow those interpreters who put their lives on the line during those difficult years in Helmand to be able to move to the UK.

A scathing report by the Commons Defence Select Committee last month found that not a single interpreter had been allowed to the UK under the scheme. A Daily Mail-backed petition over the treatment of translators was signed by more than 178,000 people, including former generals and politicians.

A former Afghan interpreter for the SAS who was hunted relentlessly by the Taliban is among those whose cases will now be reviewed. Abdul, who worked on the frontline for nearly five years, was forced to hide after the property where he was staying was sprayed with bullets as part of a terrifying campaign of intimidation. He stated:

'This is very good news and I pray that I will be included with my wife and children. We have been hiding from the Taliban for too long.'

Abdul began working for UK forces in 2007 but stopped in June 2012 when his contract ended and he did not try to renew it because of death threats. Because he stopped working before the December 2012 qualification date, he was not entitled to come to Britain under the UK's relocation scheme.

£10.5 Billion pound, 14 Aircraft PFI Contract
Amazingly, another example of the Mod having mandarins who know nothing about the military yet dictate what the defence budget is spent on. In July 2018, it was announced by a national newspaper that the cash-strapped Ministry of Defence blows £10.5billion on military jets which are leased by the PFI company, AirTanker, to Thomas Cook and Jet2 to fly tourists en-route to the their Mediterranean and US holidays. AirTanker is a consortium of Airbus and engine-maker Rolls-Royce, under a Private Finance Initiative arrangement. This allows the commercial group to potentially make millions more by renting up to four of the unused aircraft to holiday firms at the expense of service personnel.

The aircraft are supposed to transport British troops to military bases around the world and refuel fighters and bombers in mid-air during combat sorties. The aircraft are among 14 Airbus A330s acquired by the MoD under a controversial leasing agreement which costs around £400 million a year. The Voyager aircraft are supposed to be used to refuel fighters and bombers in mid-air during combat sorties. The MoD would also be forced to pay more for any of the planes if they fly into war zones because AirTanker does not insure them. AirTanker also charged £94 million for an aircraft hangar at Brize Norton, which experts say should have cost much less.

The controversial agreement between the MoD and AirTanker was signed off in March 2008 when Gordon Brown was Prime Minister, Alistair Darling was Chancellor and Des Browne was Defence Secretary. In one contract, Airbus was selling A330s for around £50 million in 2007, so a fleet of 14 would have cost £700 million to buy outright. The details of the contract suggest that the deal the MoD signed was based on a figure closer to £200 million for each plane, with the rest of the £10.5 billion covering financing, operating the service and infrastructure. The total could even rise to £12.3 billion once staffing and fuel costs are included. The costs are paid back over 27 years, with repayments expected to peak at £593 million in 2034. In 2015, the Royal Australian Air Force bought Airbus refuelling and passenger jets for just over £100 million each.

The Voyager deal was heavily criticised soon after it was signed. A report by the National Audit Office said it was too expensive, uncompetitive and overly complicated, and that the MoD lacked the expertise to manage the project. It would cost the MoD £3.5 billion to buy its way out of the Voyager contract. Military experts say the money spent on this deal would have been better used on equipment which could have saved soldiers' lives in Iraq and Afghanistan, such as armoured vehicles to protect squaddies from roadside bombs. Former Armed Forces Minister John Spellar said:

"The bottom line is that bad deals like this cost lives. Voyager has left the MoD so short of cash that troops have gone without top-grade equipment. They've also been paid less and been forced to live in inadequate accommodation. Billions of pounds have been wasted and a private consortium has been able to cream off huge profits."

One of the Voyagers was also given a £10 million refit so it could be used by the Prime Minister, senior Ministers and members of the Royal Family, including Prince Charles, for use on official long-distance trips. The MoD said: *"Voyagers are playing a key role in protecting British airspace and in the fight against Islamic State, and while our core fleet is doing the job we need* it to, we can call in the extra aircraft at short notice if we need them. When we're not using them it makes sense to have them performing other roles, as that reduces our costs and means they can be ready for operations quicker than if they were held in storage. This is a cost-effective deal that is delivering an outstanding service for the RAF."

Lord Dannatt, then the Chief of General Staff, said:

"Buying something you couldn't really afford was taken to a new level in the 1990s under the Private Finance Initiative. The government of Tony Blair and Gordon Brown seized on the concept to produce shiny new schools and hospitals across the country, especially in marginal constituencies.
But the Voyager PFI deal has to rank as the worst of the lot. Even at face value, £10.5 billion to lease 14 aircraft does not seem like value for money. The project was led not by an RAF officer, but by an Army brigadier, so that there was no undue service bias.

But this brigadier was so alarmed at the way it was going that he came to me in 2008, while I was Chief of the General Staff, to ask if I could try to get this deal stopped. I asked for a briefing, having been told there were much cheaper ways to meet the RAF's air-to-air refuelling and strategic lift requirement. At the briefing, all other options were dismissed for one spurious reason or another, leading to the curious conclusion that the £10.5 billion procurement of 14 A330 airliners, assembled at Airbus Industrie's factory near Madrid, was the answer.

In the end, the politics of European industrial collaboration was the winner, the MoD was the loser, and now bucket-and-spade holiday-makers are travelling to sunny places overseas at British taxpayers' expense. Is that value for money?"

If the money was to have been utilised in a more appropriate way than paying way over the odds for aircraft you are unable to use, and allowing the lease company to make millions on top by sub- letting them to holiday companies, you could have purchased 50 Apache Helicopters (£1.8 billion), 2 Queen Elizabeth carriers (£6.2 billion) and 28 typhoon aircraft(£2.4 billion). Not a bad deal dad, they'r useless aircraft against the alternative, or even caring for your service personnel, letting them live in a good standard of accommodation, looking after their medical needs during and post service, not to mention but a few. Adding insult to injury, giving just a pittance of £20 million over ten years to look after former service personnel.

AMPUTATION AND PROSTHETICS

History of the Prosthetic

Prosthesis is derived from the Greek word meaning 'addition' (pros=to, thesis= a placing). Advances in prosthetics have evolved through time, some of which are listed below.

950–710 B.C. –The earliest-known prosthetic was a toe made from wood and leather. It was discovered in the 1800s attached to an Egyptian mummy. This prosthesis is commonly known as "the Cairo Toe" as it was shaped and stained to look like the wearer's big toe. The toe consisted of two wooden pieces which were lashed together by leather thread through holes bored into the wood. The toe also had a leather strap which secured the toe to the foot through more leather threads.

600 B.C. – The Greville Chester toe, created by the Egyptians and discovered in 2000 near what is now known as Luxor, is made of cartonnage — a papier maché material made out of linen, glue, and plaster. This attention to the aesthetic appeal of prostheses is fairly common among ancient devices and may even have been more important than helping to improve function. Another prosthetic device from the ancient world known as the "Cartonnage Toe," which dates to about 600 BC, may have been made strictly for cosmetic purposes

300 B.C. – The oldest known prosthetic leg — the Capua leg — was crafted by the Romans from a combination of bronze and iron with a wooden core for strength. It was originally housed in the Royal College of Surgeons, but was destroyed during a Second World War bombing raid. A replica is now housed at the Science Museum in London.

476–1000 (Middle Ages) – Peg legs and hand hooks were common for those who could afford to have them fitted. Knights were often fitted with prostheses designed to hold a shield or fit in stirrups, but functionality was not an important point at this time. An increasing number of tradesmen crafted prosthetics which often used gears and springs to give limbs more detailed functionality.

1400s–1800s (The Renaissance) – Many of the medical discoveries that enabled those undergoing major limb amputations to enjoy much better survival rates came from the work of one French doctor, Ambroise Paré. Much of Paré's work overturned many of the widely held medical beliefs of the time, some of which actually did more harm than good. For example, Paré found that the application of oils to the site of a gunshot wound or other injury, which was thought to help induce healing, actually had a negative effect on the wounds. Cauterization was another widely-practised technique that Paré proved ineffective. Instead, Paré found success in tying arteries, becoming possibly the first doctor to do so.

Another pioneering doctor was Dutch surgeon Pieter Verduyn who created a non-locking below-knee prosthesis in 1696. A little more than 100 years later, in 1800, James Potts of London developed an articulated knee-and-foot prosthesis which became popular.

In 1800 a Londoner, James Potts, designed a prosthesis made of a wooden shank and socket, a steel knee joint and an articulated foot that was controlled by catgut tendons from the knee to the ankle. It would become known as the "Anglesey Leg" after the Marquess of Anglesey, who lost his leg in the Battle of Waterloo and wore the leg. William Selpho would later take the leg to the U.S. in 1839 where it became known as the "Selpho Leg."

William Selpho, an apprentice of James Potts, would eventually go on to apply for patents for his prosthetic devices and was awarded U.S. Patent No. 18021, entitled Artificial Hand. The prosthesis was secured to an arm by securing a loop around the shoulder of the opposite arm.

In 1843 Sir James Syme discovered a new method of ankle amputation that did not involve amputating at the thigh. This was welcome among the amputee community because it meant that there was a possibility of walking again with a foot prosthesis versus a leg prosthesis.

1863 – During the American Civil War, the U.S. started to see advancements in the field of prosthetics. The cosmetic rubber hand was introduced with fingers that could move and various attachments, such as brushes and hooks. Dubois Parmlee invented an advanced prosthesis with a suction socket, polycentric knee and multi-articulated foot. Later, Gustav Hermann suggested in 1868 the use of aluminium instead of steel to make artificial limbs lighter and more functional. However, the lighter device would have to wait until 1912, when Marcel Desoutter, a famous English aviator, lost his leg in an airplane accident, and made the first aluminium prosthesis with the help of his brother Charles, an engineer.

In 1906, a female pianist played a show at London's Royal Albert Hall using a right-hand prosthetic with fingers spaced to play an octave on the piano.

1914-1918 The First World War created thousands of casualties from new weapons such as the machine gun, when large field artillery caused unprecedented damage to soldiers' bodies. Hospitals were set up in any available buildings. Often these Casualty Clearing Stations (CCS) were set up in tents in a field.

Surgery was often performed at the CCS. Arms and legs were amputated, wounds were operated on and thousands of soldiers had to have limbs amputated by a guillotine. Following on from this and hoping the amputated limb was not infected the soldier, once back home in Britain, would be assessed and fitted with his new limb.

Captain Valentine H Blake devised an amputation shield which was a semi-circular sheet of brass hinged by a single rivet and slightly dished to give the hand and saw free play. A circular slot in the centre allows the shield to be adjusted to the bone.

1915 Two US prosthetic companies, Hanger and Rowley, were invited by government to establish the Roehampton Limb Centre for Great War amputees.

1916 Ministry of Pensions established. Responsibility for war pensioners included prosthetics which, uniquely, were free to veterans.

1945 – Following the Second World War, most limbs were made of a combination of wood and leather. While these materials provided the wearer with several benefits, the prosthetics were heavy, and leather can be difficult to keep clean, especially since it absorbs perspiration.

1945 War pensioner amputees peak at 45,000.

1948 Inception of the NHS. Prosthetics became free, subject to an undertaking that war pensioners would have priority. Subsequently limb service transferred between departments of state and agencies with different arrangements in England, Wales, Scotland and Northern Ireland.

1970s–1990s – Plastics, polycarbonates, resins, and laminates were introduced as light, easy-to-clean alternatives to wood and leather models. Prosthetics also started being made from lightweight materials such as carbon fibre. Synthetic sockets were custom fitted for each patient to provide an individualized, comfortable, and hygienic fit.

1986 In the McColl Report Professor (now Lord) Ian McColl was highly critical of UK limb services.

1987 Disablement Services Authority (DSA) created post-McColl to oversee the limb service, standardise provision nationwide and enunciate entitlement.

1991 DSA abolished and limb service transferred to NHS.

1999 Otto Bock C-Leg available. Fitted at Defence Medical Rehabilitation Centre, Headley Court from 2006.

2000 - date – Prosthetic design has advanced to highly specialized prosthetics, including high-performance, lightweight running blades, responsive legs and feet for navigating varying terrain, and motorized hand prosthetics controlled by sensors and microprocessors.

2003 (March) Significant numbers of amputees start to arrive from Iraq and Afghanistan with a sharp upsurge from 2009.

2010 (January) Mr Mike O'Brien, Minister of State for Health, issues unfinanced instructions for Headley Court-type provision to be available for veterans. Message inadequately received, understood and acted upon.

2010 (August) Fighting Fit recommendations on veterans' mental health accepted in full by government. Second department of health guidance note issued requiring Headley Court standard of prosthetics for veterans.

2011 (January) Terms of Reference for review into prosthetic provision for veterans.

2012 Warranties for high end prosthetics start to expire at the same time as users return to civilian life.

Counter IED (Crown Copyright / MoD)

RAF regiment Searching for IED's (Crown Copyright / MoD)

COURAGE AFTER THE BATTLE

Bomb Disposal Officer (Crown Copyright / MoD)

Thanks to new technologies and the improvements in materials, prosthetics have come a long way since the first known wooden toe. Developments in technologies such as robotics, brain-computer interfaces and 3-D printing have the potential to lead to future advancements the field of prosthetics.

In today's battlefield environment, the Royal Centre for Defence Medicine (RCDM) is the primary receiving unit for all military patients. The centre works in partnership with the University Hospital Birmingham NHS Foundation Trust (UHBFT) and a number of other NHS hospitals in the Birmingham area. Since June 2010 all operational casualties have been treated in the Queen Elizabeth Hospital Birmingham. In November 2011, the RCDM headquarters re-located from the old Selly Oak site and this completed the move to Queen Elizabeth Hospital Birmingham.

As well as the clinical needs, RCDM also look after patient's administrative and welfare requirements. The Military Patient Admin Cell (MPAC) raise all signals and work closely with Joint Casualty and

Compassionate Cell (JCCC). The aeromedical department plan the transit and arrival of casualties from across the globe. Military Liaison officers, including those drawn from the deployed units, provide the vital link between RCDM, the family and the patient's home unit. Accommodation is provided for the families in the nearby SSAFA-staffed Fisher House and Norton House and, if required, local hotels.

The Defence Medical Rehabilitation Programme (DMRP) with its consultant based multiple-disciplinary Complex Trauma Teams (CTTs) has no equivalent in the NHS. DMRP is primarily resourced to return serving personnel to duty but in practice seeks to deliver optimal functional recovery, regardless of an amputee's likely destination.

Iraq and Afghanistan added a new generation of young amputees with multiple and more complex problems than their predecessors. These amputees often have substantial additional physical and mental problems caused by their injury. With the onset of a better understanding of the types of injuries from today's complex weaponry, modern military medicine has seen the ratio of limbs lost to patients increased from 1.11 in 2006 to 1.52 in 2010. Initial costs per patient per annum are around £20,000 at the Defence Medical Rehabilitation Centre Headley Court (DMRC) against £900 in the NHS. The difference is heavily influenced by the supply of microprocessor-controlled C-Legs to bilateral above-knee amputees and the multiple limbs needed to bring the veteran, so far as possible, to pre-injury occupational and fitness levels.

The mother of an amputee soldier who had received a double leg amputation injury in Afghanistan and was now, together with her son, understandably dissatisfied at his treatment by the NHS, wrote:

"Problems arose when my son had progressed to needing more physio input and better legs. We pointed out that if still at Headley he would receive 6-8 hours' physio per day, 5 days per week. The NHS could offer no more than 2 hours per week. In addition, the amputation physio had never taught a double amp to walk, and had no experience of C-Legs."

Exercise-based rehabilitation is available for as long as an amputee remains in the Armed Forces but when they leave they no longer have access to it and the likelihood is that their physical function will decline.

Source A Better Deal for Amputees   Andrew Murrison MD MP

COURAGE AFTER THE BATTLE

World War One

World War One created thousands of casualties from new weapons such as the machine gun, and large field artillery caused unprecedented damage to soldiers' bodies. This presented new challenges to doctors on both sides in the conflict, as they sought to save their patients' lives and limit the harm to their bodies. New types of treatment, organisation and medical technologies were developed to reduce the numbers of deaths. Hospitals were set up in any available buildings. Often Casualty Clearing Stations (CCS) were set up in tents in muddy fields and were kept as clean as possible within the confines of the battlefield.

There were approximately 41,000 amputees in the initial stages of the war. Debridement techniques (the removal of damaged tissue or foreign objects from a wound) which had been learnt in the Boer War were used, but these were soon shown to be mortally inadequate. Surgery was often performed at the CCS; wounds were operated on and thousands of soldiers had to have limbs amputated. A guillotine, a variation on the one used to cut off heads in the French Revolution, was used to amputate limbs. The guillotine technique was a swift circular amputation with little or no attempt to form skin flaps to close the wound and form the stump. The main thought behind this was speed and the prevention of severe loss of blood (exsanguination) and infection, along with the need to rapidly process large numbers of casualties with any number or type of injury.

As traumatic as it was, amputation saved the lives of many men as it often prevented infection. Although surgeons sought to salvage damaged limbs when possible, the priorities in military medical practice were a period in post-operative care when after further management of any infection, patients could be moved safely back to hospitals in the UK for reconstructive surgery, rehabilitation, and the fitting of prosthetic limbs.

Infection was a serious complication for the wounded in a dirty, germ-infested battlefield situation. Doctors use all the chemical weaponry in their arsenal to prevent infection. As there were no antibiotics or sulphonamides, a number of alternative methods were employed. The practice of *'debridement'* - whereby the tissue around the wound was cut away and the wound sealed – was a common way to prevent infection. Carbolic lotion was used to wash wounds, which were then wrapped in gauze soaked in the same solution. Other wounds were bipped (bismuth iodoform paraffin) and paste was smeared over severe wounds to prevent infection. Following on from this and hoping the amputated limb was not infected the soldier, once back home in Britain, would be assessed and fitted with his new limb.

Most casualties in World War One had musculoskeletal trauma as a result of damage to upper and lower limbs caused by gunshot wounds and fragments of artillery munitions. A century later, the signature injury of soldiers returning from military operations in Iraq and Afghanistan is musculoskeletal trauma mainly caused by blast and fragments from improvised explosive devices.

Despite a century's worth of surgical improvements, one feature remains common to casualties of World War One and the present day, and that is both stump and phantom limb pain. Phantom limb sensation is when the patient has kinaesthetic feelings of length, volume, or other spatial awareness of the amputated limb.

Surgeons in World War One recognised phantom limb pain as a condition in its own right, which needed their specialist care and attention. This was not a new phenomenon at the time as artificial limbs had been around for many years, so had the phenomena of stump or phantom limb pain. A famous casualty of war was Admiral Nelson. His ship's surgeon, James Farquhar, following a battle engagement off Tenerife, wrote in his journal:

Admiral Nelson suffered a compound fracture of the right arm by a musket ball passing through a little above the elbow; an artery divided; the arm was immediately amputated. His surgeon noted in his journal seven days later that Admiral Nelson's amputated arm continued getting well. Stump looked well with no bad symptoms whatever occurring. The sore has now reduced to the size of a shilling and Admiral Nelson seems to be in perfect good health. Nelson would be troubled with amputation-related pain until his death at the Battle of Trafalgar in 1805.

In general day to day life, amputations were a rare occurrence and, as such, the skills and knowledge required were somewhat limited. Industrial accidents and the like were the only times when amputations would occur. In 1913 Robert Jones, of St Thomas' Hospital in London, had created a well organised and effective infrastructure with 5,483 operations performed, and only 34 of those were amputations. This shows the rarity of the procedure at that time. Due to the relatively high risk of complications, a planned amputation is seen as a treatment of last resort. It is only used when there is no other way of preventing life-threatening and serious symptoms such as gangrene from developing.

World War One had the first mass conscriptions in Britain, which created an army of more than 2 million men. On July 1st the Battle of the Somme began and within a month surgeons in Britain had received enough limbless casualties to realise that reconstructive surgery and rehabilitation would be much more difficult than first thought. No one had seen the likes of this in the past as there was never a War to end all Wars before, and the vast numbers returning to Britain were a shock.

Although many lives were saved by amputation, they were blighted by the pain of the stump, which was a complication of the mishandling of the nerves during the amputation procedure, rather than a complication of the rapid removal and replacement of soft and hard tissue. Marmaduke Sheild, a senior consulting surgeon at two London hospitals (St George's and the Royal Waterloo) and at the No. 5 Hospital for military casualties in Exeter, UK, reported in a letter to the Lancet Medical Journal,

a source of intolerable suffering to his amputee patients, and of despair to those who fit them with artificial limbs.

He reiterated these comments in December 1916 when the Somme offensive was called off in an article in the Lancet entitled 'Some Practical Observations on the Injuries of War'. In the August issue of the British Medical Journal, (page 309) two letters about Sheild can be found. The first is from a Mr Russel Coombe of Exeter. In his letter to the Journal he wrote: *During twelve months' work as an operating surgeon I can safely say that I never saw an amputation performed nor performed one myself in which the main nerves were not cleared and divided high up clear of the flaps.*

Personally, I was following the advice laid down in the 1912 edition of Cheyne and Burghard's Surgery, which I have looked up so as to quote it correctly:

Painless Scar, - if the large nerves be divided at a higher level than the other structures in the flap, they do not become pressed upon by the cicatrix or adherent to the bone. This is a point of great importance because should the nerves become involved in the scar, bulbous enlargement will occur, neuritis will be set up and the patient will suffer from intense neuralgic pain, aggravated by the slightest pressure.

I need hardly say I heartedly concur in Mr Sheild's remarks. He is to be much thanked for again drawing attention to and emphasising this important point.

COURAGE AFTER THE BATTLE

Sheild called for surgeons on the front line to avoid, where possible, the guillotine amputation technique because it had proved to be an unsatisfactory method of wound closure. Guillotine amputations were more likely to need further amputations, and the process usually left nerves exposed, which were a substantial cause of both poor prosthetic fit and resulting stump pain.

For many of the soldiers severely wounded in the Somme who were making their way slowly home on hospital ships and trains, this warning to surgeons would come too late, but there was hope that lessons would be learned. Based on his experience of 2,000 consecutive cases, Captain Huggins, surgical specialist at the Pavilion Military Hospital in Brighton, set out a formal two-stage process for amputation and stump management. Procedures done close to the frontline were primary amputations, and the role of surgeons back in Britain was to do the secondary amputation and secure stump health. This two-stage process supported and developed several of the issues described by Sheild.

In 1917 thousands of soldiers who had been severely wounded in the battles at Arras, Verdun, and Passchendaele were among the wounded who were to suffer long-term consequences of amputation. This had become a matter of national concern so the government created a Pensions Board to cope with the increasing numbers of disabled soldiers. To restore them to the highest possible grade of health and earning power was a political and financial priority. The war showed the need to deal with not only casualties from the fighting, but also with amputees discharged from the army, healed but not cured. This was becoming a concern. In the Official Medical History of World War One, published in several volumes from 1925, there is no mention of phantom limb pain in the chapters relating to orthopaedics and amputation.

It is estimated that around 50-80% of amputees develop phantom limb pain following an amputation. The condition is more common in women than men and in this, the upper limb amputations seem to be more relevant. The causes of phantom limb pain are unclear but there are three main theories.

The Peripheral Theory – This states that the phantom limb pain may be the result of nerve endings around the stump forming into a cluster known as neuromas. These generate abnormal electrical pulses that the brain interprets as pain.

The Spinal Theory – This suggests that the lack of sensory input from the amputated limb causes chemical changes in the central nervous system. This leads to confusion in central regions of the brain which trigger symptoms of pain.

The Central Theory – The processes that the brain has a memory of the amputated limb and its associated nerve signals. Therefore, the symptoms of pain are due to the brain trying to recreate this memory but failing, because it is not receiving the feedback it is expecting.

In research carried out in 2008, it was found that when people spent 40 minutes imagining they were using their phantom limb, they experienced a reduction in pain.

Loss of a limb can have a large psychological impact on the person and many people who have had an amputation report feelings such as grief and loss of a loved one. This can be greater defined as in the following three areas:

Coping with the loss of sensation from the amputated limb
Coping with the loss of function from the amputated limb
Coping with your own and other people's perception of a body image

More often than not, after an emergency amputation, it is common to experience negative thoughts and emotions. These can be:

Depression
Anxiety
Denial – refuse to accept that you need to make changes to your life
Grief - sense of loss or bereavement
Suicidal feelings

Amongst people who have had an amputation, and in particular but not limited to service personnel, there is the distinct possibility of developing Post Traumatic Stress Disorder (PTSD). To try and alleviate this, the medical staff will do all they can to assist the person and answer any questions they may have. During the amputation process this medical team, known as the multidisciplinary team (MDT) will consist of various health professionals, most of whom will be obvious as to their role in the team.

Surgeon
Nurse – Specialist in pain relief
Psychologist – Ensure you are mentally aware of the situation and offer any advice or guidance as required
Social Worker – There to assist you in a number of ways and not just the stereotypical interfering busybody, but an important part of the team
Pharmacist
Prosthetist – Specialist in prosthetic limbs who will measure the residual limb (stump) and will oversee the prosthetic fittings and adjustments.
Dietician
Physiotherapist
Occupational Therapist – Specialist in assisting in your improvement of skills and abilities needed for daily life such as cooking and cleaning. They can provide specialist equipment or arrange for house modifications such as ramps if needed.

Once the patient has returned to the ward with the wound covered and a tube to allow excess fluid to drain out, this covering will normally be left on for around five days to assist in the risk management of infection to the wound. Once the medical staff are happy, a compression sock will be provided and the patient will be allowed to have this on through the day, but taken off at night.

THE PROSTHESIS
There are generally three categories of prosthesis.
Cosmetic Prosthesis – This has low functionality and is generally used for upper limb amputations.
Body-Powered Prosthesis – This has a moderate level of functionality that is provided by the muscle near the area of the prosthesis, and is generally used for upper limb amputations.
Myoelectric Prosthesis – A fully functioning prosthesis in comparison to the functionality of the lost limb.

COURAGE AFTER THE BATTLE

World War Two
Within a Journal of the Royal Army Medical Corps of 06 December 1944, (1945; 84 p54-65) an article entitled Psychiatric Aspects of Rehabilitation, by Major Emanuel Miller M.A, M.R.C.P, D.P.M. discussed the rehabilitation of service personnel following World War Two. The article gives a good overview of the thoughts of the day and how they intended to rehabilitate the servicemen who were to return home and ultimately to a working career. I have summarised some of the points in the article below.

In this article he notes that the subject had received the full attention of Major E. Wittower, who had looked at a study of men who had amputations of the upper and lower limbs of varying severity in the course of battle action. It was clear to Major Wittower that vocational problems among these men would prove to be a large problem. Men had lost mobility in some form due to their limb loss and quite possibly their manipulative power and dexterity, if this was an arm or hand. It was likely that upon his return to civilian life, where he would return with a fraction of his body missing, there may be social repercussions.

> To this aim he called for the following to be established:
> 1/ Vocational Testing with intelligence grading.
> 2/ An industry-wide job analysis in order to facilitate vocational guidance or redirection, both in services or industry.
> 3/ A further study of neuro-psychiatry of the recovery of the body image and its reconfiguration to meet the amputated state. A man may have become accustomed to a certain industrial role, where a body image may cast a light on his long-term capacity to do that for which in the early stages of recovery he appeared to be unsuited or destined never to be suited.
> 4/ Characterological studies of men who, some time after returning to industry, have or have not made satisfactory adjustments.

Workers with the blind in initial stages might be chosen from victims with a high degree of vision impairment so that they appreciate the handicap and their own progress on the rehabilitation road. The workers would in effect become a buddy to the person under rehabilitation, and by understanding the problems that are faced they may be in a position to discuss how they got over this problem. This in itself would be seen as a constructive way of assisting the blind victim and not patronising, which may be the case, although not intended, by an assistant who was sighted and not able to fully understand the blind issues. This can be said for any disability as a person (buddy or assistant) is trying very hard to help but, not knowing the problems the person with vision, limb loss or other problems faces first hand, they are not fully aware how this may seem to the disabled person.

Post 1945 Conflicts and Present Day

Surgeons today work as part of a multidisciplinary team including specialists in pain medicine, rehabilitation, and physical therapists who focus on symptoms, prevalence, risk factors and treatments for the various forms of medical need. Despite substantial improvements in the understanding of these disorders there is still a long way to go. There is a determination to create a new life for amputees free from the accompanying miserable pain, which will allow them to get on with their lives.

Today's field hospitals are equipped with consultant-led orthopaedic teams whose surgical response to musculoskeletal and orthopaedic wounds has moved away from using amputation first. Instead, the trauma site is managed with debridement of the soft tissues with both the limb and limb length preservation a priority.

It seems cruel with today's advanced medicine and treatments, but debridement for creeping demarcation, or even secondary amputation, are standard and not deemed a complication. Primary amputation is used only when a severely injured limb threatens the survival of the casualty. The definition of survivability versus non-survivability is constantly being revised in military medicine. The decision to amputate is made only after agreement by two surgeons and an anaesthetist and today's surgeons have learned a lot of lessons from the past, especially by understanding and treatment of blast injury. A limb removal is a matter of careful, expedient and meticulous amputation.

The wound is left open in primary amputation and debridement, and the definitive amputation and closure of the wound is done later when a viable non-infected portion of a limb is identified. Function of the remaining limb, or a replacement limb, then becomes the surgical priority. Once home, rehabilitation of a soldier begins with physiotherapy and occupational therapy.

Current Concepts and Practice

The system used by a hospital in deciding if a limb is viable or should be amputated is the *trauma score*. Over the years, the Gustilo Mendoza Williams classification for assessment and

prognostication of open limb injuries has been considered sacred. Apart from this, there have been many trauma scores which have been devised, such as the mangled extremity severity score (MESS), the limb salvage index (LSI), the predictive salvage index (PSI), the nerve injury, ischemia, soft tissue injury, skeletal injury, shock and age of patient score (NISSSA), and the Hannover fracture scale-97 (HFS-97).

All have been designed to assess a limb with combined orthopaedic and vascular injuries. A Mangled Extremity Severity Score (MESS) has been devised to predict outcome after limb polytrauma, especially for the mangled limb. Primary amputation is recommended if this score is high (≥7), or the limb is irreversibly ischaemic or gangrenous. Poor predictors of limb salvage are delayed revascularization (beyond 6–8 hours), presence of associated fractures, arterial ligation, and location of injury (popliteal). However, in some recent studies, it has been seen that successful limb salvage in patients with a MESS of ≥7 is possible with good functional outcomes. MESS of ≥7 is not a good predictor for the need for amputation in patients especially with upper limb vascular injury, although a MESS of <7 remains a good predictor for patients who do not require amputation.

	Skeletal/Soft tissue group	
Low energy	Stab wounds, simple closed fractures, small caliber gunshot wounds	1
Medium energy	Open or multiple level fracture, dislocations, moderate crush injuries	2
High energy	Shotgun blast (close range), high velocity gunshot wounds	3
Massive crush	Logging, rail road, oil rig accidents	4
	Shock group	
Normotensive hemodynamics	Blood pressure stable in field and operating room	0
Transiently hypotensive	Blood pressure unstable in field but responsive to intravenous fluids	1
Prolonged hypotensive	Systolic blood pressure <90 mmHg in field and responsive to intravenous fluids only in operating room	2
	Ischemia group	
None	Pulsatile limb without signs of ischemia	0
Mild	Diminished pulses without signs of ischemia	1
Moderate	No pulse by doppler, sluggish capillary refill, paresthesia, diminished motor activity	2
Advanced	Pulseless, cool, paralysed and numb without capillary refill	3
	Age group	
<30 years		0
30–50 years		1
>50 years		2

If ischemia time more than six hours, add 2 points.

Trauma Score Chart.

Source Management of Major Limb Injuries

Between October 2001 and June 2013 there were 363 military amputees (ranging from single fingers and toes to multiple limb loss) from Iraq (30), Afghanistan (280) and all other locations (53), of whom 107 have been medically discharged with the average time between point of wounding and discharge being five years. It is notable that due to the care, rehabilitation and high-grade prosthesis provided at public expense through the MoD, the majority of amputees have been able to continue to serve, albeit in many cases in a reduced capacity.

The NHS has been allocated specific funding for the upgrading of veteran prosthetics. The centrally held funding is available to all eligible veterans in both in England and the Devolved Administrations to cover the associated costs for services not available at their local Disablement Service Centre (DSC), such as sockets and suspension, over and above what is normally provided by the NHS. Any veteran whose limb loss is attributable to an injury sustained as a result of service is eligible to apply for this funding for prosthetic support through the DSC of their choice. However, veterans who lose limbs after they leave the military or suffer limb loss whilst in the military that is not attributable to service (for example, in a civilian road traffic accident) continue to access services as usual through their local DSC.

Residual limb pain: spontaneous or evoked pain perceived as originating in the residual limb including the stump; pain unrelated to amputation, e.g., other injuries, such as damage of the nerves above the level of amputation.

Stump pain: spontaneous or evoked pain in the amputation stump includes neuroma, muscle, and bone stump as pain sources.

Stump contractions: spontaneous movement of the stump ranging from small jerks to visible contractions.

Phantom sensation: any sensation of the missing limb, including pain.

Phantom limb pain: spontaneous or evoked pain perceived as arising in the missing limb.

COURAGE AFTER THE BATTLE

Royal Marine Colour Sergeant Lee 'Frank' Spencer served multiple tours of Iraq and Afghanistan. Unfortunately, he was helping to save the life of another driver during an incident on the M3 Motorway in Surrey. He was hit by debris and subsequently lost his leg, but this did not stop him, as he later completed the Row2Recovery Atlantic Crossing.

In true Royal Marines style, Lee has a ten-point plan on losing his leg and getting on with life.

1. Your life will change but not in the way you think.
Everyone around me kept using the term 'Life Changing Injury' and they were right. I'd been injured trying to help someone and had fought to save my own life. That fight has never left me. Even in my darkest moments it has driven me to adapt to living normally.

2. Kids will stare
Much to their parents' embarrassment, children are welcomingly tactless and often stare open mouthed before pointing out the obvious. I smile and reassure them I am aware that my leg has fallen off and my offer to give them a detailed look at my prosthetic is rarely refused.

3. People will give you things
As a Royal Marine I lived by the mantra 'grab anything going free', so it's a hard habit to break. While always grateful, I cannot fathom why I need a T-shirt because I have one less leg. I rarely wear trousers for the impracticality of removing my prosthetic, yet I've never been offered shorts.

4. You can't park where you want
A blue badge is not carte blanche to undermine every parking law invented. Indeed, I am now more aware of parking regulations than ever before, so it irks me to the point of advocating capital punishment that people misuse disabled parking bays.

5. You may improve at sport
Before my accident, my love for watching football was only equalled by my lack of skill playing it. Injury may force you into activities you may never have previously considered, uncovering latent natural talent.

6. You will forget that it's gone
Protracted wearing of a prosthetic can be painful, so I usually remove it when seated. This habitually results in me falling over when I stand back up as I keep forgetting I don't have a right leg any more.
Conversely, when sat down I instinctively stretch out my missing leg to stop my prosthetic toppling over. How ironic.

7. Phantom pain is not a myth
I am not high on medication when I say that I often suffer pain in a leg that no longer exists. It is hard describing to someone why I occasionally recoil as though an area bereft of a limb has been plugged into the National Grid, or why sometimes I feel my ex-toes have been set on fire.

8. The story of how you lost your limb will be embellished with every recounting
Mine is a pretty simple one, but by the time I'm 70 I'm sure I will enthral listeners by my heroic rescuing of a bus load of orphans before being run over by an articulated lorry carrying nuclear bombs. One thing will remain constant: Frank the Rastafarian, without whose help I would have died.

9. New opportunities abound
Losing a limb means you are likely to get involved with organisations founded to help those in similar situations. Grab those helping hands, as every opportunity quickly leads to another.
I've met the Prime Minister and Prince Harry (twice – really cool guy), but had to turn down an invitation to Buckingham Palace (Sorry Ma'am, it clashed with Glastonbury). I've partied backstage with 'A' listers, raced Superman up the Rock of Gibraltar, gone three rounds with former Super Middle Weight World Champion Glenn Catley, and rowed across the Atlantic in 46 days as part of a 4-man all amputee crew.

This brings me on to the last and by far the most important point:

10. There's life beyond injury
Since losing my leg, life is worse in many ways; I now have difficulty in doing many simple tasks. But I prefer to concentrate on all the ways it's got better and all the amazing things I've done since my injury. Forget about

better or worse, life is just 'different', and that's really important to me. There is life beyond injury, you just have to grab it in any way you can. Don't get me wrong, though: if I could go back two years and have my leg back at the expense of everything I've done, I absolutely would, in a heartbeat. I do miss my leg – even if it was rubbish at football.

Extract from an article entitled
'10 things no one tells you before you lose a limb' by a Royal Marine
Daily Telegraph 04 May 2016 Mark Time

(Yes, this is a genuine person, who is a renowned travel writer, former Royal Marine and not a service person's play on names, as if they were on the parade ground marching on the spot, which is known as marking time. It would be a fair assumption that Mark had a lot of stick (flack) due to his name when he served in the Royal Marines).

Future Prospects of Rehabilitation

Scientists are working on a number of ways to assist people in their future life prospects and they have recently restored movement in two paralysed monkeys in an operation which could soon be used to help people with damaged spines. The monkeys walked normally again after just six days, following the fitting of the pioneering device. Because humans have very similar anatomy, scientists are confident that the same result is possible in humans by the end of the decade.

The brain-spine interface bridges the spinal cord injury, in real time and wirelessly. The system decodes activity from the brain's motor cortex and then relays this information to a system of electrodes on the brain-spine interface bridge via an implant in the motor cortex of the brain which controls the movement of limbs. The brain-spine interface bridge is located over the surface of the lumbar spinal cord, below the injury. The electrical stimulation of a few volts is then delivered at precise locations in the spinal cord. This then modulates distinct networks of neurons that can activate specific muscles in the legs.

Another promising advance in medical technology is a pair of state-of-the-art exoskeleton robotic legs which are thought to cost around £100,000. Currently on trial by former Police Officer Nicki Donnelly, the exoskeleton robotic supports allow her to walk again. Nicki has said that she feels blessed and can even walk her daughter the half a mile to school.

In February 2013, it was announced that the government were to make £6.5 million available for a special reserve to guarantee that all serving personnel and veterans injured while serving in Iraq and Afghanistan will be able to upgrade the latest prosthetics technology where clinically appropriate. Some will take this as a possible back door to refusing applications, and others as a sensible way to stretch the budget to those in need. If the service personnel were sent to a war zone and were injured, why has there been a need to have a special reserve and not just look after those injured personnel properly? Further to this, why just Iraq and Afghanistan, why not include Ireland, Falklands, Balkans etc?

At a press conference to unveil the latest in a line of new prosthetics available to service personnel, the then Defence Secretary the Right Hon Philip Hammond MP said:

"Providing world-class medical care for injured personnel remained a top priority and clinicians now have freedom to choose across the range of limbs to suit the amputee. This is great news for service people going through the process. I've talked to some of the guys waiting to be fitted with new limbs and they definitely have their shopping lists ready. They know all about these limbs, they've talked to people in the States who've tried them. They're ready to go for it."

Air Marshal Paul Evans, the MoD's Surgeon General, praised the new 'intelligent' knee:

"When you put all this together, it makes a complex piece of gadgetry that works very effectively to provide a greater degree of freedom and movement."

Lead clinician at the Defence Medical Rehabilitation Centre Headley Court, Mark Thorburn, stressed:

"Each patient will be matched with the best limb depending on a range of factors including injury, socket joint, fitness and lifestyle and the Genium C-Leg® will join a range of prosthetics available."

Paralympic rower Captain Nick Beighton, who lost both legs in Afghanistan in 2009, welcomed the new artificial limbs as a 'big step up in technology'. He said:

"I'd love to try the Genium and see if it can offer me anything extra. It's not

necessarily going to work for everyone but, for people who are a bit more able on their legs, it will offer even more functionality to get out and do a bit more with your life."

The Commanding Officer at that time of Headley Court, Group Captain Clare Walton, said:
"Some of the technology is awesome. It's just really impressive to see, but in real terms it's about what it allows patients to do, and that's what we as clinicians want to know, that we're giving our patients the best care available, and this is it."

The first patients were fitted with the new artificial limbs by late spring, 2013.

In the corridors of Headley Court, the military's medical rehabilitation centre, patients move around on a mixture of full and stumpy prosthetics. The stumpy is a short trainer leg fixed to the remains of the injured thigh, which gives greater stability by lowering the patient's centre of balance, leaving their face around waist-level, their hands trailing a few inches above the floor.

This red-brick Surrey manor that has housed the military's rehabilitation services since World War Two has tripled the size of the medical centre since its inception in 2007, when it was a green portable building. In 2010, the sudden rise in complex injuries is also visible in the changed pace of activity in the prosthetics workshop. There are six prosthetists working in the workshop, busy building new prosthetics for the injured, and the original team of four technicians has also expanded to cope with the workload.

Headley Court admitted its first triple amputee. Doctors are also treating a growing number of bilateral trans femoral amputee men who have lost both legs above the knee.

In the early hours of Christmas Eve 2007, Royal Marines Commando Mark Ormrod was out on a routine foot patrol in the Helmand Province of Afghanistan when he stepped on and triggered an Improvised Explosive Device. Thanks to the swift action of the men around him and the intervention of the Medical Emergency Response Team he was airlifted via helicopter to an emergency field hospital in a desperate attempt to try and save his life. An innovative and dangerous procedure carried out onboard a Chinook helicopter en-route to the hospital did save his life. He woke up three days later in the UK in Selly Oak Hospital, Birmingham: both legs amputated above the knee and his right arm amputated above the elbow. He was the UK's first triple amputee to survive the Afghanistan conflict.

http://www.markormrod.com/about-mark/

The then Commanding Officer, Colonel Jerry Tuck of the Royal Army Medical Corps, says:
"We have a painful number of bilateral transfemoral amputees – men who have lost both legs above the knee, in a wood-panelled room in the building's main wing." Through the window behind him, gardeners are tending the landscaped grounds. "The cohort that we are dealing with is, in research terms, relatively young. We've been treating these people from first principles and we are learning from them as we go through their rehabilitation. The guys that come back with an amputation, they are the same people, but without an arm or a leg. The patients with head injuries, inevitably their personalities are going to change. Their social standing in society, their behaviour has changed; they have memory difficulties. You're not just providing them with arms and legs, but with a new way of life. These are not the same people. Marriages break down."

It has been calculated that £288 million is the cost of lifetime care (40 years as a figure) for amputee veterans from the Afghanistan conflict so the initial £6.5 million into a special reserve announced in February 2013 by Defence Secretary the Right Hon Philip Hammond MP seems a little short of the mark. The overall costs could, however, climb even higher when factoring in such things as general illnesses and bad health that would affect the person or limb which was not directly related to blast injuries; new prosthetics, ongoing clinical need and economic losses resulting in veterans being forced to drop out of the workforce due to their injuries, and thus possibly onto the social care system.

Roadside bombs or IEDs were a leading cause of injury in UK Armed Forces personnel serving in the conflict in Afghanistan, which occurred between 2001 and 2014. More servicemen and women have been surviving blast injuries in recent years because of improved medical care and the rapid evacuation of casualties. However, surviving patients have complex wounds and the long-term medical and financial impacts of their injuries are still being investigated.

The research team from The Royal British Legion Centre for Blast Injury Studies (CBIS) at Imperial College London have carried out a comprehensive analysis highlighting the extent and nature of amputations on British service personnel from the Afghan conflict and calculated the long-term healthcare costs. This is the first study to place a figure on the long-term cost of care for British amputees in this context.

There was a press campaign in 2014 against the use of body parts which had originated in the United States, coming to Britain to be *'Blown Up.'* The practice of using body parts or any such remains is tightly regulated by the Human Tissue Authority, and both the Royal British Legion and Imperial College London adhere to those guidelines. Without this research, which is defining a complicated and emotive subject, there would have been more casualties in this and future conflicts.

In the study, the researchers found that from the first roadside blast casualty in 2003, to the UK's withdrawal in 2014, there were 265 casualties who sustained 416 amputations. The most common type of amputation from IEDs was above the knee, with 153 casualties, followed by 143 below the knee. The Blast Injury Centre is focused on supporting the military to ensure the best care possible for veterans who have lost their limbs while serving their country. Understanding the cost implications is an important part of planning how to care for injured veterans in the long-term, in order to make their lives more comfortable. Ongoing evaluation of these injured soldiers will be needed to assess the level and specialisation of care required as they age. It is likely that these veterans will be subjected to chronic health problems experienced by the general population as well as specific issues as a result of their injuries. The lives of these servicemen and women could be improved if policymakers develop more effective and sustained medical and social support.

Sue Freeth, who at the time was the Royal British Legion's Director of Operations, said:

"This is the first attempt we know of to publish an independent estimate of the lifetime health care cost of the British service personnel seriously injured by IEDs in Afghanistan. The Legion has been concerned for some time that the lifetime care of seriously injured veterans was under-estimated. This paper should alert health commissioners to the scale of the problem, and help them to plan ahead to meet the lifetime health care needs of this

generation. Many of the injured veterans from Afghanistan have survived only because of the innovation of modern military and NHS medicine and medics on the battlefield, and the need for a lifetime of health care to support them is in danger of being overlooked as the spotlight moves away from this conflict."

A breakdown of the costs by the researchers shows the base cost over 40 years of single amputees was £0.87 million for a transtibial or below the knee amputee, £1.16 million for a through-knee amputee, and £1.16 million for a transfemoral or above the knee amputee.

The Royal British Legion Centre for Blast Injury Studies (CBIS) is the first collaboration of its kind in the UK where civilians, including engineers and scientists, are working alongside military doctors, supported by charitable funding, to improve protective gear and develop better treatments for people injured from roadside bombs or IEDs. Given the current trend for terror attacks, the information gleaned from these tests would more than likely be useful to large hospitals and specialists who encounter such attacks. At the time of writing, we have had two attacks in London from vehicle-borne terrorists and a bomb in an Ariana Grande concert in Manchester. Both attacks resulted in multiple deaths and injury.

Ongoing evaluation of these injured soldiers will be needed in order to assess the level and specialisation of care required as they age. It is likely that veterans will be subject to chronic health problems experienced by the general population as well as specific issues as a result of their injuries. The lives of these servicemen and women could be improved if policymakers develop more effective and sustained medical and social support. CBIS researchers are now collaborating on a study with the British Military and King's College London to investigate the health and well-being of veterans over a 20-year period. The aim is to find ways of improving the long-term support for people who have sustained blast injuries.

Mind-Controlled Prosthetics

In June 2015, it was announced that the world's first feeling artificial leg could boost life for wounded soldiers and help them stay in the military. Using special sensors attached to rewired nerve endings, the technology can for the first time allow the prosthetic limb to recreate the sensation of a real foot, allowing the patient to distinguish one terrain from another. An added advantage is that it can also reduce the effects of phantom pain, from which many amputees often suffer.

It is hoped that renewing a sense of touch to the artificial limb could improve mobility for an amputee. The Ministry of Defence said at the time that it would look at the research. An MoD spokeswoman said:
"The MoD continually looks at research and improvements in technology to ensure that our injured personnel receive the best that is available. The products and techniques that we use are continuously reviewed in line with emerging technologies; any development that may be of benefit to our personnel will be considered as part of that process."

The prototype leg has been created by Professor Hubert Egger at the University of Linz in Austria. Professor Egger and his team were behind a breakthrough in 2010 when they created a limb that could be controlled by the brain. The latest invention involves rewiring the remaining foot nerve endings from a patient's stump to healthy tissue in the thigh. Six sensors are then fitted to the foot sole of a lightweight prosthesis, and linked to stimulators inside the shaft where the stump sits. Every time pressure is applied or a step is taken, the sensors send a signal to the brain.

Professor Hubert Egger stated that:
"It is also hoped the leg will lessen or eradicate the effects of phantom pain, which is believed to be the result of the brain becoming increasingly sensitive as it seeks information about a missing limb."

Former Austrian teacher and amputee Wolfgang Rangger, who has tested the limb, said:
"It's like a second lease of life, like being reborn. It feels like I have a foot again. I no longer slip on ice and I can tell whether I walk on gravel, concrete, grass or sand. I can even feel small stones."

A Help for Heroes' ambassador, former Reservist Sergeant Craig Gadd, 42, who lost his left leg after being hit by a bomb on his second tour of Afghanistan in 2010, said:
"The limb had the potential to give more options for wounded soldiers. I would urge the Ministry of Defence to look at this technology. Anything that can improve the quality of life for an amputee, whether a soldier or others, always has to be good news."

COURAGE AFTER THE BATTLE

David Henson, who lost both legs when he accidentally stood on a roadside bomb in Afghanistan in 2011 and went on to captain the British Armed Forces team and won Gold at the Invictus Games, said:
"What this leg does allow you to do is sense the environment. It means you can sense without looking. That sense of touch is a vital skill. If the evidence is there and there is an advantage to be gained I would expect the MoD would take notice. To be fair, they have a good track record of monitoring new research and anything that has the potential to get the boys back on their feet."

Source:- http://www.telegraph.co.uk/news/uknews/defence/11660394/Worlds-first-feeling-artificial-leg-offers-hope-for-wounded-soldiers.html

Not only have feet had the 21st century treatment and allow amputated limbs to feel their surroundings, so to speak, arms are also under consideration. In 2014, it was reported that a 42-year-old man from Sweden who was fitted with the world's first mind-controlled prosthetic arm a year earlier has been able to return to work as a truck driver after the device proved to be a complete success.

He is now able to flex his fingers, catch a ball and operate a petrol pump during his normal job, as well as tie the laces on his children's skates, unpack eggs and chop wood. The new prosthetic used a technique called osseointegration, and works by connecting the prosthesis directly to his bone, nerves and muscles. Max Ortiz Catalan, research scientist at Chalmers University of Technology in Gothenberg, Sweden said:
"We have used osseointegration to create a long-term stable fusion between man and machine. We see this technology as an important step towards more natural control of artificial limbs. It is the missing link for allowing sophisticated neural interfaces to control sophisticated prostheses. So far, this has only been possible in short experiments within controlled environments."

A system of recreating sensations to prosthetic hands using electrical stimulation, which would give the sense of feeling, is currently under development in the United States. The work is being carried out at the Case Western Reserve University and it is planned to reactivate areas of the brain that produce the sense of touch.

One person who has benefited from this research is Igor Spetic, of Madison, Ohio, who was able to identify a cotton wool ball for the first time while blindfolded after it was passed over the back of his prosthetic.
He said "I knew immediately it was cotton."

3D Prosthetics

Given the inevitable advancement, 3D printing has developed airway splints for infants, facial reconstruction parts for cancer patients, orthopaedic implants for pensioners, customised hearing-aid shells and ear moulds, dental crowns and bridges from digital scans of teeth. Jaw surgery and knee replacement operations are also routinely carried out using surgical guides printed on the machines. it was inevitable that the days of the old solid rubber prosthetics will soon be gone and people would look at the development of a prosthetic limb or other body parts such as cartilage, and possibly even one day teeth and new bones. We now have 3D-printed limbs, titanium legs and hands controlled by apps; advances in technology are revolutionising the industry.

A state-of-the-art centre in Scotland gives specialist treatment to military amputees, taking advantage of these developments, and making the technology more mainstream. The service is based at the WestMARC unit at Southern General Hospital, and at the SMART Centre in Edinburgh.

The units work alongside the existing NHS prosthetics service, and use specialist prosthetic training and imaging equipment to manufacture new socket technology.

The centre is also working on a system of cameras and motion sensors, to create a 3D image of how a limb is moving. The technology works by measuring movement and force to help assess ways for a patient to get around more easily and put less pressure on their muscles. It then advises patients how to walk more naturally. Another application being researched is using a smart phone application.

Autodesk, a company which is normally associated with engineers, designers, and architects are working with the University of Toronto, experimenting with different ways of scanning limbs and creating customised 3D prosthetic socket models. Autodesk is using a variant of their design software called Autodesk MeshMixer. One of the other uses is in models of the brain's vasculature (blood vessels) which are then being used for surgical training or when planning complex neurosurgery procedures such as repair of brain aneurysms.

As well as large companies, there are small inventors out there looking at the options of 3D limbs. These tend to be more flexible in their design and the specific needs of the patient, such as a Spiderman hand for a little boy or a pink prosthetic for a little girl. One person undertaking this task is Inventor Stephen Davies in South Wales, who was himself born without a left lower arm and never forgot the stigma of the NHS prosthetic he wore as a child. Stephen has been designing and building his prosthetics after several years of not using one. He began looking at designs available on the NHS – only to discover they had barely improved in three decades - and the more sophisticated ones were in the region of £30,000 and upwards. Having learned how far lighter limbs could be created on a 3D printer, he began to experiment and eventually set up *Team UnLimbited*, which creates customised limbs for children.

Hanger Prosthetics USA
One of the preferred manufacturer options for veterans in the United States is Hanger Prosthetics. This company is used to dealing with veterans and is one of the companies well placed to know exactly what a veteran needs. It all started on June 1, 1861, when an 18-year-old engineering student, James Edward Hanger, left his family to join his brothers in the Confederate Army. On June 3rd, less than two days after enlisting, a cannonball tore through his leg early in the Battle of Philippi, making James the first amputee of the Civil War. The young Hanger survived an excruciating battlefield amputation by Dr. James D. Robinson, which was necessary to save his life.

James Edward Hanger was later to say:
"I cannot look back upon those days in the hospital without a shudder. No one can know what such a loss means unless he has suffered a similar catastrophe. In the twinkling of an eye, life's fondest hopes seemed dead. I was the prey of despair. What could the world hold for a maimed, crippled man!"

A prisoner of war until August 1861, upon returning home to Churchville, Virginia, Hanger requested solitude. His family assumed he was writhing in despair; however, unbeknownst to anyone else, he immediately began work on what would prove to be a revolutionizing prosthetic solution.

Whittled from barrel staves, the "Hanger Limb" was first worn by Hanger in November 1861 as he descended the steps of his home, to the astonishment of his family, who didn't know what he was doing while locked away for months in his upstairs bedroom.

In the same year, Hanger secured two patents from the Confederate government and was commissioned to develop prosthetic limbs for veteran soldiers. In 1891, Hanger was granted a U.S. patent for his prosthetic innovation. By the time of his death in June 1919, the J.E. Hanger Company had branches in Atlanta, Philadelphia, Pittsburgh, St. Louis, London, and Paris.

Hanger Clinic has developed many prosthetic solutions including the ComfortFlex™ Socket System, Insignia™ Laser Scanning System and the WalkAide.® Few parts of the human body are as important and complex as the hands. Thanks to four movable fingers and a thumb that can be separately positioned, the Michelangelo® Prosthetic Hand offers gripping kinematics, giving those with upper extremity limb loss new degrees of freedom and restoring numerous hand functions for the user. In order to achieve a natural movement pattern, the hand is equipped with two drive units. The main drive is responsible for gripping movements and gripping strength while the thumb drive allows the thumb to be electronically positioned in one additional axis of movement.

Prosthetic Options

The world of prosthetics is changing and is constantly evolving into even more amazing devices. When you thought you had seen the possibility of things getting better, along comes another amazing advancement. A person now has a number of options open to then, providing their residual limb and other considerations are suitable.

The first option is choosing not to wear a prosthesis. For some people, this is the best choice and the one with which they are most comfortable. Other reasons may be a negative experience with their first prosthesis or the prospect of revision surgery, which is sometimes necessary for a successful prosthetic fit.

Passive Prosthesis

The passive prosthesis, which is a cosmetic restoration, is another option for upper limb loss people. It is a choice for those people who do not require precise hand control or grip, but still seek a cosmetically pleasing prosthesis.

Conventional or Body-Powered Prosthesis

A conventional or body-powered prosthesis is a choice many upper limb users make. This prosthesis is suspended from a harness fastened around the person's shoulder or upper torso. It is controlled by upper body movements that utilize a cable connected to the harness at one end, and to a mechanical hand, hook or elbow at the other end. Many people feel this type of prosthesis grants them a wide range of basic function and control.

Electrically Powered Prosthesis

Another option is the electrically powered prosthesis that utilizes motors to open and close the hand, and can also flex and extend the elbow or rotate the wrist. This option offers many control choices.

Myoelectric Prosthesis

The user controls the prosthesis by contracting the muscles in the residual limb, generating signals that activate the motor in the elbow, wrist or hand. Some people find that this type of prosthesis allows a greater range of motion, a more natural appearance, and enhanced work ability. It is also more comfortable since the harness is either smaller or is eliminated completely.

Hybrid Prosthesis

Combining elements of the conventional and the electrically powered prosthesis create another option - the hybrid. A hybrid prosthesis provides the user with the unique ability to operate the elbow and the hand at the same time. This feature can dramatically increase the rehabilitation potential of some individuals.

Adaptive or Activity-Specific Prosthesis

This type of prosthesis is meant for the individual whose specialized requirements cannot be met by the other options. Various terminal devices can be utilized depending on the specialized activity. For example, custom adaptations can be fabricated for photography, swimming, basketball, baseball, golf, fishing, pool and most other recreational activities.

Prosthetic Leg Solutions

The loss of a leg changes how you move through life. There is an amazing technological revolution happening in prosthetics. Advanced materials and designs are restoring mobility to people of all ages and from every background, whether you are challenged by illness, injury or accident.

Since Ottobock introduced the first computer-controlled knee, the C-Leg®, in 1999, the advantages of microprocessor-controlled knees have been well established. Microprocessor knees improve mobility and reduce the risk of injury from falls, which leads to better overall health and wellbeing for wearers. The technology continues to evolve, offering prosthetic wearers even smarter knees with improved sensors and longer battery life.

All computerized knees include a microprocessor, software, sensors, a hydraulic or pneumatic resistance system and a battery. Sensors monitor and detect changes in the environment, such as walking on a different surface, going up or down a slope or walking at a different speed. Based on that feedback, the microprocessor adjusts the resistance to knee bending and straightening to accommodate walking speed and terrain. This enhances stability and security along with other features which are typically included, such as stumble recovery, controlled descent of ramps and controlled recline into a seated position.

Microprocessor Prosthetic Feet

Microprocessor controlled feet respond to constant feedback from sensors to the onboard computer, which changes the resistance to downward motion and upward motion of the foot based on walking speed, incline, decline and type of terrain. Adjustments are made in real time. Some designs communicate with smartphones via Bluetooth. Microprocessor controlled feet require nightly recharging, similar to a mobile phone.

The details and descriptions above have been adapted from http://www.hangerclinic.com/

Thought Prosthetics

A prosthetic which is controlled by thought seems to be something out of science fiction, but this sort of development is becoming increasingly believable. Existing prosthetic arms rely on a patient twitching the muscles in the stump of their damaged arms. Existing prosthetics only allow one or two grasping actions and this is the main reason people abandon their prosthetics.

Dr Dario Farina, at Imperial College London, and colleagues in Europe, Canada and US stated:

"When an arm is amputated the nerve fibres and muscles are also severed, which means that it is very difficult to get meaningful signals from them to operate a prosthetic. This means that our technology can detect and decode signals more clearly, opening up the possibility of robotic prosthetics that could be far more intuitive and useful for patients. It is a very exciting time to be in this field of research."

The researchers carried out lab-based experiments with six volunteers at the University of Vienna, who were either amputees from the shoulder down or just above the elbow. Experts have now created the new prosthetic arm by linking the nerves from the spine into an intact piece of muscle, allowing a patient to control it by directly thinking about actions. By linking the nerves from the spine into an intact piece of muscle, either in the patient's chest or biceps, patients are able to carry out a much wider repertoire of movements. To control the new prosthetic, the patient simply has to think in a similar fashion to that of control for a phantom arm.

While an alternative approach is using brain implants, the advantage of using a nerve from the spine is that the approach is compatible with existing prosthetic arms, against the option of brain implants where wires would be needed to be inserted into the brain to control the device.

By doing this, the signal is carried by the nerves to the muscle and the prosthetic responds to the opening and closing of the hand, rotating the wrist, touching fingertips of the same hand. Although at an early stage, it is hoped that this type of prosthetic can be advanced and made more adaptable in the future.

Prosthetic Face Implants

3D face prosthetics have now been possible from the simple iPhone. Dr Rodrigo Salazar from Paulista University (UNIP) in Sao Paulo used a free app called Autodesk 123D Catch, which turns photos into 3D models. He took 15 images of the trauma area. The photos were uploaded and converted into a virtual model of Mr Conceiçao's face. Married former salesman

COURAGE AFTER THE BATTLE

Carlito Conceiçao has lived with a hole in his face and an uncomfortable prosthetic that kept falling off since 2008, following a cancerous tumour which ravaged one side of his face. His new face, which is finished in silicon, is attached by magnets to three titanium screws under his eyebrow and can easily be removed to be washed. It has transformed his life by restoring his self-esteem.

The rationale for using a smartphone is that all modern mobile devices have an integrated accelerometer and a gyroscope sensor, which are automatically run by the application to guide the operator's 3D position during the photo capture sequence. Dr Luciano Dib, a maxillofacial surgeon who is involved in the project, performed the two-hour integration operation.

'It means wearers can confidently go to the beach, take a shower, go to the gym and run without fear of the prosthesis falling off. And they can take it off at night to clean it.'

It is unclear how long the prosthetic will last before it needs to be replaced, but a silicone facial prosthesis typically lasts between one and three years, depending on a number of factors, such as work and home environment, sun exposure, skin type and hygiene.

FACIAL WOUNDS, FACE MASKS, DEAFNESS AND BLINDNESS

Amid the horrors of war, when you think of war wounded you naturally think loss of limb, stomach or chest wounds, but you never think about the person having half of their face blown away, or the face being disfigured by a bullet. The large-calibre artillery shell with their power to atomize bodies or quite simply rip them apart and leave an open wound, particularly a facial wound, is a common sight in the battlefield. These men are not merely broken but shattered by the very nature of warfare. A common misconception with the soldiers in World War One was understanding the principles of a machine gun. They seemed to think they could pop their heads up over a trench and move quickly enough to dodge the hail of bullets before returning their heads to the safety of the trench. This proved an impossible task and resulted in some of the most horrific facial injuries.

One such example was of an American soldier who, recalling the incident of June 1918 when a German bullet smashed into his skull, in the Bois de Belleau, said:

"It sounded to me like someone had dropped a glass bottle into a porcelain bathtub, a barrel of whitewash tipped over and it seemed that everything in the world turned white."

Today's combat injuries will include high-velocity/high-energy and low-velocity missiles. Blasts caused by high explosives often contain metal fragments, such as Claymore mines, which are curved charges placed upright in the ground and explode with such force towards the enemy that the contents can effectively rip into them. This sends hundreds of metal pellets which are packed inside the device towards the enemy at high speed, much like a shotgun cartridge. Victims who are close to the centre of the explosion barely survive such fatal and horrific injuries.

The severity of a bullet or ballistic injury is related to the shape and size of the projectile (the actual front section of the bullet) and the distance it has travelled, and the resulting kinetic energy at the point of impact. High-velocity bullets (rounds) fired from an assault rifle have special ballistic properties, including high-impact kinetic energy of around 3250 ft/s (feet per second) which creates a transient cavitation space with a small entrance wound and a much larger exit wound. This type of perforating injury usually causes enormous damage to soft and hard tissues, with severe comminution of the facial skeleton. Low-velocity missile injuries are quite different, due to the fact that the projectiles possess only about one-third of the kinetic energy compared with high-velocity projectiles. Such missiles generally cause penetrating injuries, which inflict multiple fractures and skin lacerations. The hallmark of high-velocity ballistic injuries to the face is fractures of the facial skeleton. There will also be the inevitable damage and destruction to soft tissue such as muscle, tendons, and even blood vessels and arteries.

In all cases, the soldier's face will have to be rebuilt on what, if anything, still exists of his original face. During World War One the soldiers, or Tommies, called a small room within 3rd London General Hospital, 'The Tin Nose Shop,' but it was officially called Masks for Facial Disfigurement Department. Within this room teams of surgeons and artists were trying hard to restore both function and form to deformities, and they crudely practised, with little real attention given to aesthetics. The artists created likenesses and sculptures of what the men had looked like before their injuries in an effort to restore, as much as possible, a mutilated man's original face.

On a single day in early July 1916, following the first engagement of the Battle of the Somme - a day for which the London Times casualty list covered not columns, but pages - Sir Harold Gillies, a pioneer in the art of facial reconstruction and modern plastic surgery who refined and then mass-produced critical techniques, (many of which are still important to modern plastic surgery) and his colleagues were sent approximately 2,000 patients. Ironically, pioneering work in skin grafting had been undertaken in both Germany and the Soviet Union, but to the credit of Sir Harold Gillies, the clinically honest before-and-after photographs which were published shortly after the war revealed how unbelievably successful he and his team were in such a pioneering area of medicine.

Too old for active duty when war broke out, Francis Derwent Wood, who had enlisted as a private in the Royal Army Medical Corps at the age of 44, and a trained artist, said:

"My work begins where the work of the surgeon is completed."

He took upon himself the task of designing sophisticated splints for patients, and then realized that he would be better employed in constructing masks for the irreparably facially disfigured. His new metallic masks, lightweight and more permanent than the rubber prosthetics previously used, were custom designed to look more like the pre-war portrait of each solider. It was accepted that facial disfigurement was the most traumatic of the multitude of horrific damages the war inflicted. Nurses were told to always look straight into the patient's face as the patient would be looking at them for any indications of horror or fright at the sight of the soldier's injuries.

Francis Wood established his mask-making unit in March 1916 and was quoted in an article in The Lancet, the British Medical Journal:

"My cases are generally extreme cases that plastic surgery has, perforce, had to abandon; but, as in plastic surgery, the psychological effect is the same. The patient acquires his old self-respect, self-assurance, self-reliance, takes once more a pride in his personal appearance. His presence is no longer a source of melancholy to himself nor of sadness to his relatives and friends."

Once the wound has completely healed, then the mask making process can start. This is initially made by using clay or plasticine. The cast will be a suffocating and sometimes painful experience, but to enable the artist to effectively make a new face, the cast material will have to reach all cracks, crevices and even eye sockets.

Another prominent mask maker was Anna Coleman Ladd, an American-born sculptor who studied in Paris and Rome, and soldiers would come to her studio to have a cast made of their faces, which would then be used to help construct the prosthetic.

The mask itself would be made from galvanized copper one thirty second of an inch thick (0.79mm) and depended on whether it covered the entire face or, as was often the case, only the upper or lower half. The mask weighed between four ounces (113g) and nine ounces (255g) and was normally held on by spectacles. The greatest artistic challenge lay in painting the metallic surface the colour of skin. After experiments with oil paint, which chipped, a hard enamel that was washable and had a dull, flesh-like finish was chosen. The mask was painted while the man himself was wearing it, so as to match as closely as possible his own colouring. A single mask can take up to a month to make.

The journey that led a soldier from the field or trench to Wood's department was lengthy, disjointed and full of dread. Once taken out of the mud and stench of the battlefield to the Casualty Clearing Station, then on to the constantly overstrained field hospital for initial treatment, there followed evacuation via ship across the Channel to England, where the wounded men were left unattended in long windy corridors before coming under the care of surgeons. Multiple operations inevitably followed and one nurse, Enid Bagnold, a volunteer nurse (and later the author of National Velvet) speaking about a badly wounded patient, said:

"He lay with his profile to me, only he has no profile, as we know a man's. Like an ape, he has only his bumpy forehead and his protruding lips; the nose, the left eye, gone."

By contrast, modern warfare sees the injured soldier evacuated from the battlefield with great speed and efficiency by helicopter and treated during their flight back to the hospital by a skilled medical team. This is a far cry from the basic systems used in World War One, where it may have taken days to get back to a full hospital environment to get treatment. That golden hour we hear about all the time was never in anyone's mind during World War One, along with the most basic of facilities and equipment.

A special facial hospital was set up in Sidcup, England, the town that was home to Sir Harold Gillies. Some park benches were painted blue; a code that warned townspeople that any man sitting on one would be distressful to view. Just imagine what this would have felt like for the man having to sit on a blue park bench to effectively silently tell others he was disfigured by a war to end all wars. Mirrors were banned in most wards, and men who somehow managed an illicit peek had been known to collapse in shock. The psychological effect on a man who has to go through life as an object of horror, to himself as well as to others, is beyond description. It is a fairly common experience for the maladjusted person to feel like a stranger to his world. It must be unmitigated hell to feel like a stranger to yourself.

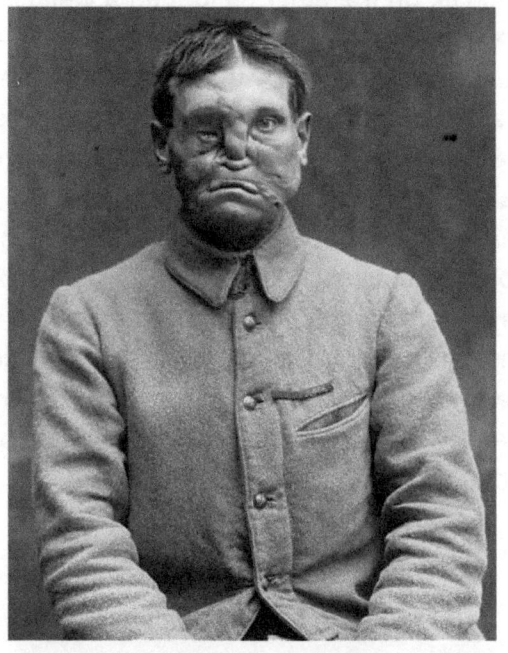

Soldier Before and After Prosthetic Mask

COURAGE AFTER THE BATTLE

Today, the only images of these men in their masks come from black and white photographs which are set for all time in a single moment's expression of afflicted soldier. He, on the other hand, had a lifetime of viewing this in mirrors and shop windows, and the indignity of people inevitably staring. The question was mentally asked by the soldier of himself: how would his children flee in terror at the sight of their father's expressionless face, or find him repulsive? Am I going to be able to regain all the usual functions of my face, such as the ability to chew or swallow, or even smile?

Wood's department was disbanded in 1919 and almost no record of the men who wore the masks survives, but it was clear that a mask had a life of only a few years. It was noted that most of the wearers were still wearing them past their usable time, despite the fact that they were very battered and looked awful. This, I suppose, was better than the disfigured face they had been left with or the looks and comments of people repulsed by their appearance.

COURAGE AFTER THE BATTLE

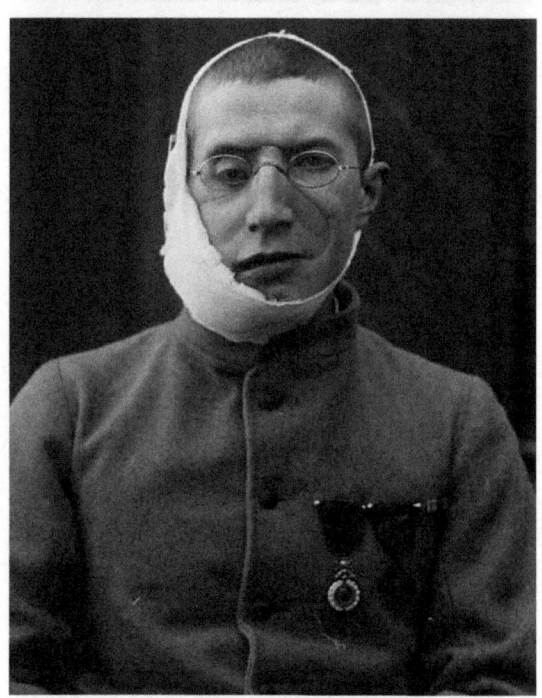

Images 22 A-B Soldier Before and After Prosthetic Mask

COURAGE AFTER THE BATTLE

Images 23 A-B Soldier Before and After Prosthetic Mask

COURAGE AFTER THE BATTLE

Images 24 A-B Soldier Before and After Prosthetic Mask

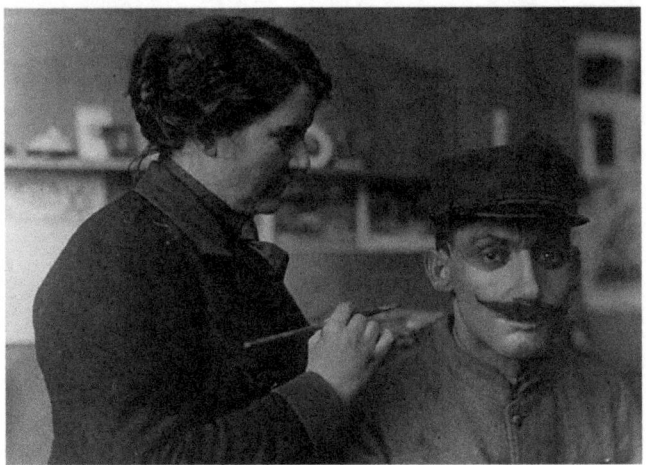

Anna Coleman Ladd working on a Prosthetic Mask

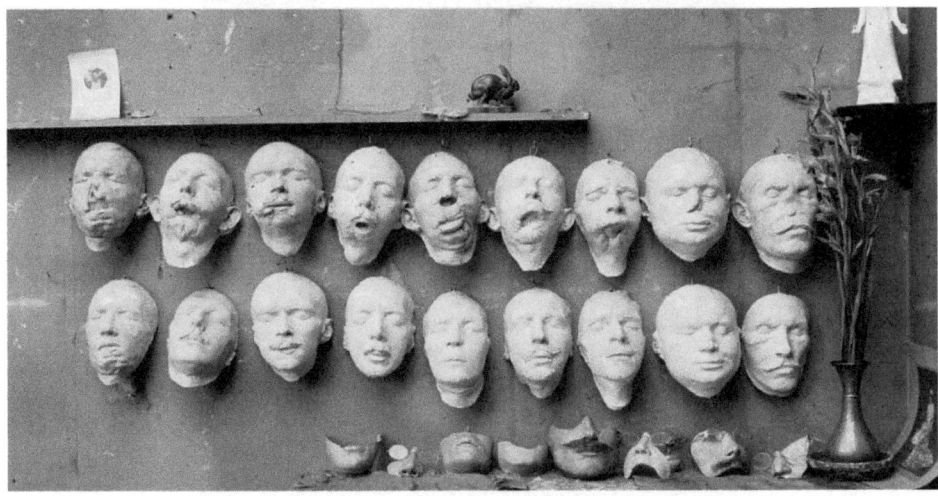

Wall of Prosthetic Masks

Today, despite the steady and spectacular advance of medical techniques, even sophisticated modern reconstructive surgery can still not adequately treat the kinds of injuries that condemned men of World War One to live behind their masks. A blast can throw all sorts of debris into the face and eyes, but these will not stop the momentum and the next stop is the soft tissue inside the skull.

The treatment of catastrophic casualties during World War One led to enormous advances in most branches of medicine, advances that would be used to treat the catastrophic casualties of World War Two and beyond.

COURAGE AFTER THE BATTLE

Only recently have we developed 3D face masks and, more recently, ones that stay in place by small magnets drilled into the adjoining bone structure and look like real skin.

If the trenches of World War One exposed men to face a daily barrage of shrapnel, which brought rise to unprecedented surgeries to reconstruct what remained, then the battlegrounds of Korea and Vietnam would therefore give birth to techniques for repairing severed arteries and veins to salvage limbs. Most recently, the IEDs that littered the streets and battlefields of Iraq and Afghanistan led to innovations in combat medicine and evacuation procedures. These advances, combined with enhanced protective equipment, which then had the adverse effect of weighing the person down, and in extreme heat, helped produce some of the highest combat survival rates in history. Today less than 10 percent of combat casualties die from their wounds, compared with 19 percent in World War Two and 16 percent in Vietnam. Iraq and Afghanistan left surgeons struggling to fix harrowing facial injuries in numbers unrivalled since World War One.

An IED blast can commonly blow a large amount of dirt and debris into the area of the wound caused by the initial blast, which can drive dust and dirty shards of metal through the new wound. In facial wounds, missing or crushed facial bones and melted skin on the face are common injuries. The flames that destroy the skin allow microbes to invade the wound and amass into slimy sheets of bacteria called biofilms. Biofilms can form within hours of injury and cause lingering, difficult-to-treat infections that, even when they don't kill, provoke inflammation which is a major impediment to seamless healing.

Surgeons prevent biofilms in limbs by removing all the wounded tissue, amputating when necessary, but they can't amputate a face. Conventional antibiotic and disinfectant treatments don't work well on face burns; the area is usually washed out to control infection and then waits for the blistered skin to fall off. If the damaged area still retains sections of bone and tissue that may be saved, the immediate surgical team may put pins through remnants of skin to temporarily hold bone fragments together, prepare the patient for evacuation and hope for the best.

During World War Two, a high percentage of the wounded soldiers, particularly those from Dunkirk and Narvik, had suffered from severe burns. An even higher percentage of sailors were wounded in action by enemy aircraft and torpedo attacks which resulted in them having their ship sunk and entering the burning sea, with horrible injuries and burns. Many of the fighter pilots escaping from their crippled aircraft landed safely but were badly burnt about the face, hands and legs. The pain suffered by these patients is indescribable. This seems to stamp an impression on the patient's mind and many, even the most stoical, suffered from tragic psychological collapse. Some remained " nervous wrecks", others became "chronic alcoholics". A famous club, the Guinea Pigs Club, was formed by the RAF Pilots and their pioneering surgeon. The Guinea Pigs Club is the name given to the pilots injured in the Battle of Britain who were treated by Sir Archibald McIndoe at the burns unit of Queen Victoria's Hospital in East Grinstead, West Sussex. The Guinea Pigs were given this name simply because McIndoe had no choice but to try out his ideas on the men, as he had no book to refer to or guide him. There were 649 Guinea Pigs at the end of the war, and 62% were British, 20% Canadians, 6% Australians, 6% New Zealanders and 6% from many other countries, including those who escaped the German invasion.

There are three degrees of burn. which are generally agreed as a bench mark for diagnosis.

1st Degree, scorching of the skin and erythema.
2nd Degree, blistering and partial skin destruction.
3rd Degree, at least full-thickness skin destruction but including those that are deeper

During this time, the standard initial treatment for burns was as follows:

The injured surface is gently cleansed with swabs wrung out, of warm saline and all dirty and blistered epithelium removed. When particularly dirty or oily, ether soap and ether are used for cleansing. A 1 percent water solution of gentian violet is then painted over the raw surface by means of gauze. Apart from its antiseptic and coagulating action, this solution clearly demarcates the raw area. The surface is dried by a current of hot air from an electric hair-dryer. Using gauze, a freshly made 10 per cent solution of tannic acid is then applied and, while still moist, the area is painted with solution of 10 per cent silver nitrate applied in the same manner. Immediate coagulation takes place and the area is again dried by hot air. A further application of gentian violet is made, particular attention being paid to the edges of the damaged area.

On returning to the ward, the patients were nursed under a shock cradle. As a routine, the coagulum was dehydrated four-hourly with methylated ether, and painted with 1 per cent gentian violet in spirit. Areas which appeared moist or thin were treated hourly if necessary. Burned hands and arms were raised on pillows to reduce oedema (a condition characterized by an excess of watery fluid collecting in the cavities or tissues of the body).

Source: Journal of Royal Army Medical Corps Treatment of Burns in War-Time (1941 77: p14-18)

Once the initial work to save the patient's face is complete, they can start the reconstruction process. Such things as creating lips from tongues, fashioning jaws from leg bones, papering faces with skin taken from wherever he could get it. To enable body areas to be rebuilt, it is preferable to use the patient's own skin and body fat to prevent rejection. For instance, if you were to rebuild a person's cheek, you may cut a slit in the shoulders and insert a deflated tissue expander under the skin, much like a surgeon would do to Siamese twins to allow additional skin growth prior to the operation to separate them.

Adding a saline solution twice a week for three months and then carving flaps of skin from each of the shoulders, flipping the free ends up to the cheeks, forms so-called supraclavicular flaps which use the blood supply from the supraclavicular artery at the base of the neck to nourish the graft. But the procedure requires the patient's shoulders to stay stitched to his cheeks for a month.

Facial trauma forces doctors to abandon a fundamental principle of plastic surgery in that they normally replace like with like. The problem with facial surgery is that the face has skin which has to be supple enough to smile and frown. Today, we see that it is possible to get a full-face transplant and as medical progress is made we may even one day be able to grow certain parts from our own bodies to be replaced when required.

Blindness

As a result of all the facial injuries, there is a good chance that the person has lost part or, in most cases, all of their sight. This starts off a whole new ball game for the injured service man or woman. Founded in 1915, St Dunstan's became the byword for care of those who have lost their sight, and the founder, Mr C Arthur Pearson, who was himself blind, was to become a major component in what will become a lifeline for most blind veterans who thought their life was effectively over.

During World War One, blind men were news and there is one story in particular, that of a Tommy from Cardiff. The news of the men now blind through battle spread and people volunteered to assist these poor men in the Military Hospitals. During December of 1914, one of these volunteers was the daughter of a wealthy Cardiff Shipbroker whose own sight was in danger. She had been taught Braille and the Medical Officer arranged for her to give the Tommy lessons in how to use the Braille system. Her father further assisted by bringing this Tommy into contact with people who were able to show him how to cope with his blindness.

One of the particular features for blindness during World War One was the number of cases of functional blindness due to the violent explosions caused by high explosive shells, bombs, and hand grenades. The causalities may not have sustained viewable organic injury, but the clinical symptoms characterizing their functional nature are very clearly marked. Usually the casualty is unconscious and on regaining consciousness he finds that he is unable to see. When examined he has eyes which are kept closed, the lids may be frequently fluttered, or twinkling. Attempting to open the lids the casualty resists but when this is overcome to a sufficient extent the eye is rolled upwards, and the pupils are always kept covered by the lids; which results in great difficulty in looking downwards. The casualty will complain of pain and photophobia, and will show marked fatigue.

Early in the war this injury was treated in several ways, all with disappointing results. The main principles on which treatment was given were rest, tonics, deprivation or punishments, such as abstention from tobacco; confinement to bed or in isolation rooms; persuasion; encouragement; counter-irritation and talking, but all proved to be ineffective until suggestion and hypnosis were tried.

The method employed was to have the men singly in a darkened room, quiet, and resting in the most comfortable armchair the ward could provide. They were instructed as to what was to be attempted, and no demur was ever made by any of them, but on the contrary, after the first experience, they were always eager to continue the treatment. The casualty had his eyes closed so that the assistance of light could not be obtained, but he was told to think of something pleasant and agreeable, not to take the slightest notice of the operator, and to relax his mind by attempting to stop all incoming thoughts and to make his mind, as far as possible, a blank.

The casualty was then hypnotised, although some men resisted the treatment and were unable to be hypnotised. The treatment carried on for a few minutes, and having obtained the sleepiness or light hypnosis necessary, the casualty was subjected to a forcible suggestion from the operator, who reiterated the casualty's ability to see and to open his eyes, and to assert very vehemently that he was not blind as he imagined, but that his eyes were perfectly sound and that he could see.

On the 29th January 1915 Mr Pearson, then the president of the National Institute of the Blind, called a meeting at York House in London to establish a Blinded Soldiers and Sailors Care Committee (BSSCC). He was aware that 22 blinded soldiers needed to be promptly and sympathetically dealt with. He requested that they be taught to read and write in the Braille (Embossed Type) System and trained to a standard that would allow them to become self-reliant and self-helpful. One of the main objects of the committee was to establish a home which was equipped to enable the residents to maintain their training. Under the Blind Persons Act 1920, Local Authorities were responsible for promoting the welfare of blind residents within their geographical area of responsibility.

Braille was invented in 1829 by Louise Braille who was a young blind student who had adapted a French army code called night writing, which used a raised dots system which was small enough to be covered by a single finger, and allowed soldiers to communicate silently at night without light. Within this system there are six dots in all, arranged in a similar layout to the number six on a domino. Throughout the code, to enable the blind person to differentiate the various letters and numbers, the dots are arranged in various configurations.

Braille alphabet card

Wear dots... raise lots

Braille letters are made of raised dots so they can be read by touch. This card shows you the braille alphabet and numbers. A braille "cell" is made up of six dots like a domino, with each letter using a different pattern.

A	B	C	D	E	F	G	H	I	J

K	L	M	N	O	P	Q	R	S	T

U	V	W	X	Y	Z	.	,	"	"

To make numbers in braille we put this special numeral symbol before the letters **A** to **I** for numbers **1** to **9** so A = 1, B = 2 and so on. **J** is used for **zero**.

So **6** is the numeral symbol followed by the braille letter '**F**' like this:

And the number **160** is like this:

© RNIB 2016. RNIB charity nos. 226227 and SC039316

Braille Alphabet (RNIB)

The first step in the rehabilitation was a Braille watch to enable the blinded casualty to tell the time of day. The watch had strengthened hands and raised dots which could be felt by the wearer and this was an important psychological first step to realising blindness was not a total and complete disaster. Some of the past descriptions of a blind person were 'Asylum for the Blind,' and 'Society for the Relief of the Indignant Blind.' Other descriptions were Blind, Nearly Blind and Idiotic.

Due to the larger numbers of blind and partially blind coming home from the battlefield, local sympathy was strong for the men who had fought for their country and were now inflicted with this disability. One particular Tommy was Billy Clough from Lancashire who had a poem written for him.

On every front throughout the war some lads from Rams they have been,
In Egypt and Salonika, France and Russia, fighting they have seen,
And when the war is over what are we going to do,
To help these gallant lads of ours who've help to pull us through?
Some will be crippled many ways; one we know is blind,
We must try to help poor Billy Clough and also bear in mind,
The government may provide an arm or leg and make it work alright,
But is it beyond the power of human aid to give a blind man sight.

Source – In the Mind's Eye – The Blind veterans of St Dunstan's by David Castleton

During the 1929 General Election, blind veterans were having difficulty casting their vote due to privacy issues as they had to have the presiding officer accompany them into the booth to place their mark on the paper. This was brought to the attention of Parliament by Mr Ian Fraser, MP (later to be Lord Fraser of Lonsdale) himself a blind person, who argued that a blind person should be able to take a trusted friend or relative into the booth with them. From this discussion, he was able to have the Blind Voters Bill introduced in 1934.

Prior to the Blind Voters Bill being introduced, there was an option of introducing a white walking stick for blind people. In 1931 the General Secretary of the National Safety-First Association brought these proposals forward in the hope that there would be a national recognition of blind people. A further advancement was guide dogs, which were introduced in 1916, but this was initially in France and later Germany, before they were introduced to Britain. The first dog was actually given to a German soldier after his doctor was called away whilst he was being walked around the hospital grounds.

The doctor had left his German Shepherd with the man to let him know he was not alone and was subsequently so impressed with the dog's behaviour that he decided to start experiments in training dogs to act as guides for the blind. By 1919 there were 539 blind men with guide dogs. By 1923 a guide dog training centre had been established at Potsdam, which trained several thousand dogs in the next ten years. The work of this guide dog school came to the attention of a wealthy American, Mrs Dorothy Harrison Eustis, who was breeding and training German Shepherds in Switzerland for the customs service, the army and the police. After visiting the Potsdam centre, Mrs Eustis was impressed and wrote an article for the American Saturday Evening Post of October 1927. Mrs Eustis then set up a guide dog centre, L 'Oeil qui Voit' (The Seeing Eye), at Vevey in Switzerland and later established the first school for training dogs in the United States.

Early in 1930 the work of the Seeing Eye appeared in British newspapers and although a lot of blind people became interested in it, there were no plans to set up a similar organisation in this country. Shortly after this, a letter appeared in the Liverpool Echo (local evening newspaper for the Wirral and Liverpool areas) asking if anyone could supply a guide dog for a blind man and if so, to get in touch with the Royal National Institute for the Blind (RNIB) in Liverpool.

The letter was read by Miss Muriel Crooke, a German Shepherd enthusiast who lived in Wallasey, who then spoke to her friend Mrs Rosamund Bond, a long time breeder and exhibitor of German Shepherds. These ladies had some experience in training dogs for obedience testing and trials so they decided to contact the RNIB and, as it happened, theirs was the only reply. The Secretary, Mr Musgrave Frankland, himself blind, suggested that if they were serious they should get in touch with Mrs Eustis direct. They decided to write to Mrs Eustis and so what we now know as guide dogs for the blind started its path through history.

Mrs Eustis was pleased that Muriel and Rosamund were interested in setting up a Seeing Eye organisation but warned them of the hard work and problems involved. For example, there was no book on the subject, there weren't many trainers and it would cost a lot of money. However, the two Wallasey women remained enthusiastic and they met Mrs Eustis in London on 23 September 1930 to discuss their plans. The original plan was to use Mrs Bond's country estate in Yorkshire as the training base. However, Mrs Eustis insisted that all the training had to be done in town to get the dogs used to traffic, and it had to be done under the immediate supervision of one of the sponsors. So, Wallasey it was, and Mrs Eustis offered to lend a trainer to run a trial scheme for four or five dogs and blind people. All that was needed now was money and somewhere to do the training.

Miss Crooke was born Muriel Elise Crooke on 14 June 1901 in Egremont, and was the daughter of a well-known surgeon by the name of Dr William Crooke. By 1911 the family were living at 3 Warren Drive, New Brighton. She died in 1975. It was at 3 Warren Drive that the first meetings were held which led to the formation of the first Guide Dogs Committee, as it was known.

During 1930-31 they set up an organisation to raise money and find a suitable training spot. In February 1931, Miss Crooke and Mrs Bond, together with two new supporters, Captain Alan Sington and Lady Kitty Ritson, went to London for a meeting with the National Institute for the Blind. Here they discovered to their dismay that they had been acting illegally in raising £284 for their training scheme, because they were not a registered charity. That said, the Guide Dog Committee, as it had become known, were determined to go ahead and a solution was found by affiliating the Committee to the Institute.

The trainer lent by Mrs Eustis, Mr William Debetaz, arrived in England from Switzerland on 31 July 1931 accompanied by Elliott Humphrey, Mrs Eustis' Director of Genetics and Training. Mr Humphrey was a world-famous expert on animals of all kinds and he selected seven of 28 German Shepherd bitches that had been acquired from various sources. Mr Humphrey returned to Switzerland and Mr Debetaz began the work of training the dogs. When the training was completed Mr Humphrey returned to test the dogs and help in the first part of turning them over to the blind.

After the training, which lasted about four weeks, the four men left with their dogs. After six months they were asked to report on their experiences. All were enthusiastic:

Allen Caldwell wrote:

"Not only has my dog given me glorious freedom and independence, never known since pre-war days, but delightful companionship."

Thomas AP Rhys wrote:

"I do not mind walking at the fastest pace or even running with her."

He was to use guide dogs for the next 48 years and died in 1979 at the age of 82 while retraining with his sixth dog.

Late in 1934 the Wallasey Corporation offered for a peppercorn rent what will always be thought of as the first real home of the Association - The Cliff. This was an almost derelict house (over 100 years old) on the seashore and, with a fierce wind blowing off the Irish Sea piling sand feet high round it, the building hardly seemed ideal. But when things had been put into some sort of order, everything was able to be all under one roof. For the first time everything was brought together: the kennels, the administrative office and lodgings for the blind people and the trainer. This established the principle of providing a home in which the blind students are guests for four weeks, which is still the basis on which the training courses are run today. At about the same time as moving to The Cliff, the Guide Dogs Committee changed its name to the Guide Dogs for the Blind Association.

Now settled in his new home, Captain Liakhoff set about introducing new training methods. His impact on the guide dog movement was incalculable. He made goggles that simulated blindness (the Association's very first 'sim specs') and designed guide dog harnesses that would be familiar to guide dog owners today. He did a lot of work on bloodlines and planned a breeding programme as early as the 1940s. He actually invented puppy walking - his two daughters were the world's first puppy walkers. Crucially, and perhaps most impressively, he worked out - from scratch - training methods that are still in daily use around the world today.

Adapted from A Wallasey First the Guide Dogs For The Blind Association –

http://www.historyofwallasey.co.uk/wallasey/Guide_Dogs_For_The_Blind/index.html

Image 28 RNID Memorial Outside New Brighton Floral Pavilion, Wirral (Author)

Image 29 RNID Memorial Outside New Brighton Floral Pavilion, Wirral (Author)

COURAGE AFTER THE BATTLE

Further establishing the blind person's rights, the Disabled Persons Act of 1944 was introduced. This act required any employer who had more than 20 workers to employ a set quota of able workers to disabled workers. Mr Ian Fraser put forward his comments on the prospect for a greater emphasis on soldiers returning from long periods away defending their country. In a speech to the House of Commons in April 1945 he said:

"The signs are that the organised war with Germany will soon be over. We have got to beat thousands of swords into ploughshares and in the process we have got to absorb into our economic life five and a half million men and women who have been out of it for years. Except where the Reinstatement of Employment Act positively requires, and rightly requires, that a man should give up his job to an ex-service man who has left the same job to go and fight, the trades unionists and others cannot, and in my view, should not, be asked to go into unemployment to make jobs for returning men and women. But whatever vacancies occur there should be a priority for those who have been away."

One example of this act being placed into a working situation, Mr Henry Ford of the Ford motor company, not long after the ending of World War One, stated:

"If one out of every thousand persons is deaf then one in every thousand of Ford workers must be a deaf man. If one in every six thousand is blind then one in every six thousand should be blind."

World War Two veteran rehabilitation specialist Richard E Hoover is credited with developing the standard technique for using a white cane in 1944. Orientation and mobility specialists still teach the Hoover Method of holding a cane in the centre of the body and swinging it back and forth to detect any obstacles in the way.

Enchroma glasses

Alex Gruetzmacher's daughter bought her father a pair of Enchroma glasses for Father's Day in 2015, and it completely changed his life. Alex is unable to comprehend the new life and constantly compares new to old by taking off his glasses to look at the same object. And its colours.

Alex's condition is described as a 'strong deutan', a type of red-green colour blindness which causes red, green, orange and browns to appear as if the same colour, while also making it difficult to distinguish between blues and pink. He could not believe it when he spotted a pink potted

COURAGE AFTER THE BATTLE

plant for the first time and he was able to define the colour.

Alex was turned down by the US Army after failing 13 out of 14 colour blindness tests. That evening he went to see the sunset, something you and I take for granted every day, but a blind or partially sighted person may never see the likes of it. Alex looked at his first sunset in full colour and he was completely overwhelmed by all the beautiful colours

Deafness / Hearing Loss

On 9th June 1911 Leo Bonn, a deaf merchant banker, created The National Bureau for Promoting the General Welfare of the Deaf in London. This was inspired by his personal experience of deafness, and the foundation would become the RNID. From the start, his aims were ambitious in that he wanted to support and care for people with hearing loss, to educate those at risk of damaging their hearing, and to raise awareness of how isolating hearing loss can be.

1939 – 1945 the RNID sent out hearing aids to deaf prisoners of war. These could be converted into miniature radio receivers for espionage purposes.

1948 marked a significant moment in history when the new National Health Service agreed with the RNID and provided free hearing aids and batteries UK-wide for the first time.

1991 was another major landmark event when the telephone relay service, Typetalk, was launched with a £4m donation from BT. Typetalk is a telephone with a Qwerty keyboard as part of the phone and a small screen. This allows the deaf person to make a call via an operator. The deaf person will type the message on the keyboard, and this is displayed on their phone and the operator's screen. The operator will then speak to the person being called and relay their reply back to the deaf person via a keyboard. This message will appear on the deaf person's screen, thus making communications possible.

In 2001 the Royal National Institute for the Deaf (RNID, which is now known as Action on Hearing Loss) persuaded the government to increase subtitling requirements on terrestrial TV from 50% to 80%. It is still not up to 80%, and a lot of the time either the subtitles run so far behind that they miss large areas of conversation, or they show something completely unrelated, and on occasions make no sense at all.

In December 2009, it was reported that service personnel returning from Afghanistan were suffering severe and permanent hearing damage following a study into one of the less well known side-effects of the conflict in Helmand. Internal MoD documents revealed that of 1,250 Royal Marines from 42 Commando, who served in Afghanistan from April to October 2008, 69% suffered Noise Induced Hearing Loss (NIHL) due to the intense noise of combat. Complaints such as Tinnitus, to almost complete deafness, were greater than previously recorded.

The Ministry of Defence study showed that the intensity of the conflict in Helmand and its close combat fighting, along with the numerous roadside devices and the noise of low flying coalition aircraft, had caused the problems. Analysis by the defence audiology service found that 865 of the Marines displayed signs of severe hearing damage and of these, 410 were classified as extreme cases.

Dr Chris Pearson, author of the report, warned that:

"The known scale of the problem may prove to be the tip of the iceberg because only the most severe forms of hearing loss, grave enough to bar troops from frontline service, are officially recorded."

Professor Mark Haggard, Honorary Vice-President of Deafness Research UK, commented:

"The issue has become systematic, endemic. Combat gunfire and explosions mean significant numbers are turning up with significant hearing problems."

British employers must not subject staff to noise levels over 85dB (Decibels) for prolonged periods. A pneumatic drill, the sort you see used to dig up roads, would measure around 126dB whilst an alarm clock would be around 40dB. A soldier would see levels for a personal weapon (rifle or another similar weapon) or medium explosion create 140dB. This is equivalent to hearing a jet plane taking off approximately 40 metres away, but they are in very close proximity to this constantly during a battle. Compared to audiology tests in the UK, with RAF land-based personnel only 5.2% of RAF personnel had severe hearing damage.

Within a Journal of the Royal Army Medical Corps of 6 December 1944, (1945; 84 p54-65) an article entitled 'Psychiatric Aspects of Rehabilitation' by Major Emanuel Miller M.A, M.R.C.P, D.P.M. discussed the rehabilitation of service personnel following World War Two. The article gives a good overview of the thoughts of the day and how they intended to rehabilitate the servicemen who were to return home and, ultimately, to a working career. I have summarised some of the points in the article below:

> With men who have suffered a deafness, more often from a head injury, every effort should be made to acquaint the deaf as soon as diagnosed with the nature of their deafness and the need, if any, for the acquisition of lip reading. The common command of speech seems to undergo a change in a deaf person in that due to their inability to hear their voice, they are unable to mentally gather the correct pronunciation level of their voice. It must be noted that human sympathy for the deaf is not so forthcoming as for the blind, and it is therefore necessary that personnel dealing with deaf soldiers should be carefully chosen and/ or educated to appreciate the psychological and social problems of the deaf.
>
> Vocational training will call for special criteria of trainability.
>
> 1/ The deaf cannot be set to tasks in which the recognition of sounds of machinery and the ring of materials is all important. Certain kinds of clerical duties are open to them but others are not. For example, the deaf will be useless for shorthand taking, but adequate as ordinary typists. (Bearing in mind that in the 40's typing was generally seen as a woman's job and a man would be doing men's jobs. Would a returning soldier want to be seen typing and in a room full of women?)
>
> 2/ Spatial orientation is disturbed, if not actually lost, and although human hearing is not highly geared as it is in animals to appreciation of the exact source of the sounds, there is a disturbance of dexterity and sinistrality which rule out certain kinds of work on machinery.
>
> 3/ Social training – this is not to be underestimated as a condition which disturbs the interpersonal relations so profoundly. As early as possible, the sufferer must be aided in cultivating human contact by recreative work, both in and out of doors, and by the provision of adequate occupation therapy designed to discuss what a man can do, and not merely to give him something to do.

As conflicts change and weapons get even more powerful, the soldier in the battlefield has to cope with this, as does his body. Bearing in mind that a large percentage of the body (up to 60%) is water, this is quite a fragile piece of kit or equipment, whichever way you look at it. There is an even more fragile item, the grey matter or brain which sits quite happily in the top section of the body and is open to all manner of outside forces. In Iraq and Afghanistan, soldiers had protective armour to keep their body and vital organs safe, but that does not protect a brain or other exposed body part from a closed blast injury.

Notwithstanding the close battle situations, IEDs and low flying fighter aircraft and helicopters, soldiers will now also have to contend with the threat of so-called less lethal weapons. These are designed to target people's sight and hearing.

This adds to the problems of the battlefield when soldiers prefer not to use hearing protection as it reduces or makes it very difficult to hear orders during the battle. These orders can be other soldiers communicating and letting you know their intentions as the battle moves forward, they are changing magazines or have a stoppage (weapon jammed), requests for covering fire to other troops in the area. The list is endless, but the need to communicate is vital during a battle and fast moving situations, as decisions are made in an instant and these have to be successfully communicated to everyone.

This is not a modern problem and veterans from all conflicts and wars have come across the same problem, with the results being hearing or other damage.

The following personal stories were taken from a Sense.Org article of deafblind service personnel by Sarah Butler, with interviews by Megan Mann.

https://www.sense.org.uk/content/talking-sense-deafblind-war-veterans

Bob Miller, born in 1915
Bob was 25 and the Manager of a greengrocer's shop when he was called up in 1940. In the army, he was responsible for maintaining gun batteries.

"I didn't know anything about vehicles, and I had to be able to ride a motorbike, I went in to the battery commander and told him I didn't know how to ride one. He said 'Well, you've got a week to learn!'"

Bob's first active service was on D-Day, when he landed in France at the end of the first day of the invasion. He stated:

"If anybody said they weren't afraid I think they'd be telling lies. The worst part was landing on the beach, being shelled and mortared and

everything coming at us."

A German bomb landed close to Bob and exploded, leaving shrapnel in the back of his right ear. He was treated in a field hospital, only the most serious cases were evacuated, and carried on fighting, sporting a large bandage round his head. Despite this, and the incredible noise of gunfire all around him during the invasion, Bob's hearing was fine when he was demobbed.

Bob's hearing loss developed in the 1980s:

"I applied for a pension and they put it in writing that it was through the fault of the war. But it wasn't bad enough to get a pension: they said, "If it gets worse, apply again", but by then they weren't giving pensions."

Bob now also has macular degeneration, and says:

"My deafness has not affected me as much as my blindness."

He receives good support in his sheltered accommodation: he has help with his pills in the morning and, if he needs it, with his breakfast and making his bed:

"although I keep on trying to do it myself."

Vista, a charity that supports people with sight loss in Leicester, Leicestershire and Rutland (www.vistablind.org.uk), provides Bob with talking newspapers, and run regular outings. Bob also attends a local Sense forum for older deafblind people.

George Walter, born in 1917:

"I was always told you don't cry when you start school, and I don't think I've cried since."

George joined up in January 1940 when he was 22 years old.

"I was a firing point instructor and you can't wear earplugs because you've got to be head to head with the man, in conversation with him, and hear the officer, and you've got cannons on the right, cannons on the left, Bren guns in the middle. The recruits only have to go through it once, but we had to go through it every time, and it was all day. At night, your ears used to ring."

That's when it (George's hearing loss) started:

"I only went to the medical officer once (about my hearing). He didn't do anything. I thought it was temporary. (After the war) I knew I didn't hear as well as other people but I just soldiered on."

George has macular degeneration and cataracts, and Charles Bonnet syndrome causes him to see things that aren't there. He is greatly supported by St Dunstan's:

"I had a week in Sheffield for rehabilitation and training, and it was a busy week, but they did treat us well. They've given us three weeks' holiday, we paid, but they collected us from the door and took us to Brighton. That's a big help."

Ken Barrett, born in 1924:

Ken joined the navy in 1942. His service took him along the coast of Africa and into the Indian Ocean protecting convoys. He returned to Europe for D-Day, and afterwards joined a minesweeper.

"In the navy they didn't provide any protective clothing. We were always subjected to gunfire. Different guns have different noises and some affected you more than others, especially anti-aircraft guns, the Bofors; they had a horrible crack. If you were behind the gun you didn't feel it so badly, but if you were exposed on the upper deck when they were firing, that's when it really affected you."

In 1945, near Thailand, they came under attack from the Japanese:

"Unfortunately, there was a Bofors gun firing within three metres of my head and it went on for at least half an hour, and believe me it was agony, the pain in your ears was terrific. I knew then there was something wrong with them.

We were seven ships and only one had a doctor on board. We had what was called a sick bay tiffy, who was a nurse, and he was useless. I couldn't report it to anybody, though I knew my ears were damaged."

Ken's hearing loss was assessed as 40 per cent, but 'it wasn't until the 1980s that it was made known that servicemen that had suffered injuries during the war could claim a pension, and when we claimed we didn't get any back pay at all.'

After the war Ken began a long career with the Colonial service, which took him round the world. In 1990 he received the MBE for services to the Medical Research Council (for whom he worked in Gambia for 15 years).

Ken's vision was damaged when he contracted river blindness in Sierra Leone, although he didn't realise until seven years later. He was cured, but suffered permanent scarring of the back of his eyes. He now also has rapidly progressing macular degeneration in both eyes.

"All I can say is that I've been really so pleased that I was introduced to

COURAGE AFTER THE BATTLE

Sense. It's made me many, many friends. I've enjoyed the forums, meeting different people, people in the same position as myself. And the help from the staff at Sense is wonderful. It's a bit traumatic when you lose your sight and also, you've got hearing problems, but Sense has helped me over that period. I'm very happy with my way of life now. I've settled that I'm deafblind, and that's it."

William Roache, born in 1932.

William Roache, better known as Ken Barlow from Coronation Street, describes how military training damaged his hearing but happily didn't hold back his acting career.

"I was in charge of a three-inch mortar platoon and we were doing a training exercise with live ammunition. The drill is, when you drop the bomb, if it doesn't go off, you are supposed to gently shake the tube. However, a guy I was training with pulled it upright and shot a live bomb straight up into the air. We had thirty seconds. It's no good running as you don't know where the bomb is going to land. You just have to get down and wait. Fortunately, it exploded about three hundred yards away. For three weeks I couldn't hear anything, but slowly my hearing returned. I always knew, though, that I'd been left with a problem. I couldn't hear, for example, clocks ticking or people speaking in noisy atmospheres."

When did you find out the extent of your hearing loss?

"It wasn't until fifteen years later. I had a hearing test and they confirmed that I'd lost fifty per cent of my hearing during the training exercise. The extent of the loss shocked me."

How has it affected your life?

"I live in a cotton wool world. Sometimes it feels quite cosy and I think I don't want to hear everything. When I have tried hearing aids, I found I didn't like the clattering of a knife and fork on a plate or a newspaper rustling. But there have been obvious downsides. When I can't hear someone, they'll often ask "What's the matter with you?" My late wife used to say "Why don't you tell people you are deaf?", but I didn't like to. I try and try to hear, I lean forward and it looks as if you are peering down ladies' dresses! If I go to a ball and there is background noise it's totally useless."

Has it been difficult to combine your hearing loss with your role in Coronation Street?

"I couldn't be in a better job. Everything is scripted, so I know what *people are going to say and most actors speak with some clarity, so it's not a problem."*

Since 2015 a team at The Royal British Legion Centre for Blast Injury Studies has been investigating hearing loss amongst veterans, and possible remedies. Research (published in 2009) on infantry soldiers found that up to 14 per cent of those returning from Afghanistan in 2007-08 had hearing loss, whilst a study in the United States found that more than half of US Army veterans suffer from Auditory Processing Disorder (APD), a hearing problem that affects the ability to distinguish between competing noises, with sufferers often struggling to make out a human voice against conflicting background noise.

Dr Tobias Reichenbach, leading the research at Imperial College, is a scientist with a background in auditory neuroscience. He said:

"At the moment, there is no treatment available, but we hope to change that. A loss of hearing in any capacity can have a significant impact on your professional and personal life. APD is a common problem among veterans, but I don't think it's really been picked up before because it's not fatal.

The US research shows that APD can be a consequence of blast exposure, and many veterans who have been in a combat situation have experienced blast exposure."

"APD isn't a result of damage done to the ear, which can be in perfect working order. It's due to neurological impairment. When exposed to a blast, a high-pressure blast wave goes over you, and that has impact on the head. Also, people can be thrown against a wall or hit on the head, causing injury to the brain."

In the first stages of the research the team used electroencephalography (EEG) to measure brain activity during speech processing. Each subject was asked to wear a cap fitted with electrodes and to listen to two competing human voices through a set of headphones. The electrodes on the cap were used to track the signals from the brain used to understand speech.

"Our preliminary results indicate that cortical oscillations (rhythmic neural activity) are impaired in veterans with APD. We are now building on these findings to develop neuro-stimulation techniques for rehabilitation. At the moment there is no treatment available, but we hope to change that. Some people are born with APD and in those people, it is difficult to cure. In veterans, APD has been acquired so we are hoping it can be reversed

through auditory training, such as brain stimulation, which involves applying small currents to the brain to make the brain able to learn more easily."

Research has also shown that some veterans who do not have APD also have difficulty with understanding speech in noise, a finding which is now being explored in more detail. This includes investigating whether problems with understanding speech in noise can also result from damage to the auditory-nerve fibres and the brainstem that link the ear to the central brain areas.

WAR WIDOWS

You may initially think this is a strange chapter to put in a book about how people get on with their lives following the stress and trauma of battle. War widows are as relevant today as they were at their inception and if you consider a wife who has lost her husband in the Falklands, Bosnia, Iraq, Afghanistan, or even a husband who has lost his wife, they are all war widows / widowers in the present day.

The War Widows' Association of Great Britain (WWA) highlights the plight of Britain's forgotten women. Today the Association has around 3,000 members, and its original aim was to fight for the removal of the tax burden from the War Widows' Pension. All the work, including responding to emails and telephone enquiries, is undertaken by volunteers as the Association has no offices and is managed by a committee of trustees. They are exceptionally grateful for the support of The Royal British Legion in providing a mail room facility.

Since its formation the Association has achieved, among other things:

Retention of War Widows' Pensions for life from 1st April 2015
Removal of income tax from the War Widows' Pension
Extra age allowance for War Widows
Improved pension for pre-1973 War Widows
Reinstatement of pension to War Widows on cessation of second or subsequent marriage
Renewal of opportunity for War Widows to visit the grave of their husband through sponsored pilgrimage
Retention of the attributable MOD occupational pension on remarriage

COURAGE AFTER THE BATTLE

Retention of the War Widows' Pension for pre-'73 widows.

The definition of who is classed as a war widow in the eyes of the government has changed considerably over the years. When you think of your idea of a war widow, you would imagine a lady in her later years who has lost her husband during active service. But what if a woman's husband dies after his service, as a result of injuries he sustained in battle? How many years until his death can no longer be attributed to those injuries, and can you prove that the injuries were to be the cause of his death later in life? What if a traumatised soldier commits suicide? How does the law consider civil partnerships in this context? These questions have been key to the various definitions of war widowhood for centuries. It's worth taking a closer look at the struggles they have had with the pensions and who defines war widowhood, and how.

At the beginning of the 20th century the only general support was through the Poor Law. Only a small minority of white-collar and public service workers had access to pensions from employment. Though many workers had some mutual insurance, the Friendly Societies did not cover old age. Following pioneering surveys showing the extent of poverty among the elderly, there was intense debate over how to provide better support. This finally resulted in Lloyd George's Old Age Pensions Act 1908. From January 1909, a non - contributory pension of 5 shillings (25 pence) a week became payable to each person over 70 with an income less than 8 shillings a week. Reduced amounts were paid to those with incomes up to 12 shillings a week.

The Liberal Government went on to introduce contributory insurance against sickness and unemployment in the National Insurance Act 1911. In 1925 the contributory principle was extended to pensions by the Widows, Orphans and Old Age Contributory Pensions Act. Coming into effect in 1928, the Act provided maintenance outside the Poor Law for widows and grafted contributory pensions from age 65 over the existing non-contributory scheme. Pensions required contributions in the five years before 65; those without a recent contribution record were still subject to a means test at age 70. Like other insurance benefits under the 1911 Act, National Insurance pension coverage was not universal and was aimed mainly at lower paid and manual workers. It did not provide support for dependants. However, a married woman could use her husband's contribution record to gain a pension when she reached 65.

During this period, occupational pensions grew steadily. The Finance Act 1921 introduced tax relief on pension scheme contributions and investments, placing them on the same footing as savings through Friendly Societies and life insurance. The Finance Act 1947 introduced limits on the amount of tax relief allowable on pensions.

By the outbreak of the Second World War, the foundations had been laid for a basic flat-rate state pension entitlement, but the system was by no means comprehensive. The flat-rate benefit of 10 shillings (50 pence) was not enough by itself to meet subsistence needs, but no additional help was available except through the Poor Law. Benefits had not increased since 1919.

In 1935, a new national means tested assistance scheme had been introduced for the unemployed. This was intended to meet full subsistence needs, including housing costs. The old Age and Widows Pensions Act 1940 of the war-time National Government now extended this supplementary assistance to pensioners and widows, removing them from the scope of the Poor Law. In addition, the Act reduced women's pension age to 60.

Source: Pension Trends – Office of National Statistics 2005

According to the Poor Law Amendment Act (1834), widows were entitled to outdoor relief – and did have the option to apply for further relief after their initial six months of widowhood, but the application of the law was highly inconsistent from region to region. In addition, the physical, financial, and psychological cost involved in repeatedly travelling to, appearing before, and answering the probing questions of the Board of Guardians could be considerable for some women.

As a direct consequence of the Crimean War (1853–56), in 1854 the Royal Patriotic Fund Corporation (RPFC) was created to help 'on-the-strength' widows of other ranks. When the Second Expeditionary Force set sail for Egypt in February 1885, Major (later Colonel Sir) James Gildea wrote a letter to The Times appealing for money and volunteers to help the military families left behind at home. A fund was set up to provide allowances. Soon Her Royal Highness the Princess of Wales (the future Queen Alexandra) became the first president of what was then called the Soldiers' and Sailors' Families Association (SSFA).

SSFA was established to alleviate the hardship faced by widows of ordinary soldiers You may now know this as SSAFA (Soldiers', Sailors' & Airmen's Families Association). While numerous similar charitable organizations and Friendly Societies would spring up during the Victorian period, the provision for war widows remained highly sporadic and inconsistent.

Many charities including the RPFC and SSFA also abided by the principles set out by the Charity Organisation Society (COS), founded in 1869. The COS advocated a home visiting system to assess whether households were deserving or undeserving of assistance, and this was usually determined by women's adherence to middle-class standards of respectability, housekeeping, and parenting. The image of the poor these narrow criteria perpetuated is perhaps best illustrated in the comment of a defender of the COS in 1881. They insisted that, in a substantial proportion of instances, investigation shows that nothing can be done, that advice would be pearls before swine, that money given would go straight to the publican, or that the applicant trades in obtaining charity by false representation. Indeed, in the same year the COS's own monthly journal makes clear the organisation's views as to the causes of poverty among the working classes. Poverty and destitution, they explain, result from improvident habits and thriftlessness, which could only be addressed through self-denial, temperance and forethought.

Many widows had to survive on a combination of a meagre pension, relief through the Poor Law, charity from friends, family, and benevolent societies, and whatever work they were able to secure. It's not surprising that newspapers and periodicals sometimes featured calls for donations for the widows of men who had been well regarded in society, or for widows whose circumstances were particularly dramatic. The pieces would usually detail the widow's and, where applicable, her children's situation, illustrating her husband's importance and/ or achievements to convey her deservingness.

COURAGE AFTER THE BATTLE

In March 1844, for example, Punch reported that Colonel Fawcett's widow, despite his distinguished military career, was refused a pension because her husband had died in a duel. A fortnight later, Punch published an article entitled 'A Handsome Thing Handsomely Done', announcing: The Duke of Wellington, Earls Winchelsea and Cardigan, the Attorney-General for Ireland, and other distinguished heroes of twelve paces will charge themselves with the payment of the pension denied to her by Sir Robert Peel. (Sir Robert Peel, 2nd Baronet, FRS, PC (5 February 1788 – 2 July 1850), a British statesman and member of the Conservative Party, served twice as Prime Minister of the United Kingdom (1834–1835 and 1841–1846) and twice as Home Secretary (1822–1827 and 1828–1830). He is regarded as the father of modern British policing and as one of the founders of the modern Conservative Party.)

A small number of widows were granted a civil pension for the services their husbands had rendered to the country, but ironically these pensions were usually reserved for the wives of high-ranking military heroes, politicians and, on occasion, scientists and authors of note; that is, those who were unlikely to be in need of financial assistance. One commentator, Douglas Jerrold, cynically observed that in order to receive £200 via the civil pensions lists, a widow would first have to convince the Prime Minister that she was already worth at least £10,000.

When no state-funded war widows' pension scheme existed, each branch of the armed forces had different processes in place to help war widows. In 1830, for example, to be eligible for any support from the army, a widow's husband had to have held at least the rank of officer and had to have served for ten or more years on full pay, or been killed in action. This was no matter what financial state or rather non-existent financial state the family of an ordinary soldier or seaman were left in prior to and following the husband's death. Many charities also applied moral criteria to whether a war widow was eligible for their assistance or not, and this moral policing of war widows became even more pronounced with the introduction of state-funded war widows' pensions during the First World War.

Despite the small amounts paid, women under the scheme applying for a war widow's pension treated it as a badge of pride in the absence of any other form of public recognition for their loss. Today the criteria for War Widow / Widower Pension and for Armed Forces Survivors Benefits are much wider, and acknowledge that war widowhood can look different from person to person. For a War Widow / Widower Pension, the criteria are as follows:

One of the following must apply. Your husband, wife or civil partner:

Died as result of their service in HM Armed Forces before 6 April 2005

Was a civil defence volunteer or a civilian and their death was a result of the 1939-1945 war

Was a merchant seaman, a member of the Naval auxiliary services, or a coastguard, and their death was a result of an injury or disease they got during a war or because they were a prisoner of war

Died as a result of their service as a member of the Polish Forces under British command during the 1939-1945 war, or in the Polish Resettlement Forces

Was in receipt of a War Pensions Constant Attendance Allowance at the time of their death, or would have been had they not been in hospital

Was in receipt of a War Disablement Pension at the 80% rate or higher and was getting Unemployability Supplement

Those widowed after 6 April 2005 are eligible for Armed Forces Survivors Benefits rather than a War Widow / Widower Pension.
The Ministry of Defence criteria for this payment is as follows:

A surviving adult dependant is someone who is cohabiting and in a substantial and exclusive relationship with the deceased serviceperson, was not prevented from marrying or forming a civil partnership with them, and was financially dependent or interdependent on them. The serviceperson must not have been in a relationship with someone else.

COURAGE AFTER THE BATTLE

This description gives a much more liberal definition of the term war widow. According to the eligibility criteria for War Widow / Widower Pension, women whose partners were killed during the Second World War as civilians also classify as war widows.

Soldiers and Sailors Widows Fund (1838)

Because there was no coherent support system for war widows during the Victorian period, many well-meaning individuals set out to establish charitable organisations to help. In the letter shown below, a correspondent calls for support for his longstanding plan to establish a Soldiers and Sailors Widows Fund.

SOLDIERS AND SAILORS WIDOWS FUND
TO THE EDITOR OF THE TIMES
Sir, As there is no channel through which a humane suggestion and a benevolent measure are more likely to attract the public, and excite public sympathy, than through the pages of The Times, I hope I may be permitted to occupy a part of one of its columns by recommending the establishment of a fund for the relief of the widows of our soldiers and sailors. Several instances have for many years past come under my own eyes of widows who, by the deaths of their husbands, have been reduced to a state of the utmost poverty and distress. In losing their husbands they have in general lost their all. By the pensions with which their husbands were rewarded they were enabled to live in comparable ease and competency; that resource being withdrawn by the decease of their husbands, I have known many who, after a long life spent in the happiest of harmony, have been incapacitated from every kind of work by which they can earn a subsistence, and whose ultimate alternative has been either to starve or seek a refuge in the workhouse, to which every right-minded English male and female have a strong repugnance.

In the year 1826 I projected a measure and drew up rules and regulations to meet such piteous cases of destitution These I submitted to the Duke of York, by whom they were whole-heartedly approved. The Duke, to whom I was domestic chaplain, favoured me with two or three interviews on the subject, and offered some valuable hints and suggestions of which one was, that no widow should receive any relief from the proposed fund unless she has been married a year or two previous to her husband having obtained the pension to which his length of service entitles him. The Duke consented to become patron, and I have little doubt that the measure would have been carried into effect but for circumstances. I was unable to prosecute the plan on account of my removal from London, and more particularly in consequence of the Duke's illness, from which he was more or less a sufferer throughout the whole of 1826 and to which the valuable life of the "soldier's best friend" fell a sacrifice at the commencement of the following year. He was indeed the soldier's friend, ever kind and affable, and ready to promote the private's comfort and best interests. I attended the funeral as one of the mourners. I stood at the grave close to the Duke of Wellington, and never shall I forget the unfeigned grief with which his Grace's countenance, and that of every soldier, indeed of everyone present, appeared to be affected.

I am quite aware that there would be difficulties attending the establishment of such a measure, but none that are insuperable. It is a part of my creed to believe that there is nothing which will not succeed, if it be right in principle. A friend of mine, who is employed in carrying into effect a measure of great local interest and importance, was complaining the other day to the Duke of Wellington he met with in certain quarters. "Never Mind" said His Grace "go on; I have had in my time as much perhaps as any man living difficulties and opposition to encounter, and yet I have been able to overcome all of them." When I recollect from what small beginnings the most important measures have emanated, and by what apparently inefficient agents the noblest monuments of national benevolence have been raised, I should not for one moment despair that the proposed plan would be accomplished. I have the case of one of your most magnificent institutions in London before my eyes – The London Orphan Asylum. I well remember the time in which only three or four of us met together to project that noble charity. We had many difficulties to contend with, yet all were overcome. The cause was good, and the principle sound; and with the money which was collected from time to time a noble structure was raised from the reception and orphans whose parents had been respectable, and there the edifice stands, as I hope an imperishable monument of private benevolence and metropolitan patronage. And the same may be said of another noble charity, the Seaman's Hospital, of which I was one of the very earliest friends. Knowing, then, how these were projected, and patronized, and supported , I have not the slightest doubt that the public attention has but to be drawn to the Widows Fund to secure its successful establishment; and that some of the many friends of humanity with whom your metropolis abounds may be prompted to take it in hand is my earnest wish and prayer; and if a few words in its favour were to issue from the very able pen of the editor of The times, provided he approved of the measure, what more likely to insure its and obtain its accomplishment.

Hawkchurch Rectory Nov 5

Letter from Times Soldiers' And Sailors' Widows' Fund. The Times (9 November 1838) p.5

Mary Anne Wellington (1846)
Rev. Richard Cobbold published 'Mary Anne Wellington: The Soldier's Daughter, Wife and Widow' (1846) in the hope of raising funds for his subject: a widow who had accompanied her husband on all his postings and who, after his death, had fallen on hard times. The biography of Mary Anne Cobbold covers her childhood as a soldier's daughter, her travels and adventures as a soldier's wife, and her struggles as a soldier's widow.

What is your name? Where do you live? What age are you? How many children do you have? What are your earnings? What do your children earn? How long have you been a widow? Have you any pension? Have you no means of subsistence? Are you able-bodied? Have you no friends? To what parish did your husband belong? How come you to be so reduced? Cannot you do something for a livelihood? Are you quite destitute?

These are some of the questions Mary Anne Wellington, an army officer's widow, was asked when applying for assistance to her local Board of Guardians. The destitute widow travelling alone, wet through, undoubtedly would have stirred the feelings and sense of propriety of the middle and upper classes. A woman without a male guardian, made nervous by the prospect of having to enter and answer to a room full of men, as though she was a defendant in court.

She entered, with a heart beating violently, and limbs trembling. The poor woman stood before the Chairman, Vice-Chairman, and a numerous body of Guardians, the Clerk of the Board, the Relieving Officers, and the

Governor of the House, and had to answer publicly any question which any man there present chose to put to her. Severe cross-examination of the person asking for assistance was not uncommon. It may be said that these were not always in the gentlest terms for their accuser, judge, and jury, and the poor creature has but little chance of escaping the utmost rigour of the law. Such, however, was not the case with the Board before which the soldier's widow stood, though to her terrified vision it might appear as if she stood before it like a criminal.

The New Poor Law, according to Benjamin Disraeli, announced to the world that in England poverty is a crime, and Mary Anne Wellington, like many others, had to defend herself to receive the assistance she desperately needed. For Mary Anne, her appearance before the Board of Guardians is more terrifying than any of the scenes of war she has witnessed in her time as a soldier's wife:

"I have been in most of the Peninsular battles with my husband, and have stood with the soldiers of my country in the face of England's bitterest and most formidable enemies; but I never knew what fear was till this moment."

Like the vast majority of widows, the first expenses with which Mary Anne was faced after her husband's death were those incurred by the adherence to Victorian mourning rituals. A funeral as well as mourning clothes for herself and her daughters had to be paid, and this necessitated the sale of Mary Anne's belongings:

"When the few things which a poor widow has are sold, and the bills for her husband's funeral, and her own and her daughters' plain black gowns, are paid, there is almost nothing left financially to provide bread for the week."

Mary Anne Wellington's pension ran out soon after her husband's death, her other resources having been spent on the funeral and her own and her daughters' mourning costumes. Mary Anne Wellington was able to benefit from the charity of some wealthy benefactors. After her outdoor relief was granted by the Board of Guardians, the Chairman assured the widow he would make her case known in Westminster. The relief this act of charity provided was temporary. These donations, for a time, greatly assisted the soldier's widow, but they could not provide for her beyond a certain time. Mary Anne once again had to apply to the Board of Guardians for renewed outdoor relief, and her three shillings weekly were again allowed.

Private charity, of course, was a temporary relief only available to those who had an influential champion willing to bring their case to public attention and whose husbands had either enjoyed some form of esteem in their lifetime or had left them in circumstances dramatic enough to incite pity and outrage.

Though a steady and safe existence, it is nothing short of depressing to think that a woman who had dedicated the largest part of her life to her husband's service for their country had to spend her widowhood uncertain of her future, and live out her days in an almshouse (a house founded by charity, offering accommodation for poor people).

In a letter to *The Times* newspaper, a correspondent criticises the discontinuation of widows' pensions for boatswains, gunners, and carpenters. Nauticus, as he called himself, goes as far as to suggest that the current regulations regarding widows' pensions in the Navy amount to a war against its servicemen. These issues were much debated in parliament at the time.

Nauticus, "Naval Economy", *The Times* (12 January 1839) p.5.

The letter went as follows:

NAVAL ECONOMY
TO THE EDITOR OF THE TIMES
*Sir, With the warlike aspect of affairs and the
Present call for seamen, the injurious acts, to save
Money, committed on the navy should at once be
Done away with. If good seamen are expected to
Enter service, the benefits they formerly could
Look to on being promoted to be warrant officers
Should be immediately resumed. Pensions of 25l. to
The widows of boatswains, gunners and carpenters
Who have been warranted since 1830, have been dis-
Continued. This pension was one inducement for
Respectable seamen and mates of merchant vessels to
Enter into the navy, and was most improperly taken
Away. Not long since, an excellent warrant officer,
Who had been promoted for his good conduct, was*

COURAGE AFTER THE BATTLE

Washed overboard at sea. His widow applied for, and
Was refused a pension. His old captains tried to
Obtain it for her, but were also refused by the Admiralty.
This is but a single instance of that economy
Which has reduced the navy to the state in which it
Is at present
I am sir, your obedient servant NAUTICUS
Jan 11, 1839

A postcard published by the Women's Suffrage Atelier (London) in 1909 illustrated just how badly English laws protected women, and particularly widows with children. It highlighted that, when it came to childcare, it was a woman's legal duty to look after her children, while her husband had no duty to provide for her or them in his will. The postcard presents us with an exchange between a representative of the law and a widowed mother of three children. "A man may leave his money to whom he likes," the solicitor tells the widow, "but you must maintain your children, that is one of the laws of England."

How the Law Protects the Widow (War Widows Association)

COURAGE AFTER THE BATTLE

Since the Guardian of Infants Act (1886), a mother was appointed guardian of her children in the event of her husband's death. This meant she was legally obliged to care for them, even though there was little help available to assist her with the cost of clothes and food now that her household had lost its main source of income. Her husband was not obliged to leave her any of his property, and widows were often forced to piece together support from friends and family, charities, and through the Poor Law. The Poor Law allowed them to receive outdoor relief for the first six months of their widowhood; that is, they were entitled to assistance in the form of money, food, clothes, fuel, and medical care without having to enter the workhouse.

The debate below is one of many debates in parliament on War Widows Pensions and predates any coherent approach to war widows' pensions. Many charities only provided assistance to war widows who had been 'on-the-strength', for example, meaning women who travelled with their husbands during their postings abroad. A serviceman's cause of death has also been a determining factor throughout the history of widows' pensions.

Resolution reported: *"That a sum, not exceeding £1,468,200, be granted to His Majesty, to defray the expenses of Naval and Marine Pensions, Gratuities, and Compassionate Allowances, which will come conic in course of payment during the year ending on the 31st day of March 1912."*

Motion made, and question proposed, That the House doth agree with the Committee in the said Resolution.

> LORD C BERESFORD: I wish to ask a question about the regulations relating to the allowances to the widows of officers and men who are slain in action. There is very little given to the widows and orphans of these men who lose their lives in the service. I maintain that a man who is blown up in the boiler-room, who dies from sunstroke or dysentery through hard work, is losing his life just as much in the service of the country as the man who is killed by shot and shell, and the country should take care of those he leaves behind. The Admiralty do recognise this to a certain extent, but only in regard to the question of gratuity or compensation, and it is not a pension. I think the scale of allowance in the case of a man who is slain is 5s.

a week to the widow and 1s. 6d. per child. In the case of a second petty officer the amount is 6s., a first petty officer 7s. 6d., and a chief petty officer 9s. Gratuities are only allowed to the widows and children if the man dies within two years of the accident.

There is one case which is particularly hard, and that is the case of insanity. We have a large number of those who are injured in the spine and sent to the asylum, and in these cases the widow does not get a single penny out of that man's pay, because what he is entitled to goes to the asylum. I hope the Right Hon. Gentleman will put this matter right. This is a substantial grievance, because, although such a man does not lose his life, it is often worse for the widow, because she has to support her husband, which she would not have to do if he had been killed. I was delighted the other day when I heard the Chancellor of the Exchequer recognise these cases, and state that they were more or less a scandal to this country. This is a rich country, and these men are ready to go out and be shot perfectly cheerily any time they are called upon, and as far as the Navy goes, the men are always on active service. They are upon active service all the time, and I hope the Right Hon. Gentleman will look after these widows who are so tremendously handicapped by their husbands being injured and rendered perfectly incapable of employment.

MR. HOHLER: I wish to raise a point connected with the Greenwich Hospital Age Pension Fund. I think it is now generally recognised that the only means we have of calling attention to this matter is by debate in this House. The point I wish to raise is the question of the fulfilment of a promise which has been made publicly to the men in the Navy. I have in my hand the answer which the Parliamentary Secretary to the Admiralty made to a deputation of these men who asked that their payments should be made under the Greenwich Hospital Age Fund. On 16th November 1909, the Financial Secretary to the Admiralty put in writing his answer to the deputation as follows: — Dear Mr. O'Neal, To avoid any possible misunderstanding, I think it is desirable to repeat in writing the statement which I made this morning to the deputation from the

COURAGE AFTER THE BATTLE

Naval Pensioners' Association. I am glad to take this opportunity of stating that the Treasury have agreed that the cost of age pensions to the men of the Seamen Pensioner Reserve, which has hitherto been automatically transferred to Greenwich Hospital Funds on the men attaining fifty-five years of age, shall, as from the 1st April 1910, continue to be borne by Naval Funds until such time as these men be granted age pensions from Greenwich Hospital Funds in the ordinary course of selection from the whole body of pensioners. This concession will, I am glad to say, have the effect of adding a fairly respectable sum to the amount available for the award of fresh Age pensions. That was a very clear and definite statement. It is important to bear in mind with regard to the general body of the Navy who are eligible for this pension that they come on at the age of sixty-three and sixty-four, whereas the men belonging to the Seaman Pensioner Reserve are transferred upon attaining fifty-five years of age. We are, of course, grateful for what the Admiralty propose to do, and if I am right in the interpretation which I put upon the Financial Secretary's language it admits of no doubt as to what is meant. The Parliamentary Secretary to the Admiralty, speaking on 20th March last, said: — What we did from the Iet of April was this. We have taken off the Greenwich Hospital Fund from the age of fifty-five to the average age at which, in other circumstances, they would come upon the Greenwich Hospital Fund, all Seamen Pensioner Reserves, and made their pensions a charge upon Naval Funds.
MR HOHLER: At what age?
DR. MACNAMARA: At about sixty-four.
MR. HOHLER: I can supply the names of several at sixty-four who have not got one.
DR. MACNAMARA: We have to consider if a man has a reasonable competence, and that some other men are more necessitous. The Seamen Pension Reserves came upon the Greenwich Hospital Fund at fifty-five. We have now taken them off the Greenwich Hospital Fund at fifty-five up to the age they would otherwise come upon the Greenwich Hospital Fund, that is sixty-four, and made them a charge upon Naval Funds. If the Hon. Gentleman will refer to page 168 of the Estimates, Vote 14, he will see that under the head

of 'Pensions and Gratuities to Seamen and Marines', the amount estimated shows an increase of £45,000. I think a considerable portion of that is due to the fact that we have taken the Pensioner Reserve off and kept him on Naval Funds until he reaches the age when, together with other applicants, he might come on the Greenwich Hospital Fund.

—[OFFICIAL REPORT, 26th March. 1911, col. 188.] That is a very clear and definite statement. I thought at the time the Parliamentary Secretary to the Admiralty, though his intention was excellent, had made a mistake with regard to the figure. I desire at once to acknowledge he himself said he would look into it, and he approached me and told me that upon examination of the Vote he found he had made a mistake. The result, therefore, is that no provision has been made to carry out the promise made to these men in December 1909. If you turn to Vote 14, Sub-head C, you will find that, so far from £45,000 going to provide their pensions, the only possible increase is one of £4,000, and in fact what the Parliamentary Secretary thought he had done has not been done. I do not doubt the perfect good faith of the Admiralty in this matter, but I want that promise publicly given carried out, and I want the men of the Seamen Pensioner Reserve transferred from the Greenwich Hospital Age Fund to the Naval Fund until in the ordinary course they would come upon the Greenwich Hospital Fund—that is to say, at sixty-four, or it may be sixty-three—so as to put them exactly in the same position as the rest. This is a fund intended for the whole body of the Navy, and the Seamen Pensioner Reserve is a Reserve created for the benefit of the nation, and it should be a charge on the Naval Fund. I say unhesitatingly that the whole method of dealing with this Greenwich Age Fund has been for years nothing more nor less than a misapplication of a trust. It has been recognised, and in December 1909, the Parliamentary Secretary made a definite promise to the men that this should be done, and in the debate he stated it had been done. That is an error, and all I ask is that it should be done. Therefore, I beg to move a reduction of the Vote by £100, to try and ensure this shall be carried out.

MR. SPEAKER: I have already put the Question, "That the House doth agree with the Committee," and I cannot put the reduction, but I have no doubt the First Lord of the Admiralty or the Parliamentary Secretary will reply.

The Parliamentary Secretary to the Admiralty (DR. MACNAMARA): The Noble Lord, the Member for Portsmouth (Lord Charles Beresford), says that if a man is killed in action his widow gets a pension and his child an allowance, but if a man is killed other than in action, say by an explosion or something of that sort, the widow gets no pension and the child no allowance. I think he is wrong. If a man is killed in action, his widow gets a pension and his children an allowance from the Naval Fund. The widow of a man killed in an accident, say an explosion, gets, so I am advised, precisely the same pension and his children get precisely the same allowance, partly from the Naval Fund and partly by an augmentation from the Greenwich Hospital Fund. That is how the matter stands. If the Noble Lord will look at page 172, Vote 14 (K), he will see there is provision for augmentation from the Greenwich Hospital Fund in the case he has in mind. The Hon. Member for Chatham (Mr. Hohler) raised the question of the Seamen Pensioner Reserve and our transference of their pension from the Greenwich Hospital Fund to the Naval Fund as from 1st April last year. There seems to be a misapprehension. All the men who get the Greenwich Hospital Pension, with the exception of the Special Greenwich Pension, which is given to the men who have not served long enough to get a Naval Life Pension, are men in receipt of Naval Life Pensions. I am afraid that is not generally understood. There are men on the Greenwich Hospital Pension Fund whose Naval life pension amounts to as much as £44 per year. What we have to do is to take each case and consider the necessitous character of the applicant and the smallness of the pension and, if we can, augment it as far as the funds will allow. The Seamen Pensioner Reserve was established in 1870 and, as an inducement to recruits, an undertaking was given them that they should come upon the Greenwich Hospital Pension Fund in augmentation of their Naval life pension at fifty years of age, or five years earlier than the other Naval Life Pensioners were eligible to come on. I am not going into that proceeding. It was the subject of considerable comment. Those men remain on the Greenwich Hospital Pension Fund for the augmentation of their Naval life pension from fifty-five up to the age at which other pensioners come on the Naval Pension Fund, that is about sixty-four or sixty-five. Then we said that, as from 1st April last year, we would make the charge for this augmentation on Naval funds and not on the Greenwich Hospital Fund up to the age at which a man might ordinarily come upon Greenwich Hospital Funds. Using the words "taken off" suggested that what we did was to take off up to the age of sixty-four, or thereabouts, all the men of the Seamen Pensioner Reserve, instead of which the men of the Seamen Pensioner Reserve who are on the Greenwich Hospital Fund now remain on, but, as from 1st April, in all future cases Naval funds, and not the Greenwich Hospital Fund, will bear the augmentation from fifty-five up to about sixty-four. That is the change we have made. It is not retrospective, and I ought not to have used the words "taken off." I imagine the Hon. Member thinks that as from 1st April last year we took all the men in receipt of Greenwich Hospital pensions right off and put them on Naval Votes. That is not what happened, and I am sorry that I put the matter in such a way, which no doubt I did, as to make it appear retrospective. What we did was to let the men remain, but for the future the Seamen Pensioner Reserve will come on Naval funds for augmentation, and not on the Greenwich Hospital Pension Fund, until he reaches the age at which he would otherwise be eligible to receive the Greenwich Hospital Pension. As a matter of fact, the result of that change enabled us last year to give 70 per cent more Greenwich Hospital pensions than in the year before. In addition to that, we transferred as from the same date from the Greenwich Hospital Fund to Naval Votes the cost of the maintenance of the Lunatic Pensioners at Yarmouth, costing roughly about £2,000 a year. I hope I have made perfectly clear the change which I am glad to say took place on 1st April last year.

MR. FALLE: It is rather late in asking a question, but I should like to draw the attention of the right Hon. Gentleman to one small point on the subject of pensions. If a man who is in receipt of a pension, say, for the loss of a limb, is fortunate enough to obtain a civil appointment and a small weekly wage, his pension is immediately dropped? That seems to me to be a grossly unfair thing to do. The case I have in mind is that of a first-class petty officer in receipt of a pension for the loss of his leg. It is just enough to keep life in him and no more. When he reported himself the second year, the doctor asked him if he was not able to obtain employment. He said, very cheerfully, "I am glad to tell you, sir, I am now caretaker in a store, receiving 10s. a week," and within ten days he found his pension had been cut £4 10s. and, as he told me with a sickly smile, "none of my mates who unfortunately come into my position will, I think, be anxious to obtain civil appointments." This is a thing which, it seems to me, should be remedied and remedied at once. If a man is in receipt of a pension for the loss of a limb he should not have that pension cut if he is able or fortunate enough to obtain civil employment. There is one small point more I wish to make. The Chancellor of the Exchequer proposes to make special arrangements in the Insurance Bill for the Navy and Army. I wish to ask the right Hon. Gentleman to use his great influence with the Chancellor of the Exchequer to have this done at once. There is apparently a surplus of nearly half-a-million, and there could be no better use of that surplus than to take, say, a quarter-of-a-million to attend to the wants and absolute necessities of the men in the Navy. As my colleague truly said, men who lose their lives in the Navy through accident in a time of peace have given their lives for their country just the same as if they had been killed in a time of war, and their widows and representatives and their children should be properly looked after. The whole scale of pensions should, in my humble opinion, be largely increased.

Question, "That this House doth agree with the Committee in the said Resolution," put, and agreed to.

Source: Naval and Marine Pensions, Gratuities, and Compassionate Allowances
House of Commons Debates (18 May 1911)

COURAGE AFTER THE BATTLE

The Bars of Iron (1916) by Ethel M Dell
During the First World War, given the large numbers of men who died, it was seen as appropriate to show grief rather than display your grief through your appearance and the wearing of black attire.

Women were expected to deal with their grief and hardship in silence but the war gave rise to what we now know as the 'coper' or the 'can-do woman'. By the interwar period, the only acceptable face of independent modern femininity was that of the coper, usually the domestic manager, who made the most of the little things in life, scrimping, saving and making a meal from nothing. War widows were often the perfect embodiment of the coper: their economic hardship, the grief over their lost husbands, they had to keep calm and carry on. Much like the famous poster and the numerous derivatives we see today on posters, cups, placemats etc.

In 1916, and out of this new showing of grief, Ethel M Dell wrote a melodramatic romance book entitled 'The Bars of Iron'. Dell presented just such a person in the form of Avery Denys, the novel's heroine, who lost her husband along with her blind daughter. Avery simply reflects on her situation by summing it up as she was left with nothing to do. She finds a job that allows her to act out the mother role she misses. Avery is rational yet caring, but also submissive in the face of her eventual second husband's violence towards her and others. The novel applauds her selflessness and self-deprecation. Like many texts of the time, Dell uses the figure of the war widow to advocate a new, reticent form of womanhood and, at the same time, to remind women that despite their temporary war-time freedom they were still duty-bound to be subservient and resume their places as wives on the men's return after the war.

You can also download a digital version of The Bars of Iron by going to the following site
https://babel.hathitrust.org/cgi/pt?id=uc2.ark:/13960/t2v40kk42;view=1up;seq=2

The outbreak of the First World War prompted the British government to introduce a national War Widows' Pension scheme. All war widows were eligible, yet the weekly payments made to them under this scheme were far too little to cover their living costs, and hardship increased as the war continued and inflation rose.

The Ministry of Pensions was founded in 1916 to deal with the administration of these payments, and the Special Grants Committee became the body that assessed war widows' eligibility for War Widows' Pension. The Special Grants Committee's decision-making process was famously flawed and widely criticised: the committee determined whether women were worthy of state support by assessing, and in some cases covertly, the woman's moral and sexual behaviour, parenting practices, and housekeeping skills. The War Widows' Pension was effectively devised in such a way as to effectively confine the woman to the domestic role of mother and housekeeper whilst refusing to pay her sufficient money to keep her within the home. A payment of half the minimum wage of £1 a week was more of a token gesture than an actual caring payment to allow the woman and her family to live following the loss of the bread winner.

In 1925, Neville Chamberlain introduced the Widows', Orphans', and Old Age Contributory Pensions Act, which built on the National Insurance Act (1911). This severely limited the number of state-supported war widows. It specified that women whose husbands had not been killed in military service were ineligible for War Widows' Pension. It also determined that only those who were married to insured men and widowed after 4 January 1926 were eligible for state support. Widows of insured men who had died before this date only received a War Widows' Pension if they had children younger than fourteen, and provision would cease once their children exceeded that age. The 1929 Amendment Bill lifted these limitations, by awarding War Widows' Pension to women who were widowed before 4 January 1926, but this was providing they were of or above the age of 55 and had children who were under sixteen years of age. This meant younger, childless war widows as well as war widows with children older than sixteen were not eligible for War Widows' Pension.

During the Second World War, conditions for war widows worsened even further when War Widows' Pension began to be regarded as unearned income and was taxed at the highest rate of 50%. This meant many war widows had to deal with their grief, their children, and another severe reduction in household income. In the House of Commons, at the onset of the Second World War, Thomas Williams stated that while politicians were keen to portray widows and veterans as patriotic heroes, the provision made for them by the state was not one fitting that status, by stating:

"The government are prepared to feed these people on honour and not bread."

WAR WIDOW'S DESPERATION.

SUICIDE AFTER SHE HAD BEEN "FLEECED" OF HER MONEY.

The death of Mrs. Irene Glendinning Welsh (35), whose body was found lying outside a private hotel in Kensington, was investigated by the Coroner yesterday. She was said to have fallen out of a window.

Mrs. Kingsman identified Mrs. Welsh as a widow and a distant relative of her husband. Mrs. Welsh's health was fairly good, she said, but there had been a lot of worry about money. Mrs. Welsh had told her that she had been "fleeced."

The Coroner: Did you know how she had been "fleeced"?—She had been "fleeced" before. She had £3,000 two years ago last November, and I understood from what she said last Tuesday, when I saw her, that it had all gone, as well as her pension from the New Zealand Government for her first husband, who was killed in the war.

The Coroner: Have you any idea how she lost her money?—Yes. Someone persuaded her to invest £500 for the benefit of her little boy Anthony. Then someone else introduced her to a theatrical agent, and he told her she was to be understudy to Miss Gladys Cooper, who, she was told, she resembled very much.

She paid the man fifty guineas, and there was nothing in it. I went with her to the West End, but we could not find the man. He obtained the money by false pretences.

The Coroner: Her pension ceased last November; she had spent all her money, or nearly so; and she could not get any work?—That was just it.

The Coroner, who sat without jury, returned a verdict of suicide in a state of temporary insanity.

"War Widow's Desperation: Suicide after She Had Been 'Fleeced' of her Money", Manchester

COURAGE AFTER THE BATTLE

Guardian (26 January 1922), p.4

War Widow's Desperation

War widows' pensions rarely covered the most basic living costs for widows and their families. Many women relied on savings and the help of their family to weave together a patchwork of incomes. This meant that war widows frequently faced the grief of having lost their husband as well as the trials of severe financial hardship. Sadly, the interwar period saw a significant number of reports of war widows' suicides, which are often directly linked to poverty, debt, grief, and a fear of being a burden to family, friends or the state. The article below reports one such case. Mrs Irene Glendinning had savings, but lost all her money to a fraudster (a scenario which is reported several times in papers of the time). Conmen and fraudsters looking for easy money (much like today) would and still do prey on the vulnerable.

The Post-War Period

Members of Parliament raised the issue of widows' pensions constantly in the houses of parliament, and criticised the low amount paid and its requirement to be taxed.

One such example was Ms Laura Connelly, returned to the United Kingdom from Australia. Within Australia, the War Widows Pension was classed as tax-free, and upon being informed by the Inland Revenue that this was not the case in the United Kingdom, she refused to pay tax and subsequently found herself on the wrong side of the Inland Revenue. Ms Connelly called on all War Widows to band together and take action against this unjust scheme. The fourteen ladies who supported her formed the War Widows Association under the first Chairman, Jill Gee, and they achieved partial success in 1976 by having the tax reduced to 25%. The removal of the remainder was completed under Margaret Thatcher's premiership in 1979.

Following the introduction of the Social Security Act (1973) those who were widowed after 1975 would benefit from the new Armed Forces Pension scheme. This scheme gave them a Forces Family Pension in addition to their War Widows' Pension, but this was providing their husband had died in service or as a consequence of it. It was not until 1990 that this disparity was addressed through a Ministry of Defence supplementary pension.

Until November 2014, some widows and widowers who had lost their spouse in military service between 1973 and 2005 stopped receiving survivor's pension if they remarried, formed a civil partnership, or cohabited with a new partner. The War Widows Association fought long and hard in getting the government to correctly address this issue. Finally, almost a century after its initial meeting, the War Widows Association achieved its aim in getting parity of pensions for all war widows.

DRUGS, ALCOHOL, PRISON, HOMELESSNESS AND DEPRESSION

In the armed forces, harmful drinking has been found to be more than twice as common as in the general population (13.0% vs 5.4%); the problem is more common among deployed than non-deployed personnel. Studies have found the prevalence of PTSD among personnel deployed to Iraq and/or Afghanistan to be about 20% higher than in the general population (3.2% vs 2.7%), whereas among those not yet deployed it was found to be about the same (2.8% vs 2.7%). The rate of common mental disorders in the armed forces as a whole has been shown to be about 30% higher than in the general population (19.7% vs 15.0%), but the prevalence of self-reported self-harm has been approximately 50% lower (4.2% vs 8.0%), as has the long-term incidence of suicide.

Among personnel who have left the forces in the last decade, the prevalence of PTSD, alcohol misuse, common mental disorders and self-harm is appreciably higher in each case than that found in either current armed forces personnel or the general population. Compared with the general population, studies of ex-armed forces personnel have found that PTSD (for those deployed to Iraq and/or Afghanistan) and alcohol misuse are both more than three times as common (Alcohol: 16.8% vs 5.4%; PTSD: 9.2% vs 2.7%); prevalence of common mental disorders has been found to be about 90% higher (28.3% vs 15.0%); and self-harming behaviour approximately 30% higher (10.5% vs 8.0%). The long-term incidence of suicide among ex-forces personnel is about the same as that found in the general population.

Although veterans are less likely overall to have a criminal record, lifetime offences of a violent nature are more common than in the general population (11.0% vs 8.7%). One study found that the rate of violent offending among Iraq and Afghanistan War veterans after they returned from their deployment was twice what it was before they enlisted. The rate of self-reported post-deployment violent behaviour is also high; one study found that 12.6% of Iraq War veterans reported having behaved violently towards family members or others within weeks of returning from their tour of duty

Risk factors affecting veterans after leaving the armed forces include social exclusion, negative life events and lack of social support. For example, a study of current and former armed forces personnel found that those who said they had few or no friends were up to three times as likely, and those with family problems up to 2.5 times as likely, to report self-harming behaviour as were veterans with access to good social support Although exposure to combat is the most potent trigger of trauma-related mental health problems in general, the most important factor in their persistence is the loss of social support after leaving the forces.

Women remain a minority group in the armed forces (9.8%) and the factors impinging on their mental health are complex. In civilian life, women are more likely than men to screen positive for PTSD and common mental disorders but this difference is less pronounced in the armed forces. In common with the general population, in the armed forces fewer women than men drink heavily; even so, women in the military drink substantially more heavily than their civilian counterparts. Potential sources of traumatic stress for women in the armed forces include the behaviour of male peers: a 2006 study found that 20% of women of low rank reported a 'particularly upsetting' experience of unwanted sexual behaviour directed at them from a colleague in the previous 12 months.

Sources: Forces Watch – The Last ambush

One in four homeless people are said to be a former member of the Armed Forces, according to figures from Shelter and the government's Social Exclusion Unit. Research has shown that thousands were living rough or in sheltered homes because they could not adjust to independent living or had problems triggered by their war experiences. Many had served in the Falklands, Kosovo, Bosnia, the Gulf, Northern Ireland and even World War Two but lived on handouts in squats and hostels.

In Liverpool, for example - but it can be any city or town in the UK - the Liverpool Veterans Project (LVP), a support organisation established by Breckfield & North Everton Neighbourhood Council, has helped house or rehouse 148 local military veterans and their families over a three year period. "Homelessness and housing needs among veterans is one of the biggest issues that LVP deals with," Jimmy Culshaw, the organisation's veterans housing officer stated in a recent article:

"Veterans may have a roof over their head but the property may not meet their needs. For instance, it may have damp or be inappropriate for their mobility issues. A number of veterans may be sofa surfing, sleeping at friends' or families', and don't have a home of their own, and a small number are actually sleeping rough."

Coupled with this, former service personnel who have lost limbs during conflicts and those who have mental health problems are constantly falling through the net and ending up on drugs, having problems with alcohol, and even prison. This is despite commitments to ensure former service personnel receive priority treatment in the NHS for injuries suffered in the line of duty. Around £22million has been spent on establishing 11 specialist centres for veterans, which have now been reduced in number. A lot of veterans are not fully aware, if at all, of the Armed Forces Covenant and how to find access to specialist care which sometimes proves difficult, despite the promises of governments and local NHS trusts, and as a result some veterans are falling through the net. Shelter launched a campaign to help people leaving Britain's armed forces. It said many servicemen suffered *Combat Stress* and other mental health issues, had backgrounds in local authority care, or suffered drug and alcohol problems.

Alcohol

Alcohol misuse among UK military personnel is a significant health concern given the high level of problem drinking. Demographic characteristics associated with heavy drinking included lower rank, being young, single, not having children, having a combat role and having a parent with a drug or alcohol problem. Heavy alcohol consumption can also be associated with current military service, being unmarried or being separated/divorced.

Heavy alcohol consumption has been long recognised as an issue in the mental health of service personnel. Recent research demonstrates that excessive alcohol use among serving personnel continues to be an issue. The consequences and potential long-term impact of heavy drinking on health and social outcomes are an important concern. Given its role in the military, a balance needs to be struck between responsible and harmful levels of alcohol consumption, which is not an easy task. It is still not understood how alcohol consumption in serving personnel changes over time and on exit from the armed forces.

Prison

Military personnel are less likely than the general population to have a criminal record but offences of a violent nature have been found to be more common among military males (11.0%) than civilian males (8.7%). One study found that the rate of violent offending among Iraq and Afghanistan War

veterans after their deployment was just over twice what is was before they enlisted, indicating a strong effect of deployment on troops' behaviour afterwards.

For those former members of the armed services who fall on hard times through divorce, bad dealings in life and even PTSD, prison is not an uncommon place to end up. A high proportion of these were for PTSD after leaving the services and the common offences were drugs and alcohol-related violence. As a result of this the NAPO called on the government to tackle the mental health problems suffered by service personnel who have been in a war zone.

A report by the Veterans in Prison support group in 2010, which was assisted by prison officers looking at 74 cases and the factors that drove former service personnel to commit crimes, concluded that:

> Most of the soldiers who had served in either the Gulf or Afghanistan were suffering from post-traumatic stress. Little support or counselling was available on discharge from the services. Virtually all had become involved in heavy drinking or drug taking and in consequence involvement in violence offences, sometimes domestic-related, happened routinely.

The MoD stated:

"Robust systems are in place to treat and prevent PTSD and other stress disorders. Counselling is available to service personnel at all times, and all troops receive pre-and post-deployment briefings to help recognise the signs of stress disorders. "

In 2012 it was reported that the number of former service personnel in prisons is nearly three times higher than official government figures, according to new research. By the criminal justice campaign group, *No Offence*, as many as one in ten prisoners are military veterans, as opposed to the 3.4 per cent official figure. MPs and campaigners said the shock new figure is clear evidence of a betrayal of the military covenant. It is thought that the number of ex-servicemen in prison is likely to grow further as the 20,000 troops returning to civilian life due to defence cuts struggle to make the transition after the battlefields of Iraq and Afghanistan.

Elfyn Llwyd, at the time the Plaid Cymru MP and chair of an all-party parliamentary group focused on the plight of veterans in the criminal justice system, said:

"This is a failure of the military covenant – and it's avoidable. It is going to get far worse unless we do something to address it. The Government is in denial of the figures. Official figures fail to take account of soldiers who have served in Northern Ireland, females, reservists and anyone under the age of 21."

No Offence, stated that they estimate around 10 per cent of prisoners are military veterans, from samples of the prison population. We believe the cuts will have a significant effect on prison numbers, as thousands of troops return to civvy street before they were anticipating, so they have not had a chance to plan. The data that was captured when people go into prison was not accurate, as people do not talk about their former role unless asked, and this is apparent even today. Some veterans, when asked, do not say as there is huge pride associated with being in the military.

Trevor Philpott, a Royal Marines officer for 34 years and founder of the Veterans Change Partnership, said:

"The government figures fail to take into account anyone from Scotland or Northern Ireland, and were based on cross-referencing Ministry of Defence [MoD] and Ministry of Justice [MoJ] figures. There is a sense that the Government is reluctant to address the true figures: if there was the

slightest admission of combat causing mental health problems, there is a fear of legal action. It is usually some five years after leaving the Army that former troops end up in the justice system, after the point at which relatives fail to cope with them. The Prime Minister has pledged to care and support veterans and their families and that should extend across the board."

A highly-regimented military life results in some servicemen experiencing a dramatic culture shock when readjusting to civilian life. Many feel different and isolated. When veterans become involved with the criminal justice system it is an indication that we as a society have failed those we have put in harm's way. We need to understand the unique factors that make them a distinct group within the offender population, and therefore worthy of continued specialist support during and after any period of incarceration.

The 3.4 per cent figure officially quoted comes from a 2009 joint MoD/MoJ survey. Seven years earlier, a Home Office study suggested the proportion of prisoners who were ex-service personnel was approximately 6 per cent.

The MoD insisted the official figure was accurate and an independent report by The Howard League for Penal Reform in 2011 concluded that ex-service personnel are less likely to be in prison than civilians. The vast majority of personnel leaving the Armed Forces make a successful transition to civilian life, and there is a wide range of help and support for all those who need it.

The Ministry of Justice stated that though ex-service personnel resettlement needs are broadly similar to other offenders, we work closely with independent organisations that provide services specifically for them. It is our duty to make sure they are supported in accessing and making best use of these sources of support, to make sure they do not reoffend.

Robert Kilgour, 42, from Edgware, served in Northern Ireland, Bosnia and the first Gulf War and returned to civilian life in 1993, aged 22. Since then he has been jailed repeatedly for assaults.

"One day you're killing, the next you're saying hello. They train you up, but don't detrain you to go back to civilian life, they need to open centres for squaddies returning from war. I was getting into trouble all the time. I'd drink to suppress my feelings. I was temperamental and hard to live with, causing a split with my wife. I was diagnosed with post-traumatic stress disorder 18 months ago, which stems from losing people I cared for and taking somebody's life away. People can see a broken leg or arm, but these mental issues are invisible."

COURAGE AFTER THE BATTLE

Following the *"Former Members of the Armed Forces and Criminal Justice System"* review by Stephen Philips QC MP, the then Justice Secretary, Chris Grayling, announced in January 2015 a package of measures to identify and support veterans when they enter the prison system. He made the commitment that every prisoner coming into custody will be asked if they have been a member of the Armed Forces, and prisons will be given new guidelines about helping them during their sentence.

The Office for National Statistics (ONS) estimated that in 2007 there were approximately 3.8 million ex-service personnel in England, equating to 9.1% of the population at that time. The estimates of the number of veterans in prisons and within the probation caseload vary. However, the official estimate for 2009 suggests that former service personnel comprise around 3.5 per cent of the prison population (2,820) and around the same percentage of offenders on licence (5,860). This is less than the adult population as a whole, of whom around 10% are veterans.

From July to September 2015, there were 721 'first receptions' who were former members of the armed forces. In the same period of 2016, the numbers had fallen to 545 and in the year leading up to September 2016, there were 2,565 veterans who were consequently convicted and jailed. It has to be said that of the initial figures, there may have been a number of "first receptions" who had not declared their former Armed Forces careers for reasons best known to themselves.

Of the Former Members of the Armed Forces and Criminal Justice System review, Justice Secretary Chris Grayling stated:

"Most ex-service personnel have successful civilian lives and do not enter the criminal justice system, but I am determined to help the minority who have committed an offence turn their lives around. Society owes a large debt of gratitude to those who have served their country, which is why our commitment to support them and their families is enshrined in the Armed Forces Covenant. We will identify veterans at the earliest opportunity, so that we can take a more tailored approach to help them turn their lives away from crime. This support will extend to offender families, who also feel the sacrifices made by our service men and women."

Stephen Phillips QC MP stated:

"We were reassured to find that if you have served in the Armed Forces, you are actually less likely to find yourself on the wrong side of the law. But we cannot lose sight of the needs of the minority of veterans who do

end up in the criminal justice system. That is why it is vital for them, their families, and our communities that more is done to look at who they are and how we can support them."

Of the statement by the Justice Secretary, Professor Neil Greenberg of the Royal College of Psychiatrists, who is lead on Military Veterans Health, stated:

"The recently published review into veterans in the criminal justice system is a most welcome document which appears to have resulted from appropriate consultation and has consequentially reached logical and evidence-based conclusions. The recommendations of the report, if implemented as presented, should lead to the small proportion of veterans who come into contact with the criminal justice system being helped to access a wide range of supportive services which should improve their life trajectories with consequential benefits for them, their families and for the rest of society. In particular, by addressing their welfare and mental health needs effectively, it seems likely that their risk of reoffending will be much reduced.

Too often, offenders are not being identified as veterans – information which could help those who work with them focus more closely on their rehabilitation needs. Alongside a commitment to identify veteran offenders in prison, the government's 'Liaison and diversion' programme has also been working since April to identify veterans in police custody and courts. Where appropriate, they can then be referred to Armed Forces specific services – with excellent support available from over 2,000 voluntary sector service charities. Offenders will also benefit from the 'Transforming rehabilitation' reforms made under this government, which will ensure, for the first time in recent history, that virtually every offender released from custody will receive statutory supervision and rehabilitation in the community."

In 2016 it is thought that more than 2,500 members of the former Armed Forces entered the prison system. Experts were warning of a disproportionate number of these being jailed for serious violent and sexual offences. According to the Ministry of Justice, former service personnel represented between 4% and 5% of the UK prison population. There were also rising concerns about the impact of the Afghanistan and Iraq campaigns, along with the associated mental health issues that would follow.

Richard Streatfeild, who served in Afghanistan in 2009, wrote *Honourable Warriors: Fighting the Taliban in Afghanistan*. During six months in Helmand province, Streatfeild and his men engaged in more than 800 firefights and were the target of more than 200 IEDs. Ten men in his company were killed and 50 were wounded. He stated:

"Problems often emerged after soldiers had left the Army. You see people start to drink too much, and then there are discipline issues, and then the relationship goes, and then suddenly they're really struggling. When they're still in the Army, they are easy to identify, and everyone knows what is going on. But it is when they transfer to civilian life that it gets very complicated because people don't realise what they have been through."

Prof Sir Simon Wessely, the president of the Royal College of Psychiatrists and co-director of the King's Centre for Military Health Research, said it was important to acknowledge all the factors affecting soldiers' mental health. He stated:

"We know that most service personnel don't come back with mental health problems, though nearly all of them come back as different people. They are changed by their experiences, but that is not a mental health problem. It's never just about what happens on the battlefield, it's about an interaction between the people we recruit, what happens to them, and the societies that they come back to. It's always a combination of all three."

Patrick Rea, a director of PTSD Resolution, stated:

"The charity saw criminality and substance abuse among ex-service personnel. Most veterans are very disciplined, so their behaviour tends to be very self-harming," he said. "They quite often find us because their partner has told them: 'You have to get help because I can't do anything more.' But they do need to want help, too. A lot of veterans don't believe they can get better, so they live in a state of distress. They soldier on. I would just like to tell them that they can get better. There is a way."

A spokesperson for the Ministry of Defence stated:

"Most former service personnel return to civilian life without problems and are less likely to commit criminal offences than their civilian counterparts, but we're determined to help those who fall into difficulty, and last year awarded £4.6m to schemes targeted at tackling this issue. The government has enshrined the Armed Forces Covenant in law to make sure veterans are treated fairly and receive the support they deserve, including with mental health issues, getting on the housing ladder, and applying for civilian jobs."

Frances Crook, the chief executive of the Howard League, said:

"Several factors contributed to the number of veterans entering the prison system, including alcohol abuse and post-traumatic stress disorder.

Members of the Armed Forces represent about 5% of the prison population, but they represent a disproportionate number of serious violent offences and sexual offences, and that raises questions that need answering. These are not victimless crimes. They have a terrible effect on the victim."

Research by the Howard League found that 25% of ex-service personnel were in prison for sexual offences, compared with 11% of the civilian prison population.

As you can see from the comments and various statements, the argument about former members of the armed services in prison or committing acts of violence is quite an emotive subject in that all sides seem to be defending their ground and no truthful answer ever comes out. What will not change is the poor sod at the end of the line that politicians and others are all giving the "I think ……this …. and that" but have no idea on actual service life, but this poor sod is still suffering and crying out for help. In most cases they find it once they have got over a wall of pride and asked for the help in the first instance. They then hit other walls if they unfortunately go the wrong route. If they manage to get the right route, doors will open and assistance will be given in abundance. It is time the politicians and MoD came clean and sorted the problem out once and for all and stopped hiding behind statistics and veiled promises. After all, they are the root cause.

As mentioned earlier in the book, people can bandy around percentages and all manner of statistics, which can be manipulated to say what the author wants, but these are no good to the end user who just wants a hand up to get on with their life. Once these people, particularly politicians of all parties, realise this and stop point scoring and tell the actual truth, we may be getting somewhere. Richard Streatfeild, in his comments, is as close to the mark as is possible. Without a national survey of all serving and former armed forces in prison, or on drugs, or in alcohol rehabilitation you will never get to the truth. I suspect the survey has not been undertaken as the final number would be too frightening for the politicians to stomach. They will claim it is too large a project, or not enough people will take part etc to prevent it ever happening.

To enable the reader to put this in perspective, the following diagram shows the relationship between the Armed Forces Career Pathways and their effect on prevalence of mental health problems in young and more disadvantaged recruits compared to older, less disadvantaged recruits.

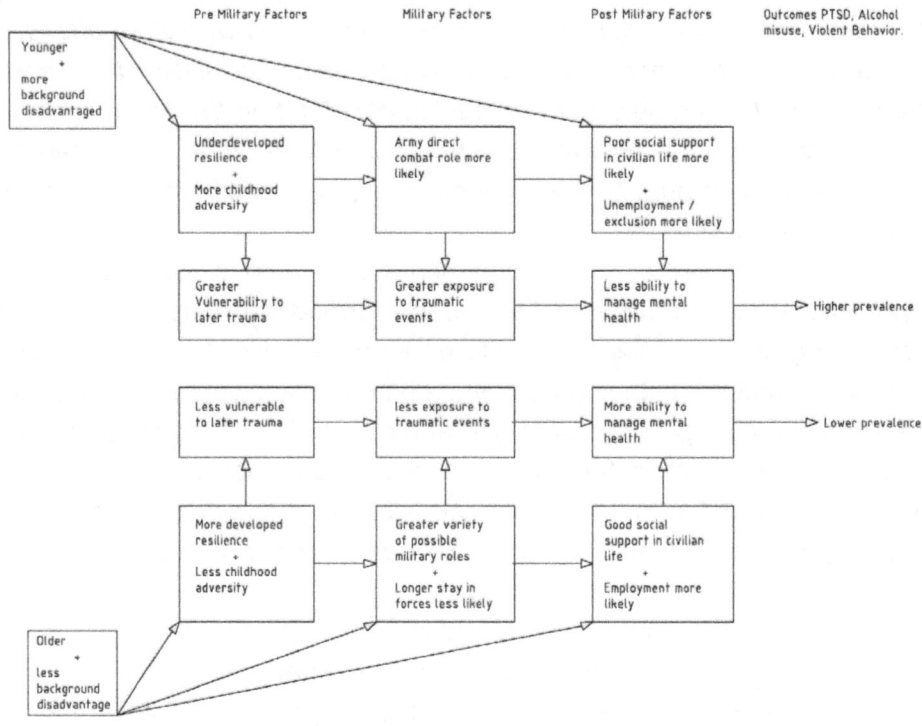

Armed Forces Career Pathways Source Forces Watch – The Last Ambush

Homelessness

Rough sleeping is the most visible form of homelessness but there are a wide range of situations that are also described as homelessness. There were an estimated 4,134 people sleeping rough in England on a single night in the Autumn of 2016. This was up by 16% on 2015.
(Source: Rough Sleepers Statistics Autumn 2016, England)

> The majority of homeless people are hidden from statistics and services as they are dealing with their situation informally. This means staying with family and friends, sofa surfing, living in unsuitable housing such as squats or in 'beds in shed' situations. When approaching local authorities for support, those deemed in 'priority need' are described as being statutory homeless because they are owed a duty by their local authority. In the 2015/16 financial year there were 57,750 households accepted as in priority need.

COURAGE AFTER THE BATTLE

Source: Statutory homelessness, July to September 2016 DCLG.

What causes homelessness? Sadly, many people view homelessness as the result of personal failings, and consider that if the economy is going well, there is no excuse for not getting on with everyday life and surviving financially. But this belief is belied by the facts, which show that homelessness is caused by a combination of factors between a person's individual circumstances and adverse structural factors outside their direct control. These problems can build up over years until the final crisis moment when a person becomes homeless.

These may include one or more of the following individual factors:

Lack of qualifications
Lack of social support
Debts, especially mortgage or rent arrears
Poor physical and mental health
Relationship breakdown
Getting involved in crime
Family background, including family breakdown and disputes
Sexual and physical abuse
An institutional background including having been in care, the armed forces, or in prison

Tackling these problems is a complex business and normally requires support from public bodies, friends and family, combined with a lot of hard work from the individual or family in trouble. Public support might include intervention, advice, counselling, training or provision of alternative accommodation by a local authority where appropriate. For many people, there's no single event that results in sudden homelessness. Instead, homelessness is due to a number of unresolved problems building up over time.

Homeless charities estimate there are around 7,000 ex-servicemen and women living rough and in desperate need of a roof over their head. The Armed Forces Covenant was introduced in 2012 as a contract stating Britain's veterans should take priority when it comes to affordable housing, and all 407 local authorities signed up to it. Too many local authorities play 'pass the parcel' when it comes to affordable housing and pass the applicant over to housing associations, meaning they have no obligation to help veterans at all. Even more damningly, desperately mentally ill ex-servicemen and women still scarred by the horrors of war, are waiting up to two years for medical help and therapy under the Government-approved channels.

By the time they get help many have attempted suicide, and too many cases of this type are actually successful. Others have faced a downward spiral into alcohol, violence, crime and substance addiction. Medical experts are now openly criticising the effectiveness of the NHS and government- funded organisations to care for homeless veterans suffering from Post-Traumatic Stress Disorder -PTSD - caused as a direct result of their service in defence of our nation.

One veteran, who was not granted housing by a local authority in England after he left the Army and had to find accommodation near his former barracks in Northern Ireland, was sent bullets through the post and his six-year-old daughter received death threats. A loophole exists because of the inefficient wording of the Covenant, which says local authorities Should Give Priority to veterans, rather than Must Give Priority to veterans

Former Royal Marines Commando Mike Hookem, a UKIP MEP, said:
"For many years, Britain's Armed Forces have been celebrated as some of the most dedicated, professional and compassionate troops in the world. But how we treat these brave men and women once their military service is over is frankly a national disgrace. With an estimated one in 10 rough sleepers thought to be from a service background, limited access to healthcare, overstretched treatment programmes for PTSD and a void of dedicated post-service care, we as a nation are failing our heroes."

Accommodation Finding Solutions once in Civvy Street
Most personnel join up from the family home and are initially housed in Single Living Accommodation (SLA). Those who marry will generally move into married quarters or Service Families' Accommodation (SFA), either on a *married patch* adjacent or commutable to their base, or a nearby *hiring* if there is insufficient capacity on the patch. Just over half of Royal Navy (including the Royal Marines) and Royal Air Force personnel, and a third of Army personnel, buy a property while serving. However, a significant minority of personnel and families enter their transitional period without having made provision for a home, either rented or owned. This absence of planning is combined with a lack of awareness about civilian housing matters.

COURAGE AFTER THE BATTLE

One option is the local Joint Service Housing Advice Office (JSHAO) which is a Tri-Service focal point for civilian housing information for service personnel and their families wishing to move to civilian accommodation at any point in their career, and provides housing advice to those during armed forces resettlement to assist the transition to civilian life. The service is delivered through briefings, the 'Housing Matters' magazine, consultations and the MoD Referral Scheme supporting Social Housing in conjunction with local authorities and their agents.

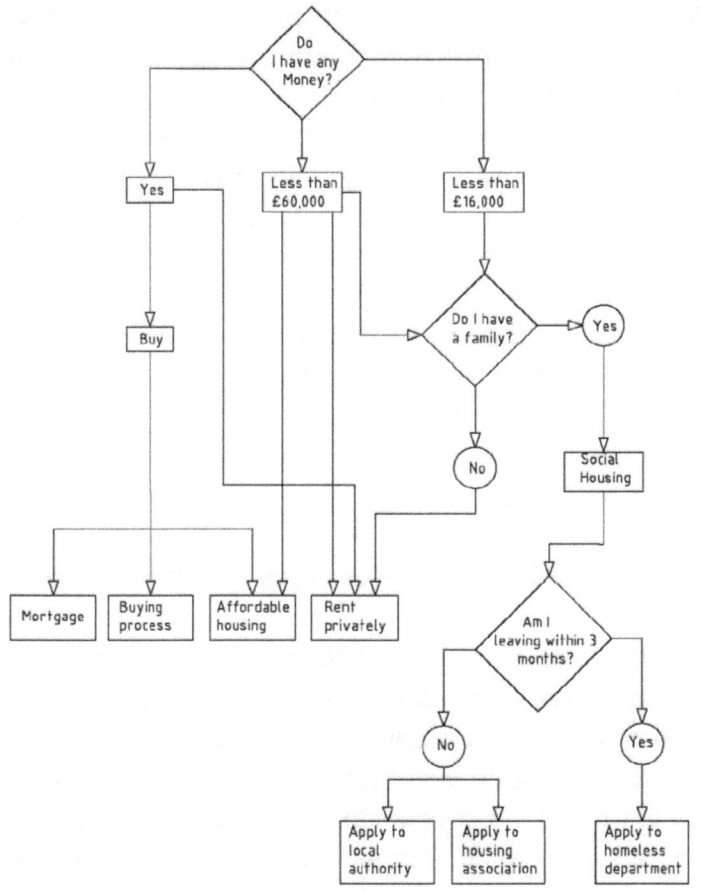

Outline of JSHAO Guides a Service Personnel Will Follow
(Lord Ashcroft Veterans Transition Review)

There are a number of organisations who are there to assist the person leaving the armed services in finding their way in civilian life, or just a home. One of these is SPACES, which is a Single Persons Accommodation Centre for the Ex Services, which also gives housing advice and targets the most vulnerable of service leavers, regardless of rank, length of service, or reason for discharge into this new world. This is particularly prevalent for those who joined as junior ranks (16-18) from a disadvantaged background and do not wish to return home.

SPACES works across the UK and is assisting in securing appropriate accommodation to reduce the risk of homelessness or rough sleeping, no matter where you are located across the UK. They will provide support for up to 12 months prior to discharge if you don't have identified accommodation. The SPACES team will maintain contact with you until suitable accommodation is secured.

SPACES have a referral pathway into most veterans' accommodation across the country via links with many other veterans' charities and housing providers, which means that they can match service personnel with the most appropriate accommodation offer. This is to ensure service personnel have a civilian structured life in comparison to the military structured life, and the transition is hoped that it avoids the pitfalls of homelessness. Service personnel may have little understanding of how to secure rented accommodation, have no experience of budgeting or setting up home, or have problems unique to veterans. This help is out there and service personnel just need to ask.

Financial Advice in Readiness for Civvy Street's Numerous Pitfalls and Bills

As mentioned above, there is an array of financial matters that you will come across after leaving the armed services and if you do not get a grip of these you may well be on the spiral to homelessness, alcohol abuse, etc. Food and accommodation was paid at source (taken out of your wages before you got them), no council tax bills or utility bills, so when you go outside you are confronted with all this responsibility and money being paid for nothing, as you will see it. All this is a bit of a shock to the system and many former vets fall foul of the system and go into an unrecoverable spiral of debt, which leads to homelessness.

There are a number of organisations out there which have official sanctions, much like SPACE and CTP Future Horizons, and there is always the trusty veteran's charity such as the Royal British Legion. The one criteria that fits all three groupsi s that you have to ask for assistance, as they are unable to come and find you to offer it on a plate.

Finding Work once in Civvy Street

Most research clearly shows that service personnel are generally at a disadvantage in the labour market and often do not know how to access the support that is available to them. Many of those who find themselves leaving the Forces early may not have been employed in a civilian job role prior to joining. As such, approaching the workplace can be especially challenging, particularly in today's competitive job market.

The Veterans Employment Transition Support Programme announced in July 2017 that they expected:

85,000 personnel to leave the armed services in the next 5 years

1:5 would be underemployed, that is doing a job that they are either overqualified or skilled for

10% would remain permanently unemployed

Given that this programme works with most of the big boys in the job prospect world, these are worrying numbers.

A 2017 study from Barclays Bank revealed that the UK economy could suffer losses of up to £1.5bn in the next five years if service leavers aren't able to find employment or are under employed upon leaving the Armed Forces. The research calculates the direct and indirect contribution of the up to 85,000 personnel that are estimated to leave the military by 2021; a figure which is equivalent to the number of people currently employed in the UK creative, arts and entertainment sector. While many veterans make a successful transition to civilian employment, the study predicts that 10% will experience long-term unemployment, and that a further 12% will be sub-optimally employed where they are effectively under-utilised by employers.

Those employers who overlook ex-military are not recognising the valuable skills and experience these highly talented individuals possess. Around two thirds of employers are expected to experience deficits in soft skills within the next five years, with more than 600,000 jobs left unfilled. By deploying more ex-military personnel into civilian job roles, one in six of these vacancies could be filled, resulting in a contribution of £12.6bn to the UK economy. This is equivalent to the annual production of the UK Pharmaceuticals industry.

A coalition of a range of leading companies, the Ministry of Defence, the Career Transition Partnership as well as Service charities are part of an organisation called the Veterans Employment Transition Support Programme (VETS). Their aim is to join up the existing transition support initiatives into a single programme that significantly improves employment outcomes for all veterans and businesses.

VETS aim is to assist service personnel regardless of rank, service or circumstances. The VETS programme recognises the corporate social responsibility and recognises the extensive skills developed through years of military service in terms of leadership, integrity, project management and the value of these to the commercial world. Working with the partners, VETS has developed a 5- stage model which shares best practice, enhances existing transition support initiatives and connects it together in a single coherent programme. This programme includes the necessary work interventions such as CV and interview workshops and access to a list of roles across all of the partner businesses. All of these are underpinned by continual support and engagement from a mentor.

Stage 1 –
Access, Registration, Assessment and Mentor Allocation. This first step includes the registration of service leavers and veterans and matching them to a suitable mentor in their preferred area of business who will assess their individual skills and aspirations.

Stage 2 –
Ready to Work. This step provides the necessary transition support activities such as CV and interview workshops, insight days, work placements and internships that can be tailored to the individual to best prepare them to apply for suitable jobs in Stage 3.

Stage 3 –
Job Application. During Step 3 candidates review the VETS jobs list with their mentor, who will assist them with their applications and provide the necessary level of support to prepare them for interview. For unsuccessful candidates, the mentor will provide guidance on whether they should

remain in Stage 3, or revert to Stage 2 for further intervention training.

Stage 4 –
In-employment Support. On receiving an offer of employment the mentor will provide ongoing advice and support to the candidate during Step 4. The key focus will be to ensure a smooth transition into their new role.

Stage 5 –
Support to the Reserves. Stage 5 of the VETS programme aims to increase the exposure of the Reserve Forces both to the coalition of businesses and to those whom they employ through engagement and sharing best practice. The programme also aims to promote the Reserve Forces to those qualifying veterans who are registered with the Scheme.
Veterans can access the model at any stage, as many times as is necessary, throughout their career.

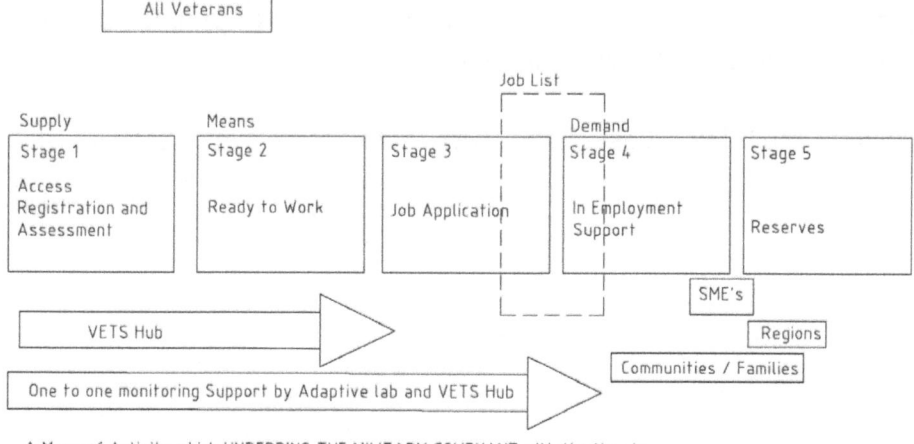

VETS Employment Route (VETS)

Many of their skills are readily transferable into the civilian working environment, especially once a veteran has progressed through the VETS process.

Leadership - Whether it is taking personal accountability or responsibility for others, service leavers are recognised for their hard-earned leadership credentials.

COURAGE AFTER THE BATTLE

Decision making - Even junior sailors, soldiers or airmen must make decisions that may have life or death implications. They willingly shoulder this personal responsibility and use their extensive training and established procedures to guide them.

Problem solving - Trained to deal with the unpredictable and unexpected, to act and to deal with complex multi-faceted issues, these individuals are creative, dynamic and effective.

Flexibility and adaptability - The military norm is to change role every 2 – 3 years. Leavers can adjust fast to new circumstances and become effective very quickly.

Integrity & moral courage - Renowned for these highly prized qualities, military veterans have a clear stance to taking a difficult but correct position over one that is easy but wrong. This is a stance that fits perfectly into a modern, multi-cultural and diverse organisation that wants to strengthen their leading role in our communities.

Source: The VETS Model - https://www.veteranemployment.co.uk/

HOW IT AFFECTS THE FAMILY

Service Family's Mental Health in the 50s
During Korea, the wellbeing and mental health of the soldier's family was seen as no easy task, but as important as the man himself. By virtue of his work, the serviceman had to be in in his place of duty, which has to be changed many times through his career, sometimes in different countries throughout the commonwealth. This constant moving would be unsettling for the family and in particular the children's ability to maintain a school career.

The absence of the father for long periods can have an effect on the mental health of the family. The wife finds herself shouldering all the responsibilities relating to the management of the home and the upbringing of her children; her husband is not at hand to advise and assist her, neither can he fulfil his role as a father, in any practical sense. The work of the housewife and mother is quite arduous enough even when her husband is at hand to help her, but when he is away the tasks which confront her are difficult in the extreme. The interruption of the normal marital relationships also has a bad psychological effect on the family.

The following paragraph could have been written today, but was actually written in an article in the Journal of the Royal Army Medical Corps entitled – The Promotion and maintenance of mental health in the military community (1951 96; p102-114)

Once war breaks out the status of the soldier immediately increases, and he suddenly finds himself especially important. Marked changes occur in the attitude of the nation as a whole towards the soldier, and he is accorded preferential treatment. People go out of their way to entertain him; some places of entertainment offer him seats at reduced prices. The soldier is applauded in the press. His friends and relatives openly admire and flatter him. The girls abandon their civilian acquaintances in his favour. Politicians woo him, because the necessary expansion of the Armed Forces make his vote a powerful factor to be reckoned with in an election. All these things strengthen the soldier's conviction of worth, and he is propelled forcibly in the positive phase of mental health.

The aim of the military community becomes more obviously identified with that of the nation as a whole. A large number of the soldier's relatives and friends are also in the services; therefore, the soldier finds himself identified with a large group composed of individuals who are *all in the same boat*. For these reasons it is easier in some respects to maintain the mental health of the army in wartime than it is in times of peace This applies particularly with regard to the soldier who, as a member of an experienced minority, acquires increased status in a community with an inexperienced majority.

Waiting for News of Safe Return
As I well know, most service personnel feel anxious about leaving the security and backing of the armed forces. They are taking a big step in life and completely changing their life for another mostly unknown one. Many have served from school or a few years later, as in my case, so writing a CV, securing employment and finding somewhere to live all present new challenges.

Once a person leaves the services, there are a number of barriers to cross to enable them to access the care and support they once took as standard. This could include registering with the local housing provider or council, GP, dentist, NHS services, schools for the children, address changes for the Royal Mail. It is hoped that they have managed to secure employment before leaving but if they have not, then they have to register and complete numerous forms and provide information. They are not used to having access to that information as it may not be relevant to their former service career.

There are systems in place to assist the service personnel leaving, but if the lecture on, say, finances is on a day they are deployed on exercise or other duty, then this critical information is missed. There is also the apathy of not paying attention, thinking they will not need this information when in actual fact it is a critical component in civvy street, such as council tax and rent.

Service children can often find themselves at a disadvantage in the allocation of school places due to parents missing deadlines for registration while deployed, as well as the frequent relocation of one or both parents. Local authorities find that they are able to do less to monitor and resolve these problems because of the loss of control of those schools which have become academies and free schools.

To try and assist those personnel leaving, the Forces in Mind Trust (FiMT) was set up with an investment from the Big Lottery Fund in 2012 to invest and spend £35 million over the next 20 years. This had the aim of supporting the psychological wellbeing and successful and sustainable transition of veterans and their families into civilian life.

> *A good transition is one that enables ex-service personnel to be sufficiently resilient to adapt successfully to civilian life, both now and in the future. This resilience includes financial, psychological and emotional resilience, and encompasses the ex-service person and their immediate families.*

Source: FiMT and The Futures Company (2013)

Many veterans' problems can stay hidden for years, and along with their families they may try to deal with matters at home. When these surface, relationships do suffer and the family can seem to be constantly walking on eggshells and tend to be in the front line for reactions. Children can find it difficult to cope with the situation too, and they are unable to grasp the whole situation or background information as to why their mother or father is behaving like this.

To illustrate this I have extracted a case from a Force Watch report entitled The Last Ambush – Aspects of Mental Health in the British Armed Forces

> *Veterans retuning from war find it more difficult to express emotion, manage strong feelings such as anger and fear, or feel at ease in a public place. Heavy drinking, risky behaviour (e.g. driving) and violence directed at others or oneself are common behavioural*

consequences, and in many cases are accompanied by bouts of depression and/or sudden swings of mood. For some, re-adjustment on return from war appears to go well, but at a cost. Empathy with others is degraded and displaced by suspicion or indifference.

Veteran David Adams was suffering from post traumatic stress disorder (PTSD) when he suddenly fell into a rage in his family home:

"I just flipped. I was withdrawn in myself and for some reason I just absolutely exploded, from the top to the bottom of the house, it got wasted. I don't know what the reason behind it was. I can remember just standing there, thinking 'What the hell have I just done!' All I remember was prior to that I was thinking about being in Iraq."

Source Force Watch – The Last Ambush

Many veterans suffer in silence due to pride and self-respect but many of the veterans who seek help have complex physical and mental health issues, including psychological injuries caused by their service in the armed forces. Some of the mental health problems suffered may include depression, anxiety, panic attacks and post traumatic stress disorder (PTSD). Alongside these, some people also have problems with misusing drugs or alcohol and for many, their substance misuse can hide the symptoms of other disorders and make it difficult for them to ask for, or find, effective help and treatment. When they do finally reach out, they often say it is their families that have made them come forward. Behind every veteran suffering in silence, there are loved ones having to do the same.

The other side of military life that is not abundantly clear, especially from a civilian point of view, is the trauma the family suffer when their loved one is away on operations, and then the fallout when their loved one returns home, with their life-changing mental or physical injuries. The families are so often the forgotten ones in all the aftermath and, in many ways, they have a tougher position than the personnel on tour.

In a US study published in the 1990s it found no significant differences in mental health between children of military families and those of civilian samples. Recent research on the impact of deployment on military families presents a different picture. Deployments to Iraq and Afghanistan appear to be more stressful compared to operations in previous years, as there is more of an unknown terrorist / guerrilla (anything goes on the enemy side, whereas the service personnel are bound by the Geneva Convention) warfare approach to recent conflicts. This in itself has seen the stress factors increase now the father, mother, brother or sister is dealing with an unknown enemy who does not wear a uniform and blends in with the public in the local area before they decide to self-detonate, take as many casualties as possible and become a martyr to the cause.

Issues for service spouses such as sudden or extended separations, frequent moves, perceived partner in danger, and social hierarchy with the military environment have been well documented in the international literature. US studies have shown that there is an increase in divorce rates for each conflict / war of the 20th century. This is particularly so for veterans of Korea and men who entered the military in later life. The factors that appear to lead to marital problems included: disruption of the life cycle, frequent moves and long periods of separation. Combat associated with PTSD and antisocial behaviour were also indirectly associated.

The personnel on tour can just get on day after day, while the families just have to sit at home wondering what is happening, if their loved one is ok and waiting for the inevitable knock on the door. This is the nightmare scenario all families dread, when their loved one is away on operations. They keenly watch the news for any sight or news that their loved one is still alive and safe, ensure they always have the mobile phone with them and fully charged, and keep calls as short as possible in case the loved one is trying to get through and it may be the last time you hear their voice or speak to them. They meet other members of the regiment family circle and try to comfort each other, and their entire life is on hold until the safe return. They effectively live on a knife edge until their loved one is home with them and they can physically touch them.

The nightmare scenario could see two well-dressed people, possibly in uniform, arriving at the front door and insisting on speaking to the next of kin. They sit the relative down and go through what has happened and arrange for them to visit the relative once they are back in the UK. At the hospital, usually the first sight of the husband, wife, son or daughter is one of shock. The family are thinking their loved one is not going to survive and will their last words to each other be ones to remember? The family will, just as all parents and loved ones want to do, just give each other a relief-filled hug to make sure they are there, safe, and this is not a dream. The family would not care if they had no arms or legs - they would love them whatever. When they do receive news that their loved one has been killed or injured or seriously wounded, so often the burden of responsibility falls to them. They become the primary carers and more often than not they are the ones left to pick up the pieces for the rest of their lives.

For many years serving personnel deployed abroad have had the opportunity to send home a small letter and have one sent to them by family and friends. I for one know the importance of these little pieces of blue paper, having sent and received them on numerous occasions. Mine were in the old-fashioned method of pen and paper but now it is all electronic and the E-Bluey, but they are still seen as a major source of keeping morale high and finding out what has happened at home, as well as letting them know you are safe and well.

Soldiers received the E-Blueys through a secure, password-protected website that their loved ones at home could access. The electronic messages were then printed out on paper at the front line so that soldiers could carry them around with them, unlike emails or social media messages, which are confined to a computer or phone. The system was also much faster than RAF airmail, reducing delivery times from weeks to hours.

However, in 2017 the penny-pinching defence chiefs decided to cut off this precious link between home and the battlefield in a sad and short-sighted move that is expected to save just £1 million a year. The E-Bluey would be no more from 31st March 2017. Army welfare groups and military wives expressed fury over the decision. About 500 British soldiers also remain in Afghanistan. Prince Charles is among those who have praised the role played by E-Blueys in maintaining morale. Speaking while his son Prince Harry, now the Duke of Sussex, was serving in Afghanistan as an Apache helicopter pilot, he said the letters to and from the war zone provided precious consolation for distressed families.

Conservative MP Johnny Mercer, who served as an Army officer in Afghanistan, called for the system to be retained, stating:

"We should definitely keep this capacity to deliver letters via the internet to troops. It would be such a shame if this was lost for ever because I remember just how meaningful the E-Blueys were to me and my wife while I was away. We would write them almost daily and there is definitely something special about receiving a letter: it is more meaningful than an

email. I'll never forget the E-Blueys being handed out and taking my letters back to my cot [bed] and reading privately for a few moments. It was far more intimate and reassuring from a morale point of view than sitting at a bank of computers at an Army base and simply reading messages online while surrounded by lots of other soldiers."

Defence sources said the move had been triggered by more troops using social media and other modern ways to keep in touch with their families. But soldiers on the front line are often ordered not to use their mobile phones and social media for security reasons, especially when there has been fatality or serious injury. The whole camp is effectively on electronic lockdown until the next of kin have officially been informed. The comment from the defence source shows a lack of understanding on any level, and even if people were using social media or other sources, the use of electronic mail would not be overtaken by such methods of communication. Again, we have a penny wise and pound foolish spokesperson, who will go home to a warm house and comfortable bed, looking for an excuse to balance the books at the expense of the men and women in the battlefield, or anywhere else apart from home.

How the 'E-Bluey' Worked
E-Blueys were invented in 2000 by Royal Logistics Corps officer Brigadier Barry Cash as an alternative to airmail. The bulging mail sacks would take up valuable space in cargo aircraft which could have been used to send first aid, ammunition and weapons instead. E-Blueys were first widely used from 2003 when British troops invaded southern Iraq. By the height of the campaigns in Iraq and Afghanistan, more than 100,000 were being sent every month.

Soldiers and their families access a secure website or use a smartphone app. Letters are typed in and photographs uploaded on to the site. They are then encrypted and sent via an MoD server to the recipient. In the war zone they are then printed out, sealed and addressed similar to traditional airmail. In Afghanistan, letters were printed at Camp Bastion and flown to outlying locations. Soldiers reply using the same system and the letters are printed in the UK. The MoD has pledged to reinvest the £1 million savings to help improve wi-fi provision at overseas locations. Troops and their families will also be able to send handwritten letters – known as Forces Free Air Letters (FFALs).

COURAGE AFTER THE BATTLE

The Army Families Federation (AFF), which represents soldiers and their relatives on welfare issues, stated the decision had caused 'distress and worry' in the military community and that the organisation had sought clarification from the MoD over why it was made. With hundreds of UK troops being sent to Estonia, security experts have raised concerns that Russia will attempt to hack British military communications, including unprotected conversations on social media platforms. The MoD said:

"The welfare of our people is very important to us and we're committed to making sure they can keep in touch with their families. That is why we're updating our service and reinvesting E-Bluey funds into ways of communicating more suited to our modern Armed Forces."

The following three stories have been extracted from a Daily Mail Article entitled:

The hidden wounds are hardest to heal

Three families who found themselves on the front line of PTSD

By Catherine O'Brien November 2016

The Story of Alex Harrison and his mum Marion

The mother of Grenadier Guardsman Alex Harrison, aged 19, remembers the time she leaped out of bed, flew down the stairs, along the hallway and flung open the front door to find two people on her doorstep as she opened the door. The first thing that went through her mind was

"Please tell me he's alive."

She was not sure if they had introduced themselves or what had happened but she was now in her lounge with a neighbour who had given her a strong cup of sweet tea. Alex, 19, had survived but was critically ill after being shot at point blank range by a Taliban fighter in Afghanistan.

The bullet had gone under his helmet, through his temple and into his eye socket, causing horrific head trauma. Twice during the emergency flight back to the UK his heart stopped and he had to be revived by defibrillator. By the time Marion was driven to the intensive care unit of the Queen Elizabeth Hospital in Birmingham, he was in a coma, looking black and blue with tubes everywhere and still covered in the dirt he had fallen in.

Alex's return from a war zone meant she was about to join a growing number of ill-prepared people by being on a front line - one which was invisible and she had neither adequate training nor support. Alex was discharged from hospital a month later, but needed ongoing treatment for his head injuries and ultimately lost the sight in his right eye. However, it was the hidden wounds of his post traumatic stress disorder that took both him and Marion to the brink of despair.

The Queen Elizabeth Hospital in Birmingham is the specialist centre for UK military personnel injured in conflict zones and a welfare officer was on hand for Marion when she arrived there to see Alex. However, once she took her son back to the family home, they were on their own.

"There was no back-up and I was thrown in at the deep end, but Alex didn't want to tell me everything that had happened. I think he was trying to spare my feelings."

Soon afterwards, what Marion describes as 'the hell' kicked in.

Alex learned that three of his best friends had been killed in Afghanistan. He kept saying:

"Why should I live if they've died?"'

Then, on top of his survivor's guilt, came the news that surgeons were not going to be able to save the sight in his right eye. That meant his Army career was over and, as far as he was concerned, he had nothing left to live for. To block out flashbacks and nightmares, Alex began drinking heavily. He admits:

"I was drunk most of the time. I'd go out till the early hours, collapse, wake up, and open another bottle of beer. I would pick fights because 'everyone was the enemy.'"

Marion recalls countless times being called by strangers who had grabbed his phone and looked up 'Mum' in his contacts.

"I'd turn up in pubs and nightclubs in my dressing gown and drag him out screaming. At home, I'd lock him in his room, only for him to climb out of the window."

One morning Marion went upstairs to find Alex tying his bedsheets together in order to hang himself from the loft hatch. On another occasion, after insisting he walked with her to the local shops to get some fresh air, she became aware that he was veering off the pavement directly into the path of an oncoming bus. He had this blank look on his face and she had two seconds to stop him, so she hit him, knocking him to the ground: it was either that or watch him die.

Alex allowed Marion to contact his sergeant, who set the wheels in motion for him to have treatment at Headley Court, the specialist Ministry of Defence rehabilitation centre in Surrey for wounded soldiers. Through his GP, he was also referred to a counsellor, who told him:

"I'm not going to be able to take away what happened to you, but I will teach you how to cope with it."

Nine years on, Alex has rebuilt his life. He lives with his partner Sarah, 28, and their two daughters Isabella, eight, and Eliza, five, and runs his own Landscaping Property Maintenance service with the help of a business mentor from the charity Supporting Wounded Veterans. Marion said:

"I could not be more proud of Alex, but he deserved better care when he was at his lowest ebb and I wouldn't wish what we went through on any other family."

The story of Lynn and Dean Hawkins

For Lynn Hawkins, that end-of-tether moment came one Saturday morning when her husband Dean had a full-blown panic attack, the consequence of PTSD that he had been suppressing for decades. The couple had popped into their local building society to sort out their children's savings accounts. The trouble was they didn't have the right documentation and when the cashier politely explained they would have to come back, the red mist descended for 55-year-old Dean.

"He just exploded; he was being verbally aggressive and thank heavens for Perspex screens, because otherwise, he later admitted, he would have pulled the guy over the counter. Instead, he started raging at a woman behind us in the queue before I managed to get him outside. He was shaking uncontrollably and it took hours for him to calm down."

Tours to Sierra Leone and Iraq had led to Dean suffering mood swings, flashes of temper and periods in which he would withdraw into himself.

"He went through some horrendous experiences, which he wouldn't talk to me about back then and that built a barrier between us. I started to find myself tiptoeing on eggshells and the children learned to do the same."

In 2006, Dean took on the highly sensitive role of Notification Officer, tasked with delivering devastating news to the families of those lost or severely injured in action. As a father of four with operational experience, he was eminently qualified for the job, but it took its toll.

"Every time you knock on another door, your heart is in your mouth because you know something of the emotional hand grenade that is about to go off. For those poor families, it is a moment they will never forget."

With hindsight, Dean can see that he was struggling with the burden of grief among the relatives he encountered.

"We are told not to build emotional bridges, but when you are doing the job, it's hard to be detached. I would come home and sit in a darkened room, talking to a bottle of wine rather than my wife. It is amazing she stuck by me. Lynn is one of the hidden wounded."

Lynn was the only one who knew the true cost to Dean's mental health at the time because innate professionalism prevented Dean from appearing anything other than strong and capable.

"As far as his colleagues were concerned, there was nothing he couldn't handle, it was at home that the stress would come out. He would break things, slam doors. We never knew how he was going to be."

Lynn admits she did contemplate leaving Dean.

"I told myself we shouldn't be living like this and worried about the effect on the children. But I feared that if we did walk out, Dean would kill himself."

She told no one what they were going through, as there seemed no one to turn to. Her husband was part of the welfare system, but there was no one there to care for the carers. There are, she explains, other complications.

"If you tell someone you husband isn't coping, first you feel as if you are being incredibly disloyal to him and, second, you worry that you might be jeopardising his career, and with that, the wage that he is bringing in and the roof over your head. There is a massive need for a confidential support network that protects military families so that they can feel safe in talking openly about mental health issues."

After Dean was diagnosed with PTSD and also chronic adjustment disorder and depression, the Army arranged for him to have counselling, which was of some help, but being signed off work meant he festered at home. Dean felt angry and bitter at being dropped after all his years of service and that made him even more withdrawn and hard to live with. It was almost two years before his regiment sent someone to check on his welfare, at which point Lynn told them furiously that they were too late.

"It's amazing she stuck by me," says Dean.

Dean embarked on his new full-time job as a facilities manager with Tesco, thanks to Supporting Wounded Veterans,

"I have the man I married back once more, and now, at last, we can be the family we were always meant to be," says Lynn.

COURAGE AFTER THE BATTLE

The story of Paul with his sister Nina

Paul, 47, is a former Royal Navy medic whose service while attached to the Royal Marines included tours of Iraq and Afghanistan, where he was involved in the rescue of countless severely wounded soldiers. Paul subsequently joined the Police Force and in 2013 was the victim of a serious assault while on duty, which triggered delayed-onset PTSD. It was his younger sister Nina Brierley to whom he turned for support after a catastrophic breakdown. Nina and Paul were not particularly close growing up, but they tolerated each other.

The change for the worse came after his second tour of Afghanistan in 2007. The family all piled down to his flat to welcome him home, but he was monosyllabic, withdrawn and very twitchy. Paul seemed to get his life together after that: he decided to leave the Navy and joined the Police Force. He was also settled with a long-term girlfriend, so although Nina was aware when she saw him that he was sometimes on a short fuse, she thought he was coping. Paul ended up with spinal and neck injuries after being called to deal with a pub fight, and his girlfriend left him. He rang Nina out of the blue and said he was having flashbacks and nightmares and couldn't sleep. He hadn't wanted to call his parents because he didn't want to worry them. He felt that as his sister, Nina was someone he could trust and that she could give him the combination of practical and emotional support he needed. Nina listened, but didn't know the right thing to say and she became desperately worried.

Fortunately, Nina had a friend who worked at Headley Court, the rehabilitation centre for wounded soldiers, who confirmed Paul needed specialist help. She spoke to Combat Stress, the mental health charity for veterans, which explained that Paul needed to be referred for counselling through his GP, which they did.

Nina said:

"When he phones, I stop doing whatever I am in the middle of and give him my 100 per cent attention. And I've learnt to gauge when I need to just listen, and when I need to give him a verbal kick up the backside. He's doing brilliantly now. He's back at work and in a new relationship and, although we both know he'll never be quite the same again, a huge positive is that he and I have become incredibly close."

Paul says:

"I am immensely grateful to my family and my work colleagues for supporting me through what we call my "rage days". But I'm not keen on anybody knowing how bad things really were. For a long time, I bottled things up - the flashbacks, the hyper vigilance and the anger. No matter what people say, you are not going to reach out for help until you are ready. Nina kept checking up on me and when I went downhill, I knew she would be the person I could talk to best. My parents have always been there for me, too, and I talk to them, but I don't have to worry about worrying Nina. She can soak up whatever I say and, thanks to her pragmatic approach, I got the professional help I needed."

If mental health remains a largely taboo subject on civvy street, a deeply embedded macho culture makes it even more difficult to talk about within military circles. According to the MoD website: 'In many ways, the stigma associated with mental health problems is more disabling than the condition itself.' But we are dealing with a massive embarrassment factor, the expectation that you should be able to cope, and fear that if you speak up, you will be putting your career, and the respect of those you value, on the line.'

Domestic Abuse
Domestic abuse affects 1 in 4 women and 1 in 6 men during their lifetime. It can affect anyone, regardless of background. The definition of domestic violence and abuse is:

Any incident or pattern of incidents of controlling, coercive, threatening behaviour, violence or abuse between those aged 16 or over who are, or have been, intimate partners or family members, regardless of gender or sexuality. The abuse can encompass, but is not limited to:

psychological
physical
sexual
financial
emotional

Research has indicated that people between the ages of 20 and 40 are at highest risk of experiencing domestic abuse and this age range is strongly represented in the Armed Forces. Regular overseas deployments and geographic separation can isolate victims by cutting them off from their family and support systems. Regular overseas deployments can make it difficult for a spouse to maintain a career, resulting in them being more economically dependent on the serving partner. Regular deployments and reunions create unique stresses on Armed Forces families.

The message behind domestic abuse is a simple one:

Domestic abuse is not right.
You are not alone.
It is more common than people think.
Trained professionals can help victims, perpetrators and children.
Help is available.

Members of the Armed Forces who are affected by domestic abuse may be concerned about specific issues when they are trying to make decisions around their future, including accommodation, and the reality of leaving the military community.

When thinking about the consequences of domestic abuse, it is important to consider the impact (mental, emotional, physical, social and financial) on the individual survivor, family and children. In addition to this there are the unseen costs for police, health and other service responses, and time off having to be taken by survivors from paid employment and caring responsibilities.

It is a misconception that domestic abuse is a rare occurrence. In fact, domestic abuse is more common than you think. One common fact that prevents domestic abuse being reported by the spouse (male or female) is the fear that their partner's career will be affected, and this could result in any number of other complications.

Service accommodation (married quarters) is provided for personnel, but if the couple separate they can remain in service accommodation for up to six months. Financial abuse can be a significant barrier to leaving an abuser. 52% of women respondents to a Women's Aid/TUC study who were still living with their abuser said they could not afford to leave because they had no money of their own.

In 2012, the Ministry of Defence conducted research of 13,000 Army personnel and found a link between combat and trauma, and violent behaviour, often towards their partners. This equates to approximately one in eight soldiers having attacked someone after coming home from a combat deployment. The study by Dr Deirdre MacManus, at The Kings Centre for Military Health Research, found an association between soldiers' experiences in Iraq and Afghanistan, and violent behaviour at home. It found that soldiers who were directly involved in combat were twice as likely as others to admit having hit someone at the end of the tour. A third of the victims were someone in the family - often a wife or girlfriend.

Ex-Royal Engineer Lewis Mackay believes screening for PTSD after a tour would solve the problem of troops not wanting to admit they were not coping with the stress.

"You don't want to admit it to yourself that you have got something wrong with you. The Army says: 'come and see us if you have something wrong.' Guys aren't going to do it."

In Afghanistan, he saw an IED search team commander lose both legs after stepping on an improvised explosive device. Mr Mackay said that when he went home to his wife Emma, he came close to hitting her.

"I had flashbacks. If I was watching telly and there was a loud bang on screen, I hit the deck, I had a very short temper. I was punching doors and walls. I was very, very aggressive. If my wife was doing something that I didn't think was right I wanted to lash out. I had to try my hardest not to by sitting on my hands or biting my fist."

Examples of this returning home and restraining yourself are noted below, some of which could be classed as abuse by the services or the other forces families.

The following brief quotes are from:

Harriet Grey – Domestic Abuse and the Public / Private Divide in the British Military

"Having the wife and kids sat at home is one thing, when you're away on tour, it keeps you going. My wife, my kids, this is why I'm doing what I'm doing. They're not going to end up talking Afghani Iraqi. (If soldiers were all single) would you get the same effort?"

"The military needs a man fit to fight. Which means the family is happy they make sure the dental service is provided, medical services, certainly abroad. So, if the family is happy, then the guy's gonna be happy. You got a happy soldier, you got a productive soldier."

"You're not your own person, you are wife of X, you are not Mrs Smith, you are wife of X. It makes you feel second rate."

"You feel like you have been stripped of your own identity and you are insignificant."

"I was just excess baggage. That's what (wives) are classed as, excess baggage."

"My husband beat me up today; I'll take it to the welfare office. Welfare office will address it with the chain of command, and then he comes back after work, 'cause he's been called by his commanding officer, he'll come back and beat me up again this evening."

"The military look after their own. They tell you that quite clearly, we're a family, we look after our own, but the head of the family happens to be … the servicewoman. So that's who they're looking after."

"They're all together. There is no separation from any of them. They're all boys club together, even the prosecution (Royal Military Police) everybody is together in the mess… Nothing in the army is separated. They're there to protect the soldier."

On average two women are killed or seriously injured by their partner or ex-partner every week in England and Wales. Domestic cases now account for 14.1% of all court prosecutions. The volume of prosecutions rose and 92.4% of defendants were male and 7.6% were women. 84% of victims were female and 16% were male. On December 29th 2015 a new criminal offence of 'domestic abuse - coercive and controlling behaviour' came into force.

Domestic abuse is a largely hidden crime, occurring mainly in homes behind closed doors. As such, it can be difficult to record the context in which abuse is being perpetrated, or accurately measure the impact of the abuse on those who experience it. Women are often afraid or unable to report domestic abuse to the commanding officer or forces welfare, and may under-report domestic abuse in surveys, particularly during face-to-face interviews, for fear or recriminations or losing the married quarters.

Researchers from King's College London looked at criminal offending rates and the possible links between them and post traumatic stress disorder, anxiety, depression and other mood disorders in a report published in 2013 which had a random sample of 13,856 serving and ex-personnel, mostly from the army. The study found that of 2,700 men serving in the armed forces under the age of 30, (20.6%) had been convicted of a violent offence, compared with 6.7% in the general population. Men who had seen combat in Iraq and Afghanistan were 53% more likely to commit a violent offence than those in non-frontline roles and personnel who had multiple experiences of combat had a 70% to 80% greater risk of being convicted of acts of violence. Violent offences covered a broad range of acts, from verbal harassment to homicide.

Dr Walter Busuttil, Director of Medical Services at Combat Stress, said:

"These findings will help us to identify which veterans are most vulnerable and in need of appropriate care and treatment after leaving the armed forces. We are planning courses for anger management and domestic violence. We are about to establish programmes that deal with alcohol abuse linked to PTSD. It would be grossly unfair and inaccurate to characterise all veterans living with PTSD as potential criminals. As noted in the report, the vast majority [83%] of serving and ex-serving UK military personnel do not have any sort of criminal record, and the likelihood of violent behaviour is lower among older veterans [aged over 45] than in the general population. What we require now is continued public education to reduce any negative connotations with seeking help for mental health issues, as well as sustained funding for services for veterans."

Going on from this, Combat Stress have successfully introduced a number of help streams for veterans and continue to do so.

Domestic Abuse Case Studies (Taken from Official Records. Names and details have been omitted.)

Case 1

A wife and daughter approached the Army Welfare Service (AWS) after the marriage had broken down. The daughter still loved her father and made a request to see him, which the wife agreed to as the marital breakdown was not the daughter's fault and it would be wrong to make her suffer by not seeing her father. The AWS worked closely with all parties to let the daughter see her father and collect belongings from the marital home as the wife was unwilling to return to the marital home.

Both the husband and wife were from the same country and the wife feared for her life if she returned. She had a good job which she loved and her daughter was doing well in school. If they moved back to their country of origin, then the daughter would have to have her schooling interrupted. The wife was ashamed of what had happened and was often blaming herself, and she was also going through an application for indefinite leave to remain.

What followed was two traumatic court cases to give evidence against her husband and details of the abuse she had suffered, along with seeing the husband she no longer recognised. She thought she would be spending the rest of her life with this man she had loved, and now she was in court against him. She initially had her request for indefinite leave to remain refused, but on appeal she was given leave to remain, which meant she was able to access benefits and work again.

The wife is now gaining education certificates to further her career and her daughter is doing well at school. The service charities are working with both the wife and daughter for as long as they need.

Case 2
A female senior member of the armed forces was abusive to her husband. They had no children. Following a complaint by the husband he was shown to have suffered both mental and physical abuse in the relationship. The member of the armed services was found to be exhibiting controlling and manipulative behaviour towards her husband. Over time this had a negative impact on the emotional and mental health of the husband. The husband took part in local assistance programmes but unfortunately they later separated.

Case 3
A wife approached the AWS to say her husband kept her short of money and this was tantamount to him blocking her financial support for the family, especially as he had £10,000 in his account. She had actively encouraged her son (18) to leave home and his two other siblings were also independent

of the family. An assessment identified emotional and verbal abuse, along with isolation of the wife and her financial control for the family. The wife felt trapped but did not want to leave the husband, so AWS assisted the wife with support and signposted her to the woman's aid support group.

Abuse is not just physical but can come in many forms, as shown above, and this can be exacerbated by a person serving in a combat area for up to six months then coming home.

Past Allegations and Current False Claims Against Serving Personnel and Veterans

Threats of After Service Prosecution Many Years Later
It is understood that Prince Harry, himself a veteran of two tours of active duty in Afghanistan as a Forward Air Controller (FAC) in Helmand Province in 2008, before retraining as a military helicopter pilot and returning for a second tour in 2012, has labelled both the Iraq Historic Allegations Team and Afghan War-centric Operation Northmoor a joke. He is said to be deeply concerned about the ordeal soldiers are being put through as they face claims of wrongdoing while on active duty.

Time and time again we see this situation with investigations which have been overseen by people who have no service background or knowledge making these "Informed" decisions, in what is effectively hindsight and the letter of the law. Yes, there is also the Geneva Convention to consider, but not all of those fighting, particularly terrorists, adhere to this, and at times the service personnel are literally fighting for their lives with their hands tied behind their backs.

"The Rules of Engagement brought about by the Geneva Convention are out of date because they only work when the Armies on both sides agree to abide by them, and take prisoners and treat them in a way that is humane. The new danger does neither, which is why the modern-day soldier feels like he is in a boxing match with a blinkered referee who is applying the Queensbury Rules completely on them but ignoring the atrocities of the opponent."

The above sentiment from a known former member of the Armed Forces can be applied to many modern soldiers. Serving and former members of the Armed Forces also have the IHAT (The Iraq Historic Allegations Team) and Northern Ireland Inquiries (Historic Enquiries Team) looking over their shoulders, only at British service personnel. Some members of the IRA, which is seen as a Terrorist Organisation, or freedom fighters, as they like to call themselves, were given pardons following the 1998 Good Friday peace deal, while others were handed Letters of Comfort or 'On the Run Letters' by Tony Blair, the then Prime Minister, promising they would never be prosecuted. You can even add the Bloody Sunday era into this and try to rake up old arguments, one side against the other, many years later. All of this adds to the pressures service personnel are under and even many years after they have left, they can still be charged with an offence. We are again back to the armchair critics who were not there or have had an inordinate amount of time to think about their answer.

In recent years successive governments, both Labour and Conservative, (including co-operation from another party to gain a majority) have indulged in a shameful betrayal of our Armed Forces. These are the very people who risk their lives to protect our country's interests and who have then been subjected to a relentless campaign of persecution, dressed up as legal investigation into abuse. Disgracefully, the politicians have not only sanctioned this continual harassment but even encouraged it through vast legal aid subsidies and compensation payments.

Almost all the allegations of maltreatment brought against British troops who served in Iraq and Afghanistan, not to mention Northern Ireland and other conflicts, have turned out to be baseless. The reluctance of successive governments to combat vigorously this constant barrage of empty charges has created its own cycle of exploitation by easy money lawyers and their clients.

In Iraq alone, the Ministry of Defence forked out £20 million to more than 300 claimants to avoid court hearings, even though it spent more than £100 million on legal fees. A whistle-blower who worked for the law firm Leigh Day (we will hear more about them later) who were at the forefront of these false money-making allegations of abuse by British military personnel in Iraq, alleged that many of these settled claims were not merely exaggerated, but they were utterly fraudulent.

Apparently, a favourite lawyers' ruse (and I hesitate in calling them lawyers as they have tainted the legal profession) was to persuade clients to alter their stories about detention, pretending they had been held by the British even if they had been taken by the Americans. This was due to the Ministry of Defence being seen as a soft target rather than the American Department of Defence, which was stringent on all aspects of any claims.

COURAGE AFTER THE BATTLE

Many Iraqi claimants simply had documents referring to the American forces but this was simply changed to the British forces as the perpetrator of the crime. Politicians look after themselves and only make a decision that may well further their career, and upholding the law and their armed forces is second, if it is on the list at all.

One of the Iraqi translators was the Manchester-based businessman, Mazin Younis, whose services were used by Leigh Day and by Public Interest Lawyers, run by disgraced human rights campaigner Phil Shiner, who was struck off as a solicitor in 2017 for making false claims against British troops. Younis was said to have been paid £1.6 million in 2009 for supplying clients to Shiner's company as well as to Leigh Day. The sum is another monument to the MoD's refusal to defend its people. Sadly, the Iraq fiasco is not an isolated case.

Such a criminal conspiracy could only have been enacted with orders from the top, but there is not a shred of evidence to support such a plot, just as there is none to support claims of Iraqi abuses.

Labour leader Jeremy Corbyn jumped on the anti-Army bandwagon by calling for an independent inquiry into alleged SAS war crimes. With the same enthusiasm he once used to denounce the recapture of the Falklands, he declared that there can be no question of a cover-up.

Senior figures in both main parties, and others with a self-interest in furthering their career or getting their face on the television, like to show their heartfelt support to take up cases against our armed forces. The British attitude explains why the MoD was so determined to hound Royal Marine Sergeant Alexander Blackman for killing a Taliban fighter, not only by securing his conviction for murder by any means, and which was rightly overturned, but also by putting all manner of resistance to his appeal.

This is a man who has served his country with distinction and was effectively left to fend for himself in a command post with very little rest and recuperation, not to mention back-up from his senior ranks. The Court Martial Judges broke with the rules and saluted the condemned Sgt Blackman on the way out of the court. Two of the five officers on the court martial panel are said to have come under very considerable pressure to change the not guilty verdicts. Would it be these officers who had actual combat experience on the panel, and where did this pressure come from? It could only have come from the highest office to protect political and legal careers with no thought for the man in the dock and his long distinctive career, and that of both his personal and Royal Marines family.

Frederick Forsyth, who spearheaded the campaign for justice for Blackman, said:

"Honourable men do not salute a perjurer and a murderer. They were sending a message and what they were saying was We've done what we were told to do."

Sgt Blackman also had his Commanding Officer Colonel Lee Royal Marines resign his commission in disgust as he had been blocked from telling the truth to the Court Martial, calling it a *failure of moral courage by the chain of command.*

The political impetus was behind the easy *pay them, as going through the courts was too expensive, so the taxpayer was saving money* option when in reality, if they had bothered to look at the facts, most if not all the cases would have been thrown out. This would show that the MoD was not an easy target. There are two main areas which these people use to *make things right* and look at a *large financial* reward. The Human Rights Act of 1998 has become a cash cow for money-grabbing lawyers, political activists and vexatious litigants. The second is Britain's membership of the International Criminal Court in The Hague, agreed by Tony Blair's government in 2001. America refused to join the International Court, because it did not want its soldiers to come under the jurisdiction of foreign regimes, or its military campaigns to be an arena for litigation.

As the latest series of claims and false accusations is showing, the perpetrators are trying to apply the legal niceties of peaceful civilian life to the lethal conflict and chaos of the battlefield, when they are two completely different animals. The result is not justice, but a cash machine for lawyers and their clients to fulfil their dreams of riches, thanks to the suffering of armed forces personnel, and it most certainly is not justice as no crime has been committed, just a figment of imagination. A central reason for this flight from common sense is that so few politicians, civil servants and even senior officers have any hardened experience of war, and they are unable or unwilling to see that the claims are false. That is not to say there may be a few genuine claims which should rightly be investigated, but a vast majority are completely fabricated.

The willingness to settle also gives credence to allegations of abuse, which in turn provides more ammunition for those who wish to exploit the system, and the tax payer loses out again. This also has a knock-on effect in that the enemy can use this information against the personnel on the ground and turn the tide of hearts and minds against them. This would then put them in more danger of retaliatory strikes and attacks. The lawyers and claimants sit safe and sound in their respective properties.

The cycle of blackening the good name of the armed service will never end until British interests are given priority. If only our politicians had the same guts as the serving men and women now under scrutiny, we would be a far better place and the armed services could relax and not look out for the next knife in their back.

July 2017, members of the SAS were placed under investigation over accusations that they executed unarmed Afghanistan civilians in cold blood. Among the charges are that the SAS used fake photography to conceal civilian deaths, falsified reports and planted Taliban weaponry on victims to disguise them as insurgents. The allegations were never proven and whilst the SAS were being investigated by the Royal Military Police (RMP), it came to light that the RMPs knew the allegations were fabricated but both the Government and RMP continued the investigation to show no one was above the law. This does not take into account the trauma suffered by the teams on the ground and in the back of their minds knowing that whatever they do could land them with spurious charges and possible jail. Nice state of mind to go into a live operation when the only way from there is down, courtesy of HM Government, aka your caring boss.

In December 2017 four Iraqi citizens were given thousands of pounds in damages against the Ministry of Defence over ill-treatment and unlawful detention during the Iraq War. This is part of a series of claims by more than 600 Iraqis in what is known as the Iraqi Civilian Litigation, who claim to have suffered and launched their claims for compensation in 2013, years after the alleged events of 2003-2009. The claims were launched in England against the MoD after they were prevented from proceeding in Iraq. The claims were given the go-ahead by the High Court in London but were blocked by the Court of Appeal because of a time bar imposed under Iraqi Law. This decision was upheld in the Supreme Court of Justice, the highest court in the land, in 2016.

At the High Court Mr Justice Leggatt ruled the four men were entitled to compensation under the Human Rights Act, with one being awarded more than £30,000. Lawyers have warned that, after the ruling on the four test cases, it could now mean the MoD faces paying out millions of pounds in compensation to more than 600 unresolved claims, but who is looking after the service personnel? It has been proved in the past that a lot of these cases were allegedly undertaken by other forces in the area but are claimed against Britain, as we are a soft option. Where are their legal and human rights?

Abd Al-Waheed, who was arrested in a house raid carried out by British soldiers in Basra city in February 2007, was awarded a total of £33,300. He was awarded £15,000 in respect of the beating he suffered after his arrest and £15,000 for what the judge described as the further inhuman and degrading treatment which he suffered, encompassing harsh interrogation, being deprived of sleep and being deprived of sight and hearing. He was further compensated £3,300 for unlawful detention for 33 days.

The judge awarded damages to two other claimants, who at the time for legal reasons could only be referred to as MRE and KSU. In March 2003 their merchant ship, moored in the Khawr az Zubayr waterway north of Umm Qasr, was boarded by coalition forces. The four crew members, including MRE and KSU, were captured. MRE was awarded a total of £28,140, made up of £10,000 for hooding with sandbags during a road journey, £1,000 for an eye injury sustained as a result of the hooding, and £15,000 for a blow struck to his head, along with £1,440 for the cost of medical treatment, and £600 for six days of unlawful imprisonment. Mr Justice Leggatt awarded damages to KSU totalling £10,600 for the hooding and the same period of unlawful detention.

Mr Justice Leggatt announced his conclusions after overseeing two High Court trials during which Iraqi citizens gave evidence in an English courtroom for the first time. The judge stated:

"This judgement follows the first full trials of these claims in which the claimants themselves and other witnesses have testified in an English courtroom. Four cases have been tried as lead cases. There is no assumption that these four cases are representative of others, but the conclusions reached on the legal issues and some of the factual issues raised, are likely to affect many of the remaining cases in the litigation."

Sapna Malik, a partner in the international claims team at Leigh Day, who represented Mr Alseran and Mr Al-Waheed, stated:

"These trials took place against an onslaught of political, military and media slurs of Iraqis bringing spurious claims, and strident criticism of us, as lawyers, representing them. Yet we have just witnessed the rule of law

in action. Our clients are grateful that the judge approached their claims without any preconception or presumption that allegations of misconduct by British soldiers are inherently unlikely to be true. Our clients' evidence has been tested at length in court and the Ministry of Defence has been found wanting. It is vital that those wronged by the UK government, whether in this country or overseas, are able to seek justice and redress. Their ability to do so in our courts is not a witch-hunt but a testament to the strength of our democracy."

Shubhaa Srinivasan, also a partner at Leigh Day, who represented MRE and KSU, stated:

"The decision sends a clear message that no one, including the British government, should be above the law."

In 2015 the then Secretary of Defence, Michael Fallon, criticised ambulance-chasing law firms as taxpayers have had to foot a £150million bill for legal fees in cases brought by people claiming human rights breaches in Iraq and Afghanistan. Maybe the government should make a stand on this as other countries have, rather than criticising the legal profession, of which there are ambulance chasers and other claims companies who regularly inflate the allegations, and they should be brought to heel.

As an example of the treatment of service personnel many years after the event, and those events being judged in hindsight by others, as shown below with Public Interest Lawyers cases, an Army Major who is facing his 8th probe over the death of an Iraqi teen says he has not had a good night's sleep in 15 years. Major Robert Campbell, 45 is still being investigated over the drowning of 19-year-old Said Shabram in May 2003.

He has now been told he will be forced to give evidence in public to the Iraq Fatality Investigations (IFI) to satisfy human rights laws. The seven investigations into the death have taken toll on his mental health and he is refusing to take part in the eighth investigation.

"No ordinary civilian would be expected to have to undergo so many investigations - and it is unfair veterans are being put through the ordeal. I don't think anything good is going to come out of this. What I want more than anything is a good night's sleep, and I haven't had one for 15 years. So, what possible good could come out of this? I have no idea.

I'm never going to speak of that day again with anyone, ever. I have fully accounted for myself in statements and that has been pored over and dissected by prosecutors and police forces. It is not fair for me to have to explain myself all over again.

My mental health is not the best and I think it is unreasonable for the MoD to expect me to go over these things over and over and over."

Major Campbell took a swipe at the disgraced lawyer Phil Shiner, who was struck off for hounding soldiers by stating deaths of Iraqi civilians have been marred by the 'Phil Shiner effect'.

"After years of bad investigating and all the money which has exchanged hands, the incentives there were for people to make allegations against British soldiers. It would be impossible now for an investigation to be fully agreed on. "

Major Campbell still serves in the Royal Engineers despite suffering injuries in Afghanistan. He has waived his right to anonymity and said his 21-year career had been poisoned by the probes.

Public Interest Lawyers

One particular person, Phil Shiner, was disqualified in his absence after a two-day hearing at the solicitors disciplinary tribunal in London in February 2017. Shiner was an Iraq human rights lawyer and was struck off by the Solicitors Regulation Authority over misconduct, and he was found guilty of multiple professional misconduct charges, including dishonesty and lack of integrity. He even had the audacity to try and save his own neck by amongst other things claiming he was too ill and in a fragile mental state to stand trial, and have the hearing in secret.

Following the trial, the Iraq Historic Allegations Team (IHAT) said it would now reassess cases referred by Shiner and his firm, Public Interest Lawyers (PIL), to decide whether they should still be pursued. An IHAT spokeswoman stated that the evidence presented at the solicitor's disciplinary tribunal casts serious doubt on the reliability of some of the remaining allegations. They would now be working closely with the Service Prosecuting Authority to determine which of the remaining allegations originating from PIL should now not be investigated. 'We will reach decisions as quickly as possible.'

If you were one of those who had been accused by PIL (and others looking to make their fortune off the back of false truths) of some form of barbaric and inhumane act, murder or any other such crime, an accused would have years thinking and wondering what was going to happen. Most of those accused were not spring chickens, with children and grandchildren, some even great grandchildren, so to look at 10-20 years in jail was terribly depressing, to say the least. This would have gone on to affect the whole family, and I would bet a few even had severe marriage or other serious problems, all due to a lawyer who was hell-bent on earning millions from the tax payer under legal aid and the cloak of doing good for the poor men, women and children of a war-torn area.

PIL was instrumental in passing on around 65% of the 3,392 allegations received by IHAT, which now has fewer than 250 active investigations. The tribunal found Shiner guilty of 22 misconduct charges. They were proved by the criminal standard of beyond reasonable doubt. Shiner was also ordered to pay for the full costs of the prosecution, starting with an interim down payment of £250,000. The Birmingham lawyer led the pursuit of legal claims against British troops for their treatment of Iraqi detainees after the 2003 invasion. Earlier courtroom victories over the case of Baha Mousa were followed by controversy around separate allegations, the most serious of which turned out to be wholly untrue.

Shiner claimed UK soldiers had captured, tortured and murdered innocent Iraqi civilians after the Battle of Danny Boy near Amara in 2004. A 2014 report by the al-Sweady inquiry demonstrated that those who died had been members of the Mahdi army militia, who ambushed a British patrol and were killed in exchanges of gunfire. Shiner subsequently admitted paying an Iraqi middleman to find claimants, a practice that is in breach of professional standards. The tribunal was told the men's purported witness accounts were fictitious and PIL stood to benefit from damages cases linked to the claim.

During the hearing, Andrew Tabachnik, prosecuting for the Solicitors Regulation Authority, accused Shiner of being "in a state of avoidance" in an attempt to prevent proceedings from going ahead in full. Shiner's defence to the dishonesty charges was effectively that he was not in full control of his mental faculties at the time and he did not know right from wrong, and what he was doing. Shiner was a sole director and 100% shareholder of PIL.

Shiner had admitted eight allegations of acting without integrity, including that he made "unsolicited direct approaches" to potential clients. He also admitted another allegation of acting recklessly. He did not attend the hearing, having written to the tribunal to say he was unwell and could not afford to pay for a defence lawyer. This from a solicitor who was only too keen in the past to put himself in front of a TV camera and argue for cases, knowing they were false and factless, which left the serving and former service personnel in a position of sheer hell. He was fine when he was collecting millions in legal aid, but when it came down to it he was unwell and unable to afford a defence lawyer. If he was that convinced the cases were able to stand up to scrutiny in court, why was he not defending himself, and stop the years of uncertainty and fear for those he was accusing?

Col James Coote, the officer commanding C Company of the 1st battalion, the Princess of Wales's Royal Regiment, when they deployed after Mahdi Army insurgents ambushed the Argyll and Sutherland Highlanders in May 2004 near Amara at the Battle of Danny Boy, stated that:

"These were highly armed men, well organised members of the Mahdi army who were out to kill British soldiers. It would be appropriate if Shiner apologised now to the soldiers and their families for what they have been through. I do not think that the legal profession should be allowed to operate in this manner with relative impunity. The last 10 years have been extremely distressing for the 200 or so soldiers who have been involved in this inquiry. They have found it difficult to understand why these allegations have been made. They were interviewed and cross-examined by the inquiry, which is a harrowing experience, particularly in the face of these allegations which were some of the most serious made since the Second World War. We have been under considerable pressure. The way the claims were investigated was unacceptable." He accused the firm of hounding British troops for a decade of sensationalism and the Iraqi claims had been investigated 'appropriately' at the time.

Paul Philip, Chief Executive of the Solicitors Regulation Authority, said:

"His misconduct has caused real distress to soldiers, their families and to the families of Iraqi people who thought that their loved ones had been murdered or tortured. More than £30m of public funds were spent on investigating what proved to be false and dishonest allegations."

Leigh Day pursued damages claims against the Ministry of Defence (MoD) over the alleged murder and torture of captives at the British-run camp following the battle. A five-year, £29million al-Sweady Inquiry earlier dismissed the claims as 'wholly baseless' and the product of 'deliberate and calculated lies'. The Solicitors Regulation Authority (SRA) alleges the law firm and solicitors Martyn Day and Sapna Malik continued to act for the claimants when they had evidence it was 'improper'.

COURAGE AFTER THE BATTLE

Paul Gott, representing Leigh Day at the tribunal stated that:

"The shredding of the English translation of a crucial document that would have exonerated British troops was down to 'human error."

He also blamed PIL for not handing over the OMS detainee list, which revealed that those captured were Mahdi army fighters and not local farmers or civilians.

Public Interest Lawyers (PIL) was founded in 1999 by Solicitor Phil Shiner. PIL soon established a reputation for having the tenacity and skill to litigate cases at the very highest level to ensure that the Rule of Law was upheld.

PIL soon began applying its exceptional brand of litigation to a wide range of Judicial Review cases. In 2002 PIL was instructed by CND to challenge the legality of the pending Iraq War. Shortly after this PIL was instructed by Colonel Daoud Mousa, the Father of Baha Mousa who had died in the custody of British troops (1QLR) in Basra shortly after his arrest, with his body bearing the hallmark of an horrendous ordeal, during which he was beaten and tortured. Those who were arrested with Baha Mousa were also tortured but survived. This led to the case of Al-Skeini and also to the Baha Mousa Inquiry. This was the beginning of a long and continuing legal battle surrounding the actions of UK forces in Iraq, during which a substantial number of Judicial reviews have been launched against the Secretary of State for Defence, each of them seeking an ECHR compliant investigation into some of the most egregious human rights breaches witnessed in modern times. The Court has recently ordered a number of Inquest-type investigations into a number of deaths, as well as ordering investigations into all of the alleged cases of unlawful detention and ill-treatment.

PIL acts in several cases arising out of the alleged unlawful actions of the UK armed forces in Afghanistan. These cases cover a wide range of issues and are presently being litigated in the Administrative Court. PIL also has cases arising out of the alleged unlawful actions of a multinational company in Africa. PIL provides a voice for the ordinary man, woman and child in Britain and beyond. We are living in a very challenging period in our history and we can expect to face a further number of difficult situations in which the executive will try to force a number of measures on a society that is already at breaking point. Our team at PIL is here to help you fight for your rights against the unfettered power of the executive when these situations arise, whether they arise on UK or foreign soil.

Extracts from the PIL website, July 2018

Northern Ireland

In May of 2018, veterans were furious to hear that the Prime Minister Theresa May had rejected any request for service personnel on Operation Banner (Northern Ireland Troubles) and she was pushing ahead with proposals to deal with the toxic legacy of the Northern Ireland Troubles without giving troops an amnesty.

Northern Ireland Secretary Karen Bradley launched a public consultation which excluded a chapter that would have limited investigations on hundreds of veterans, many now in their 60s and 70s.

The issue had earlier caused a Cabinet row, with some ministers concerned it would trigger a witch-hunt. The Government went ahead with the plans following pressure from Sinn Fein.

Sinn Féin ("ourselves" or "we ourselves") and Sinn Féin Amháin ("ourselves only / ourselves alone / solely us") are Irish-language phrases used as a political slogan by Irish nationalists in the late nineteenth and early twentieth century. It took its current form in 1970 after a split within the party (with the other side becoming the Workers' Party of Ireland) and has historically been associated with the Provisional Irish Republican Army (IRA).

Hundreds of elderly veterans now face the prospect of being quizzed about their actions four decades ago. Under the proposals, as soon as a legacy unit is set up to look at all past killings, it will have five years to investigate incidents. Northern Ireland sources say that means veterans won't be facing probes for years to come. But last night, Chelsea Pensioner David Griffin, 77, who was recently quizzed by police over the death of an IRA terrorist in an ambush in July 1972, accused the Government of treachery.

The former Royal Marine fired at the armed man in the heat of the battle to save his comrades but is now being investigated four decades later because the police have not closed the case. He said:

COURAGE AFTER THE BATTLE

"They (the Government) are putting the terrorists before us because they are scared to death the whole thing can start all over again. I'm just monumentally disappointed at the sheer treachery from the very top of our state. This is the 46th year I've had this hanging over my head."

A group of backbench MPs are calling for a statute of limitations which would stop the hounding of British war veterans. This would cover Northern Ireland, as well as Iraq and Afghanistan.

A No 10 spokesman said:

"As the Prime Minister has made clear, the current system in Northern Ireland isn't working. That is why we are consulting to get everyone's views on how we get it right."

Two senior military figures spoke out in disgust at the news. Lord Dannatt, head of the Army between 2006 and 2009, told the Sunday Express:

"War is hell. War is chaotic. And the IRA was at war with the UK."

Colonel Richard Kemp, who saw active duty in Bosnia, Iraq and Afghanistan as well as Northern Ireland, said:

"So outraged I am returning the prized commission given to me by the Queen."

Mrs Bradley insisted that the new mechanisms would be balanced, proportionate, transparent, fair and equitable. There was broad agreement that the current system was failing.

In February 2014, the Northern Ireland's first minister, Peter Robinson, threatened to resign after it emerged that the British government had written to more than 180 republican terror suspects to assure them they would not be prosecuted. Peter Robinson stated he was kept in the dark over the deal between Tony Blair's government and Sinn Fein, which saw so-called 'On the Runs' given the letters.

The crisis comes after suspect John Downey was told he would not face trial over the IRA bombing of Hyde Park in 1982, because he had one of the letters. The Provisional IRA detonated a nail bomb in the boot of a blue Morris Marina parked on South Carriage Drive in Hyde Park, central London. The blast killed four members of the Household Cavalry who were on ceremonial duty in the park: Roy Bright, Anthony Daly, Simon Tipper and Jeffrey Young. A separate bomb placed under a bandstand in Regent's Park went off two hours later, killing seven military bandsmen from the Royal Green Jackets.

COURAGE AFTER THE BATTLE

In 1987 Gilbert "Danny" McNamee was convicted of conspiring to cause explosions and sentenced to 25 years. He was released after serving 12 years under the Good Friday Agreement in 1998 and judges later ruled his conviction had been unsafe. British police said the fingerprints of John Anthony Downey, a convicted IRA member, had been found on parking tickets dispensed when the Marina was left in two NCP car parks shortly before the terror attack. Downey, now 62, and living in Donegal in the Republic of Ireland, has always protested his innocence.

In 2007 he received a letter from the British government which stated that the UK authorities were no longer seeking to prosecute him. In May 2013 Downey was arrested at Gatwick Airport. He was subsequently charged over the murder of four British soldiers and with causing an explosion, and was due to stand trial at the Old Bailey. Later Mr Justice Sweeney threw out the case, accepting defence argument that the trial would be an abuse of process. It emerged that the Police Service of Northern Ireland (PSNI) made what David Cameron described as a dreadful mistake. Despite the text of the letter, the force did know that Downey was still wanted by police on the mainland, but still sent him the letter of assurance in error.

The Good Friday Agreement granted early release to many republican and loyalist prisoners convicted of paramilitary crimes. But the status of the 'On the Runs' remained ambiguous. These were suspects who feared arrest for offences carried out before the 1998 agreement, or who had escaped from custody after being charged or convicted. 187 such letters had been sent to suspects, all of them nominated by Sinn Fein, following a deal with by Tony Blair's government. The issue was felt at the time to be a sticking point in the negotiations with Sinn Fein over the decommissioning of IRA weapons. Former Northern Ireland minister Peter Hain said:

"This was a critical part of the peace deal that has brought Northern Ireland from horror and evil to peace and hope and the idea that it could be unravelled in his (Downey's) case was astonishing to me."

The Labour government tried to find a legislative solution to the outstanding problem of 'On-the-Runs' in 2005, but a new law was rejected by all sides. The "administrative process" of sending letters continued.

"The letters do not in themselves grant immunity from prosecution."

But Mr Robinson has alleged that royal powers had also been used to pardon convicted republicans. He said:

"It appears that we are not just dealing with 'On the Runs' who received

letters, but we are also dealing with people who received the Royal Prerogative of Mercy that indicates there were offences involved. So we are not talking just about people who it is believed that the police did not have sufficient evidence to make a prosecution stick. That makes it a very serious matter."

The question must be asked that in this case the freedom to roam and get on with your life can be handed to a terrorist, but it cannot be handed to a serving or former member of the armed services, or its affiliates, for events whilst undertaking orders from the officers, who are the government's representatives, or directly from HM Government.

Why is it that they are happy to see service personnel hounded till their dying days but let terrorists roam the street, even those who have warrants against them prior to the letters being issued?

Ministry of Defence Position on the Investigations
On this subject, the Ministry of Defence has stated that they are supporting the work of both the Coroners' Inquests in Northern Ireland and Criminal Investigations concerning deaths and other potentially criminal matters during the Troubles. Some of these investigations involve veterans and serving personnel. Veterans and serving personnel may be contacted with a request for them to act as witnesses. In other cases, individuals have been questioned as suspects and in a very small number of cases, this has led to prosecutions being mounted.

The MoD continues to support both the investigations and the individual servicemen and veterans who have been approached by the investigating teams. This is normally in the form of witness tracing in support of the coroner. This process involves a search by the MoD of its records to identify and trace those individuals who may have knowledge of the incident or death being investigated. When potential witnesses can be identified and traced, they will normally be written to by a member of the Defence Inquest Unit (DIU), a specialist team established to manage the MoD's engagement with coroners. On occasion, the coroner's staff may choose to contact veterans directly. Should they do so, the advice and support offered by the MoD is still available to them (see below). With regards to criminal investigations, in most cases the investigating Home Office Police Forces have agreed to liaise with the MoD to ensure that the MoD is aware of any individuals being investigated or prosecuted. In such cases, the MoD will establish contact with the affected personnel to coordinate the necessary support.

If you are approached directly to support any of these investigations, you are advised to contact the Operational Legacy Support Team on 01264 382842 or 01264 382854. Although the team is based in Army HQ , it will support veterans from any Service.

For more information, please see the link below:

https://www.gov.uk/guidance/operational-legacy-investigations-and-inquests-help-for-veterans

ARMED FORCES COVENANT AND THE THIRD (CHARITY) SECTOR

The Official Armed Forces Covenant Promise in Full is shown below:

The Armed Forces Covenant

An Enduring Covenant Between

The People of the United Kingdom

Her Majesty's Government

– and –

All those who serve or have served in the Armed Forces of the Crown

And their Families

The first duty of Government is the defence of the realm. Our Armed Forces fulfil that
responsibility on behalf of the Government, sacrificing some civilian freedoms, facing
danger and, sometimes, suffering serious injury or death as a result of their duty.

Families also play a vital role in supporting the operational effectiveness of our
Armed Forces. In return, the whole nation has a moral obligation to the members of
the Naval Service, the Army and the Royal Air Force, together with their families.
They deserve our respect and support, and fair treatment.

Those who serve in the Armed Forces, whether Regular or Reserve, those who have
served in the past, and their families, should face no disadvantage compared to
other citizens in the provision of public and commercial services. Special consideration is appropriate in some cases, especially for those who have given
most, such as the injured and the bereaved.

This obligation involves the whole of society: it includes voluntary and charitable
bodies, private organisations, and the actions of individuals in supporting the Armed
Forces. Recognising those who have performed military duty unites the country and
demonstrates the value of their contribution. This has no greater expression than in
upholding this Covenant.

Source: https://www.gov.uk/government/uploads/system/uploads/attachment_data/file/578212/20161215-The-Armed-Forces-Covenant.pdf

What is the Armed Forces Covenant?
The Armed Forces Covenant has for the first time set out the nation's intention that former Armed Forces personnel should be treated fairly and not disadvantaged in comparison with their civilian peers or, in the case of those whose health has suffered as a result of their service, be entitled to special treatment. The Armed Forces Covenant is an agreement between the armed forces community, the nation and the government. It

encapsulates the moral obligation to those who serve, have served, their families and the bereaved. The covenant's underlying principles are that members of the armed forces community should face no disadvantage compared to other citizens in the provision of public and commercial services. In addition, that special consideration is appropriate in some cases, especially for those who have given the most, such as the injured or the bereaved.

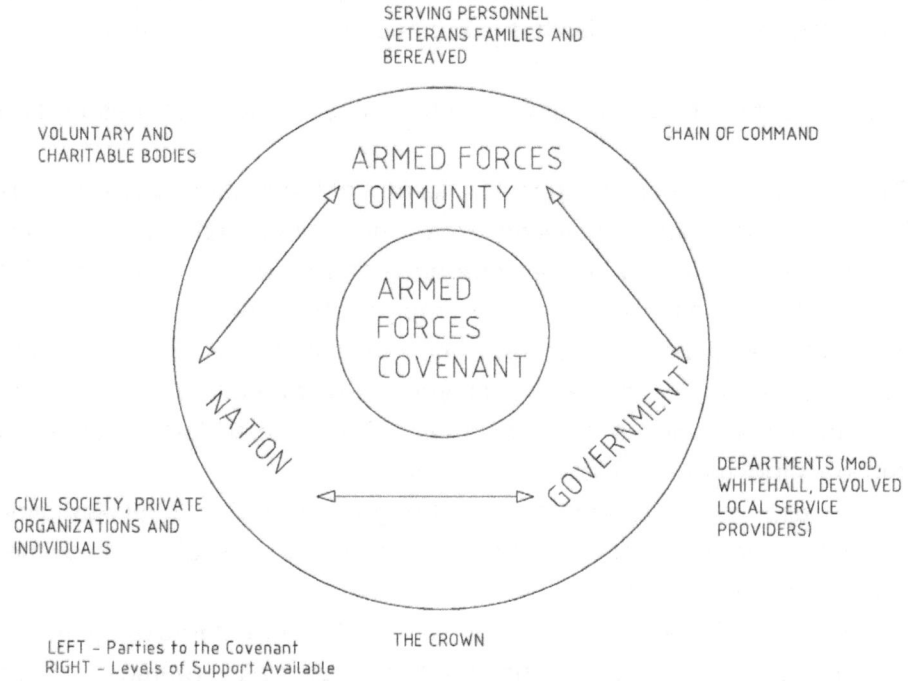

Covenant Parties and Support   Source: Lord Ashcroft Redraw and Clarify

For the purposes of the Covenant, the Armed Forces Community is defined as follows:

Regular Personnel – any current serving members of the Naval Services, (Including Royal Marines) Army or Royal Air Force
Volunteer and Regular reserves – Royal Naval Reserves, Royal Marine Reserves, Territorial Army, Royal Auxiliary Air Force, Royal Fleet Reserves, Army Reserve, Air Force Reserve, Royal Fleet Auxiliary and Merchant Navy (where they served on a civilian vessel whilst supporting the Armed Forces)

Veterans – Anyone who has served for at least a day in the Armed Forces as either a Regular or Reservist

Families of Regular Personnel, Reservists and Veterans – spouses, civil partners and children, and where appropriate can include parents, unmarried partners and other family members

Bereaved – The family members of service personnel and veterans who have died, whether that death is in connection to their service or not

Source: Our Community Our Covenant – Local Government Association

Since the initial launch in June 2011, as part of the Armed Forces Act 2011 (S2) local authorities in mainland Great Britain have signed a 'community covenant partnership' with their local armed forces and reserve forces. The community covenant is now known simply as the Armed Forces Covenant, which covers all aspect of society. Many local authorities have an 'Armed Forces Champion'. The role of a 'champion' is often to make sure that the local authority achieves its commitments to the armed forces community and any blockages are resolved.

The aims of the covenant are to bring together the Local Authorities and the armed forces community to work together to establish a covenant in their area in order to:

Encourage local communities to support the armed forces community in their areas and to nurture public understanding and awareness among the public of issues affecting the armed forces community

Recognise and remember the sacrifices faced by the armed forces community

Encourage activities which help to integrate the armed forces community into local life

Encourage the armed forces community to help and support the wider community, whether through participation in events and joint projects, or other forms of engagement

Covenants in each community may look quite different from one location to another. This is a scheme where one size does not fit all, and the nature of the support offered will be determined by both need and capacity.

From a business point of view, businesses can sign the covenant and can make a range of written and publicised promises to set out their support to members of the armed forces community who work in their business or access their products and services. The level of support will depend on the size and nature of the organisation, but the pledges may include encouraging reserve service and supporting employment of veterans and service spouses. All Armed Forces Covenants have to be signed by a person in authority who can ensure that commitments are implemented and maintained. There is also the possibility of a Gold, Silver and Bronze achievement award.

How it is supported?
In June 2013, the Chancellor announced that £10 million per annum would be allocated in perpetuity from the financial year 2015/16. This fund would be known as the Covenant Fund and it was to ensure the government's Armed Forces Covenant commitments. The Covenant Fund was to be completely new and was not a replacement for any previous grant schemes or funds. Funding priorities would be set annually by the Covenant Reference Group which is a stand-alone grant team drawing on experience from inside and outside the MOD.

The covenant is also a voluntary, non-binding commitment by local councils to support members of the armed forces community in their area. The covenant is also a written and publicised voluntary pledge from businesses and other organisations who wish to demonstrate their support for the armed forces community. The covenant can be signed by a business or other organisation of any size, and from any industry.

To address the priorities, funding is available for:
Small grants up to £20,000,
Primarily for community integration projects
Large grants up to £500,000,
For more strategic, higher impact projects
Decisions on both small and large grants are made by a national panel based on the recommendations of regional panels.

There are some Local Authorities, through the military charities and their Armed Forces Champions, that are combining together to form an Articles of Understanding. This would see a localized central point of requests for Covenant funding and better targeting of any funded events which are therefore less likely to be refused or waste the funding.

The Armed Forces Covenant wanted to improve the identity of the covenant and its meaning, so in January 2016 they launched an Armed Forces Covenant website and a media campaign which was launched in April : 2016.

https://www.armedforcescovenant.gov.uk/

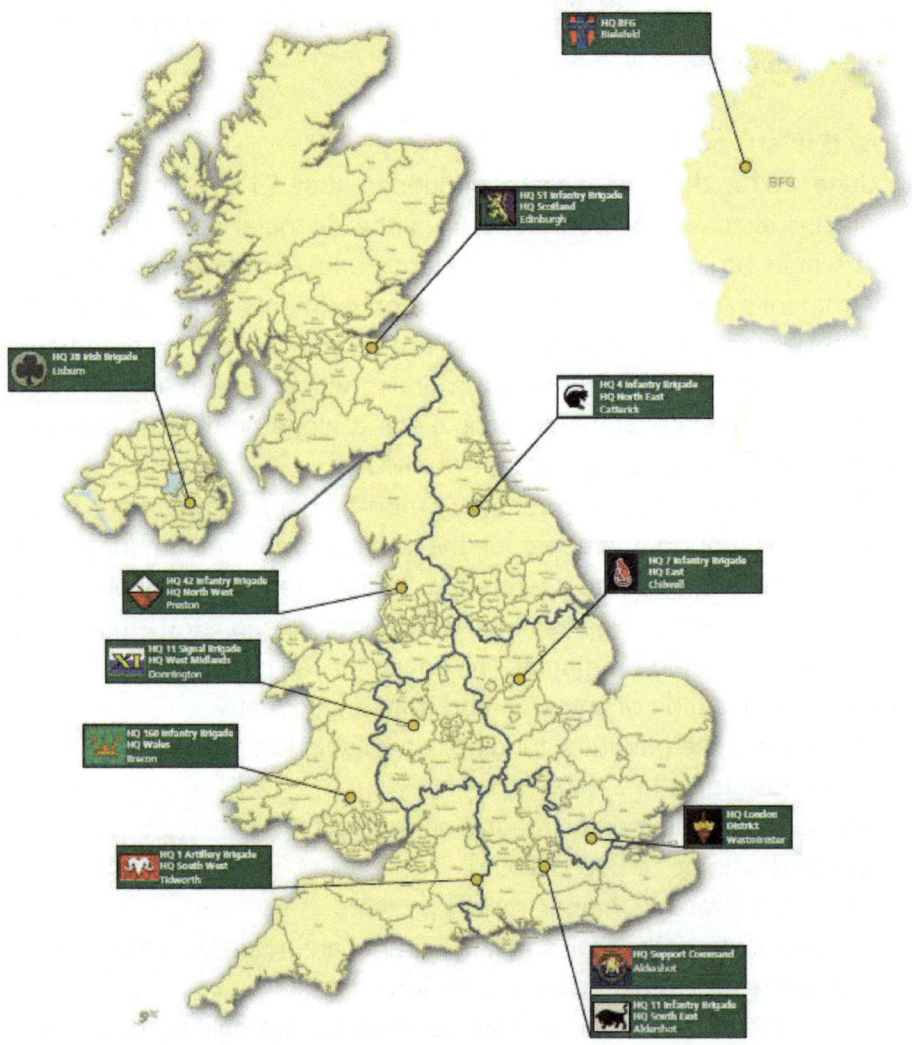

Armed Forces Covenant Board Areas (UK Government Military Covenant website)

According to Government figures, the Covenant in November 2016 is as shown below:

COVENANT IN NUMBERS 2016

The Armed Forces Covenant is a promise by the nation ensuring that those who serve or have served in the armed forces, and their families, are treated fairly.

Over 1300 UK organisations are now signed up to the covenant.

£22m Service Pupil Premium payments supporting 73,000 pupils.

100% Of Local Authorities in Great Britain have signed the covenant.

9,000 Service Personnel have become homeowners through Forces Help to Buy.

Over 150 Covenant Champions in the Services are raising awareness of the covenant within their units.

86% Of UK motor insurers are supporting overseas postings by committing to waive cancellation fees.

Over £270m Has been allocated to deliver covenant commitments since its launch in 2011.

4 Mobile phone providers are supporting overseas postings by committing to suspend contracts.

172 Projects funded to support the Armed Forces community in 2016.

Covenant Website launched to help the Armed Forces community find the help it needs: www.armedforcescovenant.gov.uk

Covenant in November 2016 (UK Government Military Covenant website)

Overseas Veterans Agencies

In comparison to the UK Armed Forces Covenant, the American, Canadian and Australian system is a little different.
https://www.va.gov/

The US has an estimated 21.2 million veterans, with 300,000 personnel transitioning in each of the next five years as the military is reduced in size. In service, personnel may access a subsidised home loan scheme and transitioning personnel may attend a five-day Transition Assistance Programme (TAP – not unlike the Career Transition Workshop provided by the UK's Career Transition Partnership) run by the Department of Labour. Each service administers its TAP separately, with the Army running a wrap-around programme known as Soldier 100 for Life. The TAP places significant responsibility on the individual to research and prepare prior to attendance, in order to achieve the required effect. Active duty National Guard and Reservists are treated as Regulars for transition entitlements and laws are in place to protect Reservists during operational deployments, but time away can be seen as damaging their long-term careers. Early Service Leavers get no transition support, while those made redundant receive only the standard package and no additional leave. Terminal leave is provided for entitled personnel based on time served plus a 30-day relocation leave package

The Veterans Agency (VA) is a department of state, separate to the Department of Defence (DOD), responsible for healthcare (through the Veterans' Healthcare Administration) and benefits and employment (through the Veterans' Benefits Agency). The VA's budget request for 2014 was $152.7 billion, and it has more than 332,000 employees. A number of negative comments made to the Review about UK policy and provision made reference to the US and the VA by comparison, so it is worth exploring some of the headlines in greater detail.

For those unable to find work, 26 weeks of unemployment benefit are paid by the DOD, then veterans devolve to the regular unemployment system. To support veteran hiring, the Department of Labour now has veterans' champions, and two schemes provide tax credits for employers to hire veterans. Returning Heroes provides a credit of up to $2,400 to employers who hire a veteran who has been unemployed for at least four weeks, expanded to give $5,600 to employers who hire veterans who've been jobless for over six months. The Wounded Warrior tax credit is worth up to $4,800 for companies who hire disabled veterans, doubled for the long-term unemployed, giving a tax break of up to $9,600 to companies that hire disabled veterans who've been unemployed longer than six months. Additionally, there is a policy of positive discrimination for veterans for jobs in many federal and state bodies.

Another major difference with the UK is the propensity of American Service Leavers to set up their own businesses. This is encouraged by the setting aside of some government contracts for companies owned by disabled veterans. Two US transition initiatives worthy of note are the Military.com website, which provides free transition assistance, and VetNet, a similar programme run by Syracuse University's Institute for Veterans and Military Families. These two models show how good transition support and advice can be made accessible to personnel, veterans and spouses for limited cost and maximum efficiency through online seminars, e-learning packages and networking tools to support job finding and entrepreneurship.

https://obamawhitehouse.archives.gov/blog/2013/09/25/blackstone-group-hosts-inaugural-veterans-hiring-summit

Canadian Vets

http://www.veterans.gc.ca/eng
http://truepatriotlove.com/

Canada has a care plan for veterans similar to that in the UK. With a national population of 35 million it has armed forces of 98,000 and 700,000 veterans, with 5,000 transitioning per year, of whom 20–25% have some form of medical issue. Canada has a Minister and Department for Veterans' Affairs responsible for information, pensions and benefits, transition support and some healthcare support in partnership with the Department for National Defence (DND). Canadian veterans have a similar pattern of employment to the rest of Canadian society, with an average employment rate of 89% and an initial drop in income on transition being common. Those who face difficulties during transition have a similar profile to their counterparts in the UK.

As a result of the 2006 Veterans Charter, Canadian veterans are supposed to have increased access to rehabilitation services, financial benefits, disability/health benefits, case management and transition services. A notable financial difference between the Charter and the previous Pension Act, however, is that the Charter offers a one-off lump-sum disability award, whereas the Pension Act offered a monthly tax-free pension for life and a survivor benefit. This means a whole-life reduction in compensation between the Charter and the Pension Act, which widens if a veteran lives longer, has more children, has a higher disability assessment or is released at a lower rank.

Canada has a much smaller military charitable sector than the UK and the US, but a notable player in the sector is Canada Company which, with the DND, provides the Military Employment Transition Programme (METP). The METP serves as a one-stop web portal for transition for serving personnel and veterans and acts as a bridge between business, community leaders and the forces. The programme seeks to educate prospective employers, including private and public sector organisations, on the benefits of hiring veterans and connects them to the service leaver population.

Aside from the transitional support charities, Canada has a fundraising, welfare and advocacy charity modelled on Help for Heroes called True Patriot Love (TPL). This is particularly worthy of mention because of its programme of multinational veterans' transition symposia which are proving central to growing an international community of understanding and practitioner network, vital to creating efficiency and effectiveness across the sector.

Canada is developing two tools of particular interest: one is the online automated veterans' benefits system mentioned in the US section above; the second is an online military skills translator being developed for the DND to focus on Canadian military course qualifications. As such, it bears further scrutiny due to the broader similarities between the Canadian and UK Armed Forces.

Australia

With a population of 23 million and a Regular and active Reserve Armed Forces of 80,000 (with a further 20,000 on standby) of whom 5–7,000 transition each year, Australia has a similar scale of transition and veterans to Canada. The government claims to provide all necessary services for transition and veterans (only those with operational service are known as veterans; all others are 'ex-services'), and charitable support is less central to provision and public perception. Australia's Department of Veterans' Affairs (DVA) has a similar remit to that of Canada and is similarly partnered with the Department of Defence, with a DVA presence on all military bases. The transition process starts on joining. Civil accreditation for military courses is widespread, and the education and preparation process is supported by the fact that the majority of personnel, married and single, live in the community rather than on a married quarter. The process of departure is supported by the Career Transition Assistance Scheme (CTAS), similar to CTP/TAP/CTAP, accessible from 12 months prior to departure, with three levels of financial and training entitlement depending on length of service.

Charity Sector
The modern armed forces charity sector can be traced back to the Soldiers' and Sailors' Families Association in 1885. Prior to SSFA, some smaller charitable funds connected to regiments of the British Army had already been established. For instance Sir James McGrigor, Director General of the Army Medical Service, set up two funds early in his tenure for widows (the Army Medical Friendly Society in 1816) and then orphans (the Army Medical Officers' Benevolent Society in 1820).

Following the outbreak of the First World War, there was an unprecedented growth and expansion of UK armed forces charities. Extra help from the public was certainly needed at a time when the British welfare state was not yet in existence. More than 6 million men served in the First World War, of which some 725,000 never returned. 1.75 million of those who did return had suffered some kind of disability and half of these men were permanently disabled.

This figure does not include the dire futures ahead for the wives and children, widows and orphans who were often left financially dependent. But even those who had come through the war relatively unscathed struggled with employment. As a result of the war, Britain's economy plummeted and in 1921 there were 2 million unemployed.

Between 1916 and 1920, 11,407 wartime charities were registered (another 6,492 were exempted from registration). Many of today's most well-known armed forces charities have their origins in that period and are still going today, almost 100 years later.

Blind Veterans UK (formerly St Dunstan's) was founded in 1915 by Sir Arthur Pearson, who then owned the Evening Standard and founded the Daily Express. Having lost his own sight through glaucoma, he was shocked at society's attitude to blindness. He decided to help those who had lost their vision in the First World War by giving them the care and rehabilitation they needed to lead constructive, self-sufficient lives.

BLESMA, The Limbless Veterans (formerly the British Limbless Ex-Service Men's Association) was founded in the years following the First World War when 40,000 service men who had lost limbs or eyes during the war faced mass unemployment and subsequent deprivation – 90% of the nation's war limbless could not find work. During this period the limbless gathered together in groups, determined that if society would not help them, they would help themselves. So the Limbless Ex-Service Men's Association was born and grew, finally achieving national status in 1932 as the British Limbless Ex-Service Men's Association.

RAF Benevolent Fund was founded by Lord Trenchard in 1919, a year after he founded the RAF, to provide direct welfare assistance to the 16,000 casualties, 2,600 widows and dependants, and 7,500 badly incapacitated men of the fledgling RAF, who often had little or no chance of employment for the rest of their lives.

The Not Forgotten Association was founded in 1920 by Marta Cunningham, American-born soprano singer and philanthropist, with the object of providing entertainment and recreation for the war-wounded to alleviate the tedium of their lives and give them something to which they could look forward.

The Royal British Legion was formed in 1921 by Lance Bombardier Tom Lister, who decided that the government of the day was not doing a good enough job of improving the lives of ex-service personnel. This eventually led to the formation of The British Legion from the amalgamation of four ex-service personnel organisations that had established themselves after the First World War. The charity was granted Royal status in 1971, and in 1981 extended its membership to serving members of Her Majesty's Forces, as well as ex-service personnel.

Modern estimates using registration figures from the Charity Commission put the number of armed forces charities registered in England and Wales at around 2,000 (Grenville 2013), with several thousand more unregistered. No figures were available for armed forces charities in Scotland or Northern Ireland.

Source: UK Armed Forces Charities – An Overview and Analysis (Sector Insight)

Defining the demographic profile of the armed forces community can be difficult tasks as you first have to define who is a veteran. The Latin root of the word comes from *vetus,* meaning 'old', and ex-service personnel can be very young. It is generally accepted, albeit not by everyone, that if a person has served even a day in the UK armed forces, excluding their dependants, they are classed as a veteran. This definition would be looked at by other former service personnel on a case by case basis for anyone calling themselves a veteran, and the reality of that person really is can someone call themselves a veteran or not if they have served a single day or just a month in the armed services?

In 2000, the UK government adopted the definition of veterans as 'Those who have served for at least a day in HM Armed Forces, whether as a Regular or as a Reservist.' This definition does not require personnel to have been deployed on active service or even that they have completed basic training.

Charitable giving has been an important manifestation of public support for the Forces since the Crimean War, when no particular provision was made for veterans by the state. Outside times of war, the Forces have been largely invisible. This was particularly the case during the 30-year-long operation in Northern Ireland, when service personnel were effectively hidden from the public for reasons of personal security. Only after 2001, the beginning of operations in Afghanistan, did the Armed Forces begin to receive significant public attention and sympathy. The number and nature of British casualties in Afghanistan and Iraq has in turn prompted a generous public response in the form of charitable giving.

There are around 2,050 directly Armed Forces-related charities in existence in the UK, with total reserves of over £1.1 billion. Many of these, such as Cadet Forces and military associations, are unrelated to service leavers and veterans. There are, however, about 350 whose objectives are relief-in-need, benevolence, resettlement, rehabilitation and mental health. This group has an annual income in the order of £400 million, though most of this is concentrated in the largest fifty. These charities range from the extremely large, such as one with an income of over £130 million, to one-person ventures. They cover a huge spectrum of need, are a mix of general and niche provision, national organisations and local, and range from the very competent to the ineffective.

Just over half (186) of the 350 Forces charities providing care and benevolence, including the biggest names in the sector, such as ABF

COURAGE AFTER THE BATTLE

The Soldiers' Charity and the Royal British Legion, are members of the Confederation of British Service and Ex-Service Organisations (COBSEO). These 186 organisations account for over 90% of all Armed Forces Third Sector income. The stated objectives of COBSEO act as a point of contact for external agencies to the members of COBSEO and support the needs and opinions of its member organisations, individually and collectively at central and local government levels. The member charities of COBSEO are organised into eight clusters.

These are:
    Research (led by the Forces in Mind Trust)
    Help Lines (led by the Forces in Mind Trust)
    Residential and Care Homes (led by the Royal British Legion)
    Housing (led by Haig Homes)
    Welfare Delivery (led by SSAFA Forces Help)
    Membership (led by the Royal Air Forces Association)
    In-Service cluster (led by the British Forces Foundation)
    Foreign and Commonwealth (led by the Army Families Federation)

Aligned with COBSEO is the Forces in Mind Trust (FiMT), whose purpose is to promote the successful transition of Armed Forces personnel, and their families, into civilian life. FiMT has been awarded a Big Lottery grant of £35 million for this work and is presently involved in commissioning research and awarding grants to support projects that enhance the understanding of transition, including related mental health and wellbeing issues. It aims to use this knowledge to advocate appropriate change to improve the likelihood of successful transition. Its first two reports were published in 2013 and they are referred to extensively in this review.

First, professionals working in the field as well as service leavers endured serious hardships on operations, and the feeling that others must be in greater need than them contributes to making them reluctant to seek help. Typical comments are:

"I've got a book full of charities but I've never used it. It's degrading to ask." Recent service leaver

"I don't want to take out of the pot when there's guys who have lost

arms and legs."

"People ask me why I didn't go for benefits, but it was like waving a flag – I've failed, let my family down, my mates who said I'd be a success. An embarrassment to the Service."

"It's instilled into you when you join up – pride, self-image. It's difficult to turn around and say 'I can't cope'. People reach rock bottom before they come to us. We're trying to design our services to stop that. Support has to be carefully designed so they don't feel social-worked."

"I was sat in a police cell, sectioned for a month, and the community psychiatric nurse gave me a card for Combat Stress. I rang it and they helped me immediately and got me here [named charity]."

"Most of the time I was on the streets, stairwells, stuff like that. It was a big struggle. I didn't know about this place. I went to get a meal, this place at a church, and a woman there rang the Legion. The area caseworker came and saw me, and four days later I got a call from [named charity]."

Another typical concern that is of grave importance is to consider the service leaver's family in the transition process. This is particularly the case for the Army which, being more mobile than the other services, provides large numbers with housing, welfare, education and healthcare.

"During my husband's transition, there was no support for families – budgeting, housing concerns, schools… My husband had trouble adjusting to the stress of it all and started drinking, which led to him becoming depressed and he lost a job. This led to him contacting Combat Stress."

"Do you have to be registered to go to a doctor? I thought you could just tip up."

"I'm only getting to grips now with paying Council Tax. I got a massive bill through. If someone had told me I was meant to be paying this, I would have done." The people giving advice are people who have been in the Army for 30 years. That's been their life. I know more about civilian life than they do!"

"My friends are either like me – bought a house and got them ready, knowing one day the game was over - or put their heads in the sand and totally ignored it."

Over the years there have been a number of comments about the armed forces charity sector which have been explored by various people and these include:

Claim
There are too many armed forces charities;
Answer
This may be driven by a lack of understanding of the huge diversity of armed forces charities and the assistance they can give to both the individual, on the one-to-one basis of the smaller charities, and the large back-up systems of the larger national charities. There is also the plethora of 'unwanted items' bags being posted in the letterbox, people standing in the street collecting, and all manner of other collection points and systems. Admittedly some of these are from unscrupulous people who have no intention of paying the money to charity, but this does nothing for the public opinion.

Claim
New entrants into the sector have created unwarranted competition and have taken income away from more established charities;
Answer
New entrants into the sector are having a generally positive effect, and they are creating more avenues of assistance to the veteran. This, in effect, creates more growth in the sector and it is hard to believe that a small one-man band or group will remove monies from a national well established charity.

Claim
There is little or no coordination in the sector.
Answer
The armed forces charity sector shows greater collaboration and cooperation than other charitable sub-sectors. There are many examples of partnership working and examples of financial support provided by armed

forces charities to other armed forces charities. The benevolent grant-making process in particular appears to be highly coordinated and flexible in responding to the needs of beneficiaries, with most of the casework generally routed through SSAFA or The Royal British Legion.

We now have the Veterans Gateway, and in Liverpool there is a particularly good example in the Veterans HQ (Formerly Liverpool Veterans).

The UK Armed Forces Charities Report in 2014 noted that the geographical distribution of armed forces welfare charities was as follows:

There are 278 armed forces welfare charities registered in England and Wales. These charities provide a wide range of support to members of the armed forces community who are in need, through the provision of welfare services (such as housing and care homes) and/or grants for relief-in-need purposes.

The majority of these charities have their main headquarters in Greater London and the South East of England (59%) (see figure 5.4). This reflects the pattern seen in the UK voluntary sector as a whole, with over 10 times more voluntary organisations per 1,000 people in some London Boroughs versus Blackpool (Clarke et al. 2012).

Only 6% of armed forces welfare charities have their main headquarters in the North West. Even fewer have their headquarters in Yorkshire and the Humber (3%), Wales (3%), the North East (1%) and Scotland (1%) (see Figure 5.4).

Source: UK Armed Forces Charities / Sector Insight Report in 2014

INVICTUS GAMES

Invictus is an adjective in Latin meaning 'unconquerable' or 'unsubdued'. It embodies the fighting spirit of the wounded, injured and sick service personnel and what these tenacious men and women can achieve, post injury. The Games harness the power of sport to inspire recovery, support rehabilitation, and generate a wider understanding and respect for those who serve their country.

Most of us will never know the full horrors of combat. Many service personnel suffer life-changing injuries, visible and non-visible, whilst serving their country. How do these extraordinary people find the motivation to move on and not be defined by their injuries? How can they be recognised for their achievements and not given sympathy? On a trip to the Warrior Games in the USA in 2013 Prince Harry noticed how the power of sport could help physically, psychologically and socially. His mind was made up. London would host the inaugural Invictus Games, an international sporting event for wounded, injured and sick service personnel.

"These Games have shone a spotlight on the 'unconquerable' character of service men and women and their families and their 'Invictus' spirit. These Games have been about seeing competitors sprinting for the finish line and then turning around to clap the last man in. They have been about teammates choosing to cross the line together, not wanting to come second, but not wanting the other guys to either. These Games have shown the very best of the human spirit." Prince Harry

Invictus Games competitors are the men and women who have come face-to-face with the reality of making a sacrifice for their country. They are the mothers, fathers, husbands and wives who put their lives on the line and suffered life-changing injuries. These people are the embodiment

COURAGE AFTER THE BATTLE

of everything the Invictus Games stands for. They have been tested and challenged, but they have not been overcome. They have proved they cannot be defeated. They have the willpower to persevere and conquer new heights. The Games shone a spotlight on the sacrifices these men and women made serving their country, and their indefatigable drive to overcome.

Generations have drawn on the words of William Ernest Henley's poem for strength during times of adversity. Henley was himself an amputee and the poem reflects his long battle with illness. The title means "unconquered" and the 16 short lines of the poem encapsulate the indefatigable human spirit, which is at the heart of the Invictus Games.

> Out of the night that covers me,
> Black as the Pit from pole to pole,
> I thank whatever gods may be
> For my unconquerable soul.
> In the fell clutch of circumstance
> I have not winced nor cried aloud.
> Under the bludgeonings of chance
> My head is bloody, but unbowed.
> Beyond this place of wrath and tears
> Looms but the Horror of the shade,
> And yet the menace of the years
> Finds, and shall find, me unafraid.
> It matters not how strait the gate,
> How charged with punishments the scroll.
> I am the master of my fate:
> I am the captain of my soul.

In 2004 it was announced that UK Sport, the British Army and the English Institute of Sport have joined forces to launch a ground breaking talent programme aimed at identifying future Olympic medallists from within the ranks. This co-operation became the Army Elite Sports Programme (AESP) launched using a £1.4m donation the British Army received for providing some of the security at the London 2012 Olympic and Paralympic Games.

This new collaboration reached out to men and women in the various disciplines that would form the 2012 Olympic Games and then onto successive Olympics to the Tokyo games in 2020. UK Sport and the English Institute of Sport have a proven track record for identifying talent, having run ten national athlete recruitment projects, assessing over 7,000 athletes who were previously unknown to the UK World Class system. These projects discovered 19 athletes who represented Great Britain at the 2012 London Olympic and Paralympic Games.

Invictus - The Beginning
On a long flight home from a shortened tour of Afghanistan, courtesy of the press, a young second Lt from the Household Cavalry was on the cramped aircraft with many other service personnel. Up front was a curtained off area which housed the wounded, and this young second was keen to glimpse what was behind the curtain. As the plane covered the many miles en-route home the curtain twitched and moved as people entered or left the area. It was at this time that the Second Lt had a glimpse of what was behind there. He had not seen death and severe injury, usually by IED, before as his only contact was over the radio as callsign W67 (Widow six seven) as he called in air support for the ground troops or an "Op Vampire" which signalled the urgent need for blood.

This young second Lt is Prince Harry and he was not a happy soul, returning home early due to press intrusion, and leaving his men behind. The plane landed in daylight at Birmingham to offload the three wounded men who would be taken to Selly Oak Hospital. The aircraft then made its way to RAF Lyneham where Prince Harry was met by Princes Charles and William. Prince Harry was driven back to Windsor and he could not stop thinking about the men he had seen on the flight and dropped off at Birmingham.

He had to do something, but what? He had more questions than answers at this stage. Prince Harry returned to do a second tour of Afghanistan in 2012-13 as a co-pilot of an Apache helicopter.

In May of 2013 Prince Harry attended the Warrior Games in America, where service personnel had their own games to compete in. The Warrior games had a handful of invited foreign personnel and it has to be said the crowds were a little sparse. This is where Harry had his 'Eureka moment' and thought the idea was good, but could be improved upon, so he did the only thing which came natural to a service person in instances like this - steal the idea and improve on it. And so the games begin.

COURAGE AFTER THE BATTLE

At this point Prince Harry was unaware that the Warrior Games had been stolen from the North-West England Limbless Sports Club (NWELSC) which had held a sports day for limbless service men since 1922 and had been opened by Earl Haig, who was the commander of the British forces on the western front in the First World War. The NWELSC had such games as the norm in that time period such as football, obstacle courses, walking races and high jump, which seems a little odd given the early days of prosthetics then.

From that point rehabilitation of service men in the form of sport was being considered a jolly good idea. A German Neurosurgeon from the Stoke Mandeville Hospital, called Dr Guttmann, organised the Stoke Mandeville Games. The games ran from 1948 and in 1960 were held alongside the Olympics in Rome. They were to become the modern-day Paralympics and some of the contestants in the Invictus Games progress to the Paralympic Games, thereby creating the circle of life and connections from 1922 to today's games.

As his idea progressed, Prince Harry had to consider how he was going to pull off the impossible.

The London Olympics were less than a year away and this would be the ideal location for the inaugural Invictus Games, but how was going to pull this off in just under a year without any specialist help or knowledge how to organise a large athletic event?

To Harry, the games were not just the mental but also the social aspect of service personnel being in an environment they could relate to. In most cases service personnel are far from understood by civilians, and this adds to the stresses of coping with life in civvy street. The games would be of a service mentality and black humour, which a civilian would not understand and more likely take offence with when comments are made about injuries and how they were obtained. The games would be a chance for the public to show their thanks for all their sacrifices.

Prince Harry turned to Sir Keith Mills, the man who invented Air Miles and of late was the deputy chair of LOCOG, the London Organising Committee of the Olympic Games and Paralympic Games. The first meeting was in November 2013 and Prince Harry broke the news that he wanted the games to be held in September 2014, less than 12 months away. With no venues, capital or other piece of the puzzle in place, this was going to be a hard task to complete. Sir Keith Mills asked Prince Harry to be hands-on, to stand any chance of this succeeding, and Prince Harry had already decided to be fully involved. In January 2014, Prince Harry left the Army and devoted himself to the Invictus Games full time.

It is only right that we acknowledge the initial board members who pulled off the inaugural games in 2014, less than a year. Those board members were:-

Prince Harry
The Prince had the games as an important part of a broader legacy of support, through a combination of ongoing care, training and employment opportunities, to the well-being of those men and women who have served their country.

Sir Keith Mills GBE
Former deputy chairman of the London Organising Committee of the Olympic Games and Paralympic Games. He founded Air Miles International and is formerly Chairman of Loyalty Management Group Ltd, the company which owns and manages the Nectar programme. Sir Keith is Chairman of the charitable sport for development Sported Foundation and a Trustee of the Royal Academy.

Sara Donaldson OBE
Strategy Director at Unspun and has overseen the delivery of many of the UK's highest profile sporting campaigns and media launches. Sara was the Chief Operating Officer of the Production Company for the London 2012 Olympic and Paralympic Opening and Closing Ceremonies.

Lt Gen Andrew Gregory CB
A serving Army Officer and the Chief of Defence Personnel, with responsibility for People policy for Service Personnel, MOD Civil Servants and Veterans, including the Defence Recovery Capability for wounded, injured and sick Service Personnel. He represents Defence on the Invictus Games Board.

Debbie Jevans CBE,
CEO of England Rugby 2015. She was formerly Director of Sport for the London 2012 Olympic and Paralympic Games. Debbie is also a member of the All England Lawn Tennis Club's Committee of Management and

Championships Committee, as well as a Sport England Board member.

Edward Lane Fox
Former captain in the Household Cavalry who served in Bosnia and Iraq. After leaving the Army he worked at financial communications firm RLM Finsbury, before joining the staff of the Royal Household in 2013.

Terry Miller
Was on the general council for the London Organising Committee of the Olympic Games and Paralympic Games. Prior to joining LOCOG Terry spent 17 years at Goldman Sachs in London as a partner and international general counsel. She was awarded an OBE in the 2013 New Year's Honours List for her services to the London 2012 Games.

Guy Monson
Has been chief investment officer at Sarasin & Partners LLP since 1997 and a managing partner at the company since 2008. He is a trustee of The Royal Foundation of The Duke and Duchess of Cambridge and Prince Harry.

Roger Mosey
Was the BBC's Director of London 2012 Olympic Games coverage and former BBC editorial director. He is now master of Selwyn College, Cambridge.

General Sir Nick Parker KBE CBE
A former British Army officer who served as Commander Land Forces (formerly Commander-in-Chief, Land Forces). He was also charged with organising the military support provided by the Armed Forces during the London 2012 Games.

Mary Reilly
A chartered accountant and former Partner at Deloitte LLP. She was previously Chair of the London Development Agency and was also on the Board of the London Organising Committee of the Olympic Games and Paralympic Games.

Chris Townsend OBE
Was the Commercial Director for the London Organising Committee of the Olympic and Paralympic Games where he was responsible for raising £2.4

billion pounds for LOCOG as well as sponsorship, ticketing and licensing. He previously worked at BSkyB and Transport for London and is now Chief Executive of BDUK, the Government's rural broadband project and Executive Board Director of DCMS.

Source: Invictus Games Web Site for the 2014 Invictus Games

Corporate Sponsorship, as in any big event, would have to be sourced and most companies allocate the funds 12-18 months in advance. However, Land Rover, Jaguar, BT, Fisher House Foundation, Ottobock, Price Waterhouse Coopers, and YESSS Electrical became official sponsors. The Royal Foundation of the Duke and Duchess of Cambridge and Prince Harry and the Ministry of Defence were the founding partners of the 2014 Invictus Games.

What was the name to be? Many names were thrown around and Major General Buster Howes, the Defence Attaché at the British Embassy in Washington DC who had first invited Prince Harry to the Warrior Games, suggested Invictus. The logo was created and picked out the "I AM" which were so prominent in the last two lines of Henley's poem.

6 March 2014 The Royal Foundation of The Duke and Duchess of Cambridge and Prince Harry, in partnership with the Ministry of Defence, announces that the 'Invictus Games' presented by Jaguar Land Rover, an international sporting event for wounded, injured and sick service personnel, will take place in London from 10 -14 September 2014. It will see more than 300 wounded, injured and sick servicemen and women, serving and veteran, competing in the Queen Elizabeth Olympic Park and the Lee Valley Athletics Centre, thanks to the Mayor of London, the London Legacy Development Corporation and the Lee Valley Regional Park Authority. Sports within the games will be Athletics, Archery, Wheelchair Basketball, Road Cycling, Indoor Rowing, Wheelchair Rugby, Swimming, Sitting Volleyball and a driving challenge. Teams will be invited from the armed forces of 13 nations that have served alongside each other, with relative newcomers to adaptive sport joining advanced athletes in an inclusive programme.

The first Invictus Games almost ended in disaster at the last hurdle. G4S, who were to have covered the security element, pulled out at the last possible moment so in stepped the armed forces into a position they knew well - security. As a result, a highly qualified security screen was around the games amongst the present-day threats of terror attack, and should the unthinkable happen, then the games were well protected by their own.

The Invictus Games Orlando 2016 featured 500 competitors from 15 nations: Afghanistan, Australia, Canada, Denmark, Estonia, France, Georgia, Germany, Iraq, Italy, Jordan, Netherlands, New Zealand, United Kingdom and the United States of America.

In September 2014, Prince Harry opened the inaugural Invictus Games with three military bands - The Irish Guards, Central Band of the RAF, and the Band of Her Majesty's Royal Marines, Collingwood. The Red Arrows performed a fly past, the Queen's Colour Squadron of the RAF gave a rifle demonstration, the King's Troop of the Royal Horse Artillery a display and the actor Idris Elba recited Henley's poem with the final lines, 'I am the master of my fate, I am the captain of my soul' reflected in the I Am badges worn by the competitors.

In November of that year, the bidding process started for the host of the 2016 and 2017 games. Such is the planning process, and it shows how hard the initial board had worked to pull off this feat of endurance in less than 12 months. At the opening of the 2016 games, there was the famous video or the President and First Lady of the United States, Barack and Michelle Obama, mentioning to Prince Harry that he should be careful what he wished for. This was in reference to Prince Harry noting to the President and First Lady they should 'bring it at the Invictus Games'. The President pointed to the camera whilst service personnel behind him made scary faces and mimed a 'boom' microphone drop.

Princes Harry initially wondered how he was going to reply to this and get the upper hand, so to speak. His reply came courtesy of Her Majesty Queen Elizabeth the Second, his grandmother. By way of reply, the Queen was seen watching the video on Prince Harry's mobile and saying witheringly, 'Oh Really. Please!' whilst Harry dropped his own imaginary microphone and sent the boom back to America.

Harry's opening speech was a less formal dress occasion than the original collar and tie back in 2014.

"I'm a long way from London tonight, but when I look out and see so many familiar faces, servicemen and women, their friends and families and all the people who have got them here, I feel like I am at home. I joined the army because for a long time I just wanted to be one of the guys. But what

COURAGE AFTER THE BATTLE

I learned through serving was that the extraordinary privileges of being a prince gave me an extraordinary opportunity to help my military family. That's why I had to create the Invictus Games – to build a platform for all those who have served to prove to the world what they have to offer.

Over the next four days you will see things that in years past just wouldn't have been possible. You will see people who by rights should have died on the battlefield, but instead they are going for gold on the track or in the pool. You will be inspired, you will be moved, and I promise you will be entertained.

While I have your attention, though, I want to briefly speak about an issue that for far too many of you is shrouded in shame and fear. An issue that is just as important for many of you watching at home as it is for those of you in this stadium tonight. It is not just physical injuries that our Invictus competitors have overcome; every single one of them will have confronted tremendous emotional and mental challenges.

When we give a standing ovation to the competitor with the missing limbs, lets also cheer our hearts out for the man who overcame anxiety so severe he couldn't leave the house. Let's cheer for the woman who fought through posttraumatic stress and let's celebrate the soldier who was brave enough to get help for his depression.

Over the next four days we will get to know these amazing competitors. They weren't too tough to admit that they struggled with the mental health, and they weren't too tough to get the help they needed. To those of you watching at home and who are suffering from mental illness in silence, whether a veteran or a civilian, a mum or a dad, a teenager or a grandparent, I hope you see the bravery of our Invictus champions who have confronted invisible injuries, and I hope you are inspired to ask for the help that you need.

To end, can I just say thank you to all of you guys. You are fierce competitors. You are role models that any parent would be proud to have their children follow. You've made me a better person. You are about to inspire the world and I'm proud to call you my friends. So let's put on a hell of a show in memory of all of our fallen comrades who didn't make it back. We are Invictus."

Throughout the short history of the Games, no matter what country you come from you are all service personnel past or present. An example of

COURAGE AFTER THE BATTLE

this was shown in the 2016 Games in Orlando, Florida. It had taken the ill-equipped Afghanistan team 24 hours to reach the location of the Games and they had not even met their team manager or had any coaches with them. In addition to this, as an Invictus Games team, they had no prosthetic limbs and hardly any sports clothing to their name, but they had travelled and were willing to compete for their country.

As with any service family, the other teams rallied round and assisted the Afghanistan team as best they could. The Americans covered the cost of the flights, hotels and food and the Australian power lifters "spotted" (watched and were the safety element) for their Afghan competitors, along with encouraging them. When the Afghans were above the French on the score tables during the sitting volley ball between the two nations, the crowd cheered for both teams. This is despite the 21st century prosthetics worn by the French and the twenty plus years old hooks and prosthetics worn by the Afghans. Will Reynolds, the US team captain who lost part of his left leg in Baghdad, said "I have got eight legs, more than I need. The general consensus was that there are other pieces of equipment that is happily or never used, so this was donated to a programme which would collect prosthetics and send them to countries such as Afghanistan. which desperately needs them.

The phrase *life changing* is almost seen as a negative one as the word *change* implies a loss of something or a reduction in its use, which both result in changes to the person's quality of life. The Invictus Games and the spirit shown by all service personnel for their family have shown that this phrase is exactly the opposite, and provides new avenues for the life ahead. Most of the competitors have stared death right in the face and effectively shown it the door.

Given this near-death experience, Prince Harry remarked in his closing speech that:

"By definition, service men and women are highly skilled, well trained and motivated people. Many of those injured are young men and women with their whole lives ahead of them. For those no longer able to serve in the Armed Forces, the future is often uncertain. We should be there to support them, if or when they need it. For a few this may mean long term physical and mental support, but for the majority, this means fulfilling employment. Not special treatment, but to be treated as they were before *injury, with respect, admiration and recognition of their considerable talent.*

And just what that talent could do! Imagine an Invictus Games competitor comes to talk to a school, for example. Imagine the sparks which that talk could fan in a child listening to those stories. Imagine those same stories being told to a youth group, or in a prison, or even an ordinary office environment. We bemoan the slickness and emptiness of our politicians, but here we are, a group which actually has something to teach us, if only we will listen."

Para Athletes

If like me you have wondered how these exceptional athletes compete, and the various categories they compete in, I have compiled a very loose description as to the meaning of the categories. A system was compiled to minimize the impact of any Impairments on sport performance and to ensure the success of an athlete is determined by skill, fitness, power, endurance, tactical ability and mental focus, and ensures everyone competes on a level playing field with no additional advantage to any one athlete.

There are eight different types of physical impairments in the Paralympic Movement:

Impaired muscle power: With impairments in this category, the force generated by muscles, such as the muscles of one limb, one side of the body or the lower half of the body is reduced, e.g. due to spinal-cord injury, spina bifida or polio.

Impaired passive range of movement: Range of movement in one or more joints is reduced in a systematic way. Acute conditions such as arthritis are not included.

Loss of limb or limb deficiency: There is a total or partial absence of bones or joints as a consequence of amputation due to illness or trauma or congenital limb deficiency (e.g. dysmelia).

Leg-length difference: Significant bone shortening occurs in one leg due to congenital deficiency or trauma.

Short stature: Standing height is reduced due to shortened legs, arms and trunk, which are due to a musculoskeletal deficit of bone or cartilage structures.

Hypertonia: Hypertonia is marked by an abnormal increase in muscle tension and reduced ability of a muscle to stretch. Hypertonia may result from injury, disease, or conditions which involve damage to the central nervous system (e.g. cerebral palsy).

Ataxia: Ataxia is an impairment that consists of a lack of co-ordination of muscle movements (e.g. cerebral palsy, Friedreich's ataxia).

Athetosis is generally characterized by unbalanced, involuntary movements and a difficulty maintaining a symmetrical posture (e.g. cerebral palsy, choreoathetosis).

In addition to the main areas above, any athlete who wishes to compete and has a physical, visual or intellectual impairment is also included in the Paralympic Movement.

Visual impairment: Visual Impairment occurs when there is damage to one or more of the components of the vision system, which can include:

impairment of the eye structure/receptors

impairment of the optic nerve/optic pathways

impairment of the visual cortex

Intellectual Impairment: Athletes with an intellectual impairment are limited in regards to intellectual functions and their adaptive behaviour, which is diagnosed before the age of 18 years.

Source: Layman's Guide to Paralympic Classification

LIST OF CHARITIES (AUGUST 2018)

Listed within this section is a list of national charities and other useful information that are able to assist in your hour of need. It is by no means a definitive list but it is intended to help you in gaining any assistance you may require. No matter how big or small or insignificant you feel your query is, all military charities are there to help you, but you need to make the initial approach. As a former Royal Marine myself, I know how pride and stubbornness can get in the way and you will "sort it myself" or "I will be fine". Please bite the bullet and ask. You will be surprised at what help is out there and how understanding the people will be towards you and your needs.

MoD 24 Hour free Military Mental Health Helpline

0800 323 4444

Veterans Gateway

0808 802 1212 Website: www.veteransgateway.org.uk

Armed Forces Act 2011

http://www.legislation.gov.uk/ukpga/2011/18/contents

https://www.gov.uk/government/publications/2010-to-2015-government-policy-armed-forces-covenant

AA Veterans Support

AA Veterans Support is a Northern Ireland-based charity set up to provide help and support for veterans and their families throughout Northern Ireland. The charity aims to provide practical, training, emotional and financial support to anyone who is serving or has ever served, along with their families.

http://www.aavsni.com

info@aavsni.com

Unit C3 Edenderry Industrial Estate
326 Crumlin Rd
Belfast
BT14 7EE

028 9074 7071

ABF The Soldiers' Charity
ABF The Soldiers' Charity, giving lifetime support to serving and former soldiers and their families. Includes making grants to individuals and specialist charities that help ex-soldiers and their families, including financial assistance to relieve hardship, grants for living costs, emergency needs, debt relief, cCare home fees, home adaptations, furnishing and equipment, mobility assistance, funding holiday breaks.

http://www.soldierscharity.org

info@soldierscharity.org

Mountbarrow House
6-20 Elizabeth Street
London
SW1W 9RB
0207 901 8900

AF & V Launchpad Ltd

Launchpad provides veterans (and their partners) of all services with affordable, self-contained flats arranged in managed houses in Newcastle (34 flats) and Liverpool (52 flats). An important part of the process is integration with the local community and mutual support. All this is provided to enable the veterans to avoid homelessness, unemployment and social exclusion.

http://www.afv-launchpad.co.uk

enquiries@afv-launchpad.co.uk

3 Hansard Mews
Holland Park
London

0300 1111 238

Aggie Weston's

Aggie Weston's is dedicated to supporting the serving men and women of the Royal Navy, Royal Marines and their families.

http://aggies.org.uk/

office@aggies.org.uk

Castaway House
311 Twyford Avenue
Portsmouth
PO2 8RN

02392 650505

Alabaré Christian Care and Support

Alabaré Christian Care and Support; ending homelessness for veterans by providing a pathway of accommodation and support to enable them to move on to a successful, independent and fulfilling life. They offer temporary supported accommodation – both higher and lower support homes, through which residents can transition to independence - and signposting to specialist support services.

http://www.alabare.co.uk

enquiries@alabare.co.uk

Riverside House
2 Watt Road
Salisbury
SP2 7UD
01722 322 882

Alexander Duckham Memorial Schools Trust
The Alexander Duckham Memorial Schools Trust aims to promote the education and welfare of children of members and former members of the RAF who are in need of financial assistance.

http://www.admst.org.uk

admin@admst.org.uk

16 Westpoint
49 Putney Hill
London
SW15 6RU

Armed Forces Para Snow Sports Team
Armed Forces Para Snow Sports Team was formed in 2011 to provide injured, wounded and service personnel and veterans support. The Winter Sports environment transforms an athlete's drive and energy to overcome adversity, provides focus during difficult recovery journeys and gives a sense of freedom that had once been lost.

http://www.afpst.co.uk

nordic@afpst.co.uk

RMA Sandhurst
Camberley
GU15 4PQ

07508 015053

Army Central Fund
The British Army's charity delivering financial support by means of grants, for the benefit of all ranks, their families and dependants of the Serving Army, including Army widows and those supporting organisations which provide expertise and assistance to the Army.

Service personnel, Units, Garrisons, Districts and Divisional HQs in UK, Northern Ireland and Germany should consult the HQ Land Forces LFSO 3206.

The ACF supports the Army chain of command in all theatres as well as the Army Families Federation (AFF) and the Army Sport Control Bd (ASCB) – thereby underwriting Strategic Welfare & Support.

Grants are awarded for Capital Projects in Units and Garrisons – often in conjunction with the Nuffield Trust for the Armed Forces and the ASCB Charitable Fund and the Army Sports Lottery.

Army-ArmyCentralFund@mod.uk

Building 8
Trenchard Lines
Upavon, Pewsey
SN9 6BE

Army Dependants' Trust
Promotion of the efficiency of the Army by the awarding of immediate financial assistance to meet the needs of dependants/next of kin of deceased soldiers or officers.

http://www.army.mod.uk/welfare-support/23214.aspx

ArmyPersSvcs-ADT-Sec@mod.uk

Building 183
Trenchard Lines
Upavon, Pewsey
SN9 6BE

Army Families Federation
AFF acts as an advocate and an independent expert witness to promote a quality of life which reflects the military covenant. Highlights problems to chain of command and service providers. Sign-posting service for assistance of every kind.

http://www.aff.org.uk
adminuk@aff.org.uk

IDL 414, Floor 1, Zone 7
Ramillies Buildings Marlborough Lines
Monxton Road ,Andover
SP11 8HJ

01264 382326

Army Widows Association
Army Widows Association offers comfort, support and friendship to widows and widowers of service people.

http://www.armywidows.org.uk

info@armywidows.org.uk
C/O AIASC - PS4
HQLF/IDL 428 Ramillies Bldg Marlborough Lines
Monxton Road ,Andover
SP11 8HJ

0300 666 0136

Association of Jewish ex-Service Men and Women
Remembrance of the sacrifices of the past, help for those in need in the present and education for the future.

http://www.ajex.org.uk

Welfare@ajex.org.uk

Shield House
Harmony Way
Hendon, London
NW4 2BZ

020 8202 2323

Big White Wall
Big White Wall delivers personalised support and recovery pathways to improve mental health and related conditions via a safe and engaging collaborative platform of peers and professionals. Big White Wall is free to all UK serving personnel (including reservists), veterans/ex-serving, and their families aged 16+, thanks to the support of Help for Heroes, the Ministry of Defence and NHS England.

Big White Wall (BWW) was one of the first five services to be endorsed by the NHS in the NHS Mental Health Apps Library (NHS Choices), and is registered with the Care Quality Commission (CQC). It is supported by Help for Heroes, NHS England and the Ministry of Defence to provide free, 24/7 mental health support to the Armed Forces community.

http://bigwhitewall.com
theteam@bigwhitewall.com

3rd Floor
16 Upper Woburn Place
London
WC1H 0BS

0203 7418080

BLESMA, The Limbless Veterans

BLESMA, The Limbless Veterans, is a national charity formed in the years following the First World War which supports all limbless ex-service men and women, their widows and dependants.

http://www.blesma.org

ChadwellHeath@blesma.org

Frankland Moore House
185-187 High Road
Chadwell Heath
RM6 6NA

020 8590 1124

Blind Veterans UK

Blind Veterans UK offers support for blind and visually impaired ex-servicemen and women.

http://www.blindveterans.org.uk/

fundraising@blindveterans.org.uk

12-14 Harcourt Street
London
W1H 4HD

020 7723 5021

Bournemouth War Memorial Homes

Provide assistance to beneficiaries with the provision of affordable accommodation ("Beneficiaries" means those who are in need or vulnerable, because of their physical or mental health or social or economic circumstances) to former members of the Merchant Navy, former service personnel of Armed Forces of the Crown and widows / widowers and surviving dependants of men and woman who have served in the Merchant Navy, Royal Navy, Army, Royal Air Force.

http://bwmh.org.uk/

estatemanager@bwmh.org.uk

15 Woodford Green
Castle Lane West
Bournemouth
BH8 9PT

01202 302881

Bridge for Heroes, The
The Bridge for Heroes was established in September 2010 by Mike and Helen Taylor with the aim of delivering direct and immediate support to the HM Armed Forces community, veterans and their families. Since its opening in June 2011 The General Dannatt Contact Centre in King's Lynn has provided support through respite breaks, compensation claims, pensions advice, veteran advice and guidance, housing advice, service records and medal applications, and military family research.

http://www.thebridgeforheroes.org/

52a South Clough Lane
Kings Lynn
PE30 1SE

01553 760230

British Ex-Services Wheelchair Sports Association
British Ex-Services Wheelchair Sports Association promotes well-being and rehabilitation of disabled ex-service personnel through sports and sports medicine.

http://www.bewsa.org

info@bewsa.org

12 Tukes Close
Falmouth
TR11 2HL

01326 318780

Building Heroes Education
Building Heroes provides ex-service personnel with a rapid transition into careers in the construction industry through retraining and employment support. We provide an intensive programme covering a range of building skills, plus relevant health and safety training, to equip our graduates to progress into employment, self-employment or further training. We have a growing network of employers able to offer job opportunities and provide appropriate individual support with your chosen career path.

http://www.buildingheroes.org.uk

info@buildingheroes.org.uk

Lodge Cottage
Brinsbury Estate
Staine Street, North Heath, Pulborough
RH20 1DJ

01798 874521

Burma Star Association
Forum and support group for Burma Star veterans. Welfare assistance is available. The list includes: top-up fees, nursing care, mobility aids, EPVs, home repairs, white goods etc, club and social events, magazine.

http://www.burmastar.org.uk

34 Grosvenor Gardens
London
SW1W 0DU

020 7823 4273

Canine Partners
Our dogs help with everyday physical tasks that disabled people find difficult, painful or even impossible to do themselves. These include opening and closing doors, retrieving items including medication, unloading and loading washing machines, undressing, taking cash and card out of an ATM and fetching help in emergencies.

The help the dogs bring with these physical tasks allows the disabled person to gain independence and confidence: but there is also a huge benefit gained on an emotional and psychological level, particularly with regard to PTSD.

http://www.caninepartners.org.uk/

info@caninepartners.org.uk

Mill Lane
Heyshott
Midhurst
GU24 0ED

Support Offered

Care After Combat
Care After Combat provide assistance and welfare to, but not restricted to, veterans in the criminal justice system by the provision of a mentor, to create a pathway back to normality for the veteran who has been in prison.

http://www.careaftercombat.org

jim@careaftercombat.org

COURAGE AFTER THE BATTLE

Troon House
4400 Parkway
Solent Business Park, Fareham
PO15 7FJ

0300 343 0255

Care For Veterans
Care For Veterans provide a multi-disciplinary approach for the care and rehabilitation of those with neurological and medical disabilities – predominantly those who have served with HM Forces.

http://www.qahh.org.uk

ceo@qahh.org.uk

Boundary Road
Worthing
BN11 4LJ

CESSAC & CESSA HA
CESSAC has been operating amenity centres for serving members of the Armed Forces and their families in establishments at home and abroad for over 125 years. CESSAC provides a number of homely, welcoming alcohol-free cafes for serving Armed Forces personnel and their families in Cyprus, Germany, Falklands & UK.
CESSA HA manages sheltered housing schemes for ex-service personnel & their families over age 60.

http://www.cessaha.co.uk

marika.stivanello@cessaha.co.uk

1 Shakespeare Terrace
126 High Street
Portsmouth
PO1 2RH

Change Step Veterans Services (CAIS)
Change Step is a veteran to veteran peer mentoring and advice service. This service is for military veterans, and others with posttraumatic stress disorder and a range of psychosocial problems, who want to make positive changes to their lives. Listen In is the sister project which supports the significant role families and friends of veterans play in promoting recovery from problems associated with military service and the transition to civilian life.

http://www.changestepwales.co.uk/

Ask@change-step.co.uk

12 Trinity Square
Llandudno
LL30 2RA

0300 777 2259

Chaplaincy Support
Chaplains work within each branch of the armed services and are located within the individual units and bases. The 'Padre', as they are occasionally known, will speak to you in the strictest confidence.

Combat Stress
Combat Stress provides effective treatment and support, delivered by qualified and understanding professionals, to veterans of the UK Armed Forces who are suffering from mental ill health.

http://www.combatstress.org.uk

contactus@combatstress.org.uk

Tyrwhitt House
Oaklawn Road
Leatherhead
KT22 0BX

01372 587 000

Defence Medical Welfare Service
Defence Medical Welfare Service delivers an independent and impartial 24-hour specialist welfare service to those members of the British Armed Forces who are receiving hospital care, their dependant relatives and entitled civilians, in order to contribute to the coherence of the recovery and rehabilitation pathway for service personnel. The crucial practical and emotional support is provided at times when it is most needed and is bound by a code of confidentiality.

http://www.dmws.org.uk

info@dmws.org.uk

The Old Stables
Redenham Park
Redenham, Andover
SP11 9AQ

01264 774000

Domestic Abuse
 There are many organisations who deal with domestic and other similar abuse cases and I have highlighted a few of those pertaining to the service community.

Female Victims
Http://www.womansaid.org.uk

Men's Advice Line
info@mensadviceline.org.uk
http://www.mensadviceline.org.uk/mens_advice.php.html

Mankind – http://mankind.org.uk

Additional support available in Scotland

http://www.abusemeninscotland.org
http://www.mapni.co.uk

Lesbian, Gay, Bisexual and Transgender Relationships
http://www.brokenarrow.org.uk
help@brokenarow.org.uk

Children and young people are often affected by domestic abuse

The Hideout – http://thehideout.org.uk/default.aspa

Childline – http://childline.org.uk/Pages/Home.aspx

http://www.childline.org.uk/explore/homefamilies/pages/domesticviolence.aspx

NSPCC – http://nspcc.org.uk/help-and-advice/worried-about-a-child/are-you-worried-hub_wdh72939.html

Parenting during and after domestic and violence abuse
http://www.nehantsdvf.co.uk/Parenting%20leaflet%20March%202012.pdf

Talking to children about domestic violence and abuse
http://nehantsdvf.co.uk/Talking%20to%20children%20leaflet%20March%202012.pdf

NSPCC – Help and Advice for Parents
http://www.nspcc.org.uk/help-and-advice/for-parents/for-parents-hub_wda96726.html

The Hideout Section for Adults – http://thehideout.org.uk/default.aspa

Families of the Fallen
Families of the Fallen's aim is to deliver EXTRA financial help to the families of British servicemen and women killed in Afghanistan and Iraq.

Families of the Fallen, 2 Eaton Gate London SW1W9BJ

http://www.familiesofthefallen.org.uk
admin@familiesofthefallen.org.uk

Families Federations

Navy Families Federation – http://www.nff.org.uk/

Army Families Federation – http://www.aff.org.uk/

RAF Families Federation – http://www.raf-ff.org.uk/

Felix Fund

Felix Fund assists with the well-being of individuals within the Explosive Ordnance Disposal (EOD) community past, present and future.

https://www.felixfund.org.uk/

melanie@felixfund.org.uk

Vauxhall Barracks
Foxhall Road
Didcot
OX11 7ES

07713 752901

FirstLight Trust

FirstLight Trust supports Veterans of the Armed Forces and Emergency Services locally at the grass roots and rehabilitates them back into their own community – whatever that looks like.

http://www.firstlighttrust.co.uk/

enquiries@firstlighttrust.co.uk

63 Newborough
Scarborough
YO11 1ET

01723 361210

Forces Children's Trust
Forces Children's Trust are devoted to working together to help children in need whose father or mother has died, or has sustained life-threatening injuries whilst serving as a member of the British Armed Forces.

https://forceschildrenstrust.org.uk/

denny.wise@forceschildrenstrust.org.uk

Quaver Rest'
65 Shawley Way
Epsom Downs
KT18 5PD

01737 361077

Forces in Mind Trust
Forces in Mind Trust is prevention and relief of poverty, the protection of mental and physical health and the relief of sickness and need amongst serving and former serving members of the armed forces by means of the provision of mentoring services, facilities and equipment to support their treatment, rehabilitation, resettlement, education, training and employment and thereby support their transition to civilian life. The protection of the mental and physical health and the relief of poverty of the families and dependants of serving and former serving members of the armed forces in all cases for the benefit of the public.

http://www.fim-trust.org/

enquiries@fim-trust.org

Forces in Mind Trust Office
Mountbarrow House
6-20 Elizabeth Street, London
SW1W 9RB

Forces in the Community
Forces in the Community is a local charity committed to supporting ex-service personnel, reservists and their families to reach their full potential. The charity supports the clients and their families, who are often disadvantaged and at a point of crisis in their lives. We provide a community focal point. The aim is to transform lives.

http://www.forces.org.uk/

info@forces.org.uk

2 Cross Street
Beeston
Nottingham
NG9 2NX

01159 220 320

Forces Pension Society
Forces Pension Society campaign on behalf of all ranks of all three services to seek improvements to the Armed Forces Pension Schemes (AFPS): we also campaign to resolve unfairness within the AFPS and we seek to ensure that all serving and retired members of the Armed Forces and their dependents receive the occupational pension to which they are entitled.

http://www.forpen.co.uk

memsec@forpen.co.uk

68 South Lambeth Road
London
SW8 1RL

020 7820 9988

Forward Assist

Forward Assist enables veterans to use their transferable military skills to do good for others through well supervised projects that support those less well off than themselves. Veterans gain the respect of the wider civilian community and significant others, thus facilitating a smoother transition to civilian life. Forward Assist have developed a portfolio of local employers who support our veteran community by working closely with our Education, Training & Employment Coordinators to facilitate vital work experience/ placements, career advice and guidance, interview skills, and realistic employment opportunities.

http://www.forward-assist.com/

admin@forwardassist.com

C/O John Willie Sams Centre
Market Street
Dudley
NE23 7HS

0191 250 4877

Future for Heroes

Formed in 2008, the charity was originally called Remount, using the strap line 'the future for heroes'. It was recognised that some armed forces personnel leaving the military needed help in making the physical and emotional adjustments necessary to successfully reintegrate into civilian life. Others can look to dependency for the answers.

http://www.f4h.org.uk/

j.paton@f4h.org.uk

C/O RHQ Stanley Barracks
Bovington
BH20 6JB

01452 505 686

Give Us Time
Give Us Time is a small, niche service charity that focuses exclusively on the military family. As a charity we provide free holiday accommodation to veterans and serving personnel and their families, as well as the families of those who have lost their lives due to military service.

https://giveustime.org.uk/

enquiries@giveustime.org.uk

73 Great Titchfield Street
London
W1W 6RD

020 7470 8877

Greenwich Hospital
Benevolence for Royal Navy and Royal Marines seafarers, grants, donations, pensions, sheltered housing and education (parent charity for the Royal Hospital School, Holbrook).

http://www.grenhosp.org.uk

enquiries@grenhosp.org.uk

Gate House
1 Farringdon Street
London

020 7396 0150

Gurkha Welfare Trust
Gurkha Welfare Trust provides welfare to enable Gurkha ex-servicemen and their dependants to live out their lives with dignity, primarily in Nepal but increasingly in UK and elsewhere.

http://www.gwt.org.uk

staffassistant@gwt.org.uk

P O Box 2170
22 Queen Street
Salisbury
SP2 2EX

Haig Housing Trust
Haig Housing is a housing provider for ex-service people and the strategic housing partner of Help for Heroes. The main object of the Trust is to provide housing assistance to the service and ex-service community and this is delivered through various options including general needs housing throughout the UK, let to ex-service people at affordable rent, and special needs housing to rent or part purchase through a shared ownership scheme, aimed at helping severely wounded and disabled service and ex-service people.

http://www.haighousing.org.uk

enquiries@haighousing.org.uk

Alban Dobson House
Green Lane
Morden
SM4 5NS

0208 685 5777

Help 4 Homeless Veterans
Provide a 'Service of Care' for veterans who for whatever reason find themselves vulnerable and living rough. The charity source and provide accommodation to ex-service personnel who are living rough or in unsatisfactory accommodation.

http://www.help4homelessveterans.co.uk

help4homelessveterans@gmail.com

105 Grange Road
Royston
Barnsley
S71 4LG

07586 777856

Help for Heroes
Help for Heroes is a charity that offers comprehensive support to those who have suffered life-changing injuries and illnesses while serving.

http://www.helpforheroes.org.uk

14 Parker's Close
Downton Business Centre
Downton
SP5 3RB

General Enquiries: 01980 846459

Welfare Support: 01980 844224

Heroes Haven Swanage
Heroes Haven Swanage offer holiday accommodation for service personnel, both serving and veterans.

http://www.heroes-haven.org.uk/

Herston Yards
Washpool Lane
Swanage
BH19 3DJ

Heropreneurs

Heropreneurs has been created by successful entrepreneurs for the benefit of new entrepreneurs. Heropreneurs helps anyone, or their families, who has served in the Armed Forces on the commercial creation of a business and its future growth strategy. It is also increasingly being asked to help more established businesses on their future strategy.

http://www.heropreneurs.co.uk/

team@heropreneurs.co.uk

2 High Street
Mildenhall
Bury St Edmunds
IP28 7EJ
020 7193 4128

HighGround

HighGround provide advice and support to service leavers, reservists and veterans about employment and vocational opportunities in the land-based sector.

http://www.highground-uk.org

95 Horseferry Road
London
SW1P 2DX

Hire a Hero

Hire a Hero is a charity established to support all service leavers with the transition to meaningful civilian employment. Hire a Hero supports service leavers, regardless of service type or length, situation or background, by doing whatever it takes for as long as it takes to provide individual support in the transition from service life.

http://www.hireaherouk.org/

info@hireahero.org.uk

Unit 3 Mamhilad Technology Park
Mamhilad
NP4 0JJ

01495 366670

HIVE Information Centres

The HIVE is an information network available to all members of the armed services community. They provide up to date information on any relevant subjects for that organisation.

Royal Navy and Royal Marines – http://www.royalnavy.mod.uk/welfae/resources
Army – http://www.Army.mod.uk/welfare-support/23438.aspx
RAF – http://www.RAF.mod.uk/community/support/RAFhiveinformationservices.cfn
Hive Overseas/Europe – http://bfgnet.de/hive-europe/

Holidays for Heroes Jersey

Holidays for Heroes Jersey aim to provide a week's holiday in Jersey for past or present members of HM Armed Forces with injuries in mind or body attributable to their service.

http://www.hols4hjersey.org.je/

hols4heroesjersey@gmail.com

2 Sion Farm Close
La Rue De Samares
St Clement
JE2 6LZ

01534 856658

COURAGE AFTER THE BATTLE

HorseBack UK

HorseBack UK is a charity which was set up in 2009 to empower service personnel and veterans suffering from life-changing injuries and posttraumatic stress disorder. Using horsemanship and outdoor activities, participants gain self-confidence and self-esteem amongst people who have experienced similar trauma.

http://www.horseback.org.uk/

emma@horseback.org.uk

Ferrar
Dinnet
Aboyne
AB34 5LD

01339 880487

Hosanna House and Children's Pilgrimage Trust
Hosanna House and Children's Pilgrimage Trust gives respite breaks for veterans of the British Forces and their dependents who have disabilities or special needs.

http://www.hcpt.org.uk/group/507/

jshhg507hq@yahoo.com

227 Austin Crescent
Crownhill
Plymouth
PL6 5QT

Housing Options Scotland
Housing Options Scotland help clients to find the right house, in the right place.

They never turn anyone away and never close a case until the client asks them to close the case.

http://www.housingoptionsscotland.org.uk

militarymatters@housingoptionsscotland.org.uk

The Melting Pot
5 Rose Street
Edinburgh
EH2 2PR

0131 247 1400

Invicta Foundation, The

The Invicta Foundation is a charity supporting individuals and forces families affected by military service in the UK. This includes wounded, injured and sick service personnel and families who may be affected as a result of military service. They endeavour to improve the welfare of these individuals and Forces families wherever impossible. With an array of fundraising events and volunteer projects planned across the year, we welcome you to join our endeavours to help support those in need.

http://www.theinvictafoundation.org.uk

enquiries@theinvictafoundation.org.uk

1st Floor Lisle House
12 Red Lion Yard
Lion Walk Shopping Centre, Colchester
CO1 1DX

01206 617001

Joint Casualty and Compassion Centre
Imjin Barracks, Gloucestershire, GL3 1HW
Emergency Number - 01452 519 951
Office hours – 01452 712 612 Ext 6090 / 7495

A guide to the Joint Casualty and Compassionate Centre

https://www.gov.uk/government/publications/a-guide-to-the-joint-casualty-and-compassionate-centre

Joint Service Housing Advisory Office
Https://www.gov.uk/housing-for-service-personnel-and-families

KartForce (Karting for Injured Troops)

KartForce (Karting for Injured Troops) introduce competitive motorsport to injured troops, starting with team endurance kart racing and progressing to team endurance car racing.

http://kartforce.org/

dave@kartforce.org

1 St Leger Court
Newbury
RG14 1TW

01635 770601 / 0782 462 8029

LINKS/Combined Forces (LYNX)
LINKS/Combined Forces is a mental health project covering Carmarthenshire, working with both civilians and ex-service personnel. The charity aims to support those who have experienced or are living with mental ill health to enable them to build self-confidence, self-esteem and to move on.

http://www.links.uk.net
susie@links.uk.net

Unit 4
The Palms, 96
Queen Victoria Road, Llanelli
SA15 2TH

Little Troopers
The object of the charity is to enhance the support already given to Armed Forces children via various sources by the following, but not exclusively; The promotion of the efficiency of the armed forces by the provision and support of facilities and activities to improve the quality of life and welfare of families of military personnel who are away from home, in particular when on active service.

http://www.littletroopers.net/

louise@littletroopers.net

4b, 80 High Street
Egham
TW20 9HE

Lord Kitchener Memorial Holiday Centre
Lord Kitchener Memorial Holiday Centre is situated on the Suffolk Coast in a Grade II listed building. The charity aims to provide seaside respite holidays and short breaks to ex-members of the armed forces and the merchant service, and to their spouses and widows/widowers.

http://www.kitchenerslowestoft.co.uk/

kitchener@lowestoft.org.uk

10 Kirkley Cliff
Lowestoft
NR33 0BY

01502 573564

COURAGE AFTER THE BATTLE

Lt Dougie Dalzell MC Memorial Trust

The Lt Dougie Dalzell MC Memorial Trust seeks to improve the quality of life of those wounded or injured who are currently serving or have served in the Armed Forces (and their dependants). Lt Dougie Dalzell MC was killed in Helmand in 2010 on his 27th birthday. The Trust, set up in his name, was formed later that year.

http://www.dougiedalzellmemorialtrust.co.uk

info@ddmt.co.uk

Causeway Farmhouse
Woolavington
Bridgwater
TA7 8EQ

Merchant Navy Association

Merchant Navy Association bringing all serving and retired seafarers together in a spirit of companionship, consideration and commitment towards a united lobby for the Community of the Sea.

http://www.mna.org.uk

mna.nat.sec@gmail.com

9 Saxon Way
Caistor
Market Rasen
LN7 6SG

Mission Motorsport

Mission Motorsport provides aid in the recovery and rehabilitation of those affected by military operations by providing opportunities through motorsport, in the coordination and provision of motor sport as a recovery activity and as Relationship Managers to the automotive industry for vocational opportunities for the wounded, injured and sick.

http://www.missionmotorsport.org/

team@missionmotorsport.org

Vantage Point Business Centre
Micheldean
GL17 0DD

03330 338338

Mutual Support
Mutual Support is the Armed Forces Multiple Sclerosis Support Group, National Support Group of the MS Society "Supporting Members of the Military family affected by MS". They offer advice and assistance in applying for state benefits, war pensions, AFCS and grants from other sources. Residential weekends with health workers.

http://www.mutual-support.org.uk

support-team@mutual-support.org.uk

c/o Mutual Support
MS Society National Centre
372 Edgware Road, London
NW2 6ND

07962 708899

National Family Mediation
National Family Mediation (NFM) helps parents who live apart stay close to their children. NFM's professional family mediators provide a voluntary, confidential process helping people reach joint decisions without using court. We offer a safe, neutral place where couples no longer in a relationship can meet with a trained professional mediator to make sustainable plans for the future. This enables families to keep control of vital day-to-day arrangements for finance, property and children. It empowers parents to agree long-term solutions and agreements that are based on the unique

circumstances of the family members. NFM is the largest provider of family mediation in England and Wales, with a network of hundreds of professional non-profit mediators.

http://www.nfm.org.uk/

general@nfm.org.uk

1st Floor
Civic Centre
Paris Street, Exeter
EX1 1JN

0300 4000 636

National Gulf Veterans & Families Association

The NGVFA provides practical support and help to veterans and their families and our aim is to improve the quality of the day-to-day lives of those who have been affected by the 1990-91 and 2003 Gulf conflicts, as well as the present Afghanistan and all other future desert conflicts. We also help veterans from other conflicts that are in need of our advice and support.

http://www.ngvfa.org.uk

info@ngvfa.org.uk

Building E, Office 8
Chamberlain Business Centre
Chamberlain Road, Hull
HU8 8HL

0845 257 4853

Naval Families Federation

The NFF offers an independent voice to Royal Naval and Royal Marines personnel and ALL members of their extended family. The NFF can provide support and guidance on day-to-day issues that occur as a result of being part of a Naval Service family. The NFF has direct access to the chain of command, the MoD and the Government. The organisation ensures that the unique challenges faced by Naval Service families are considered in the 'purple arena' and when policies are reviewed.

http://www.nff.org.uk

admin@nff.org.uk

Rooms 1&2
Building 25
HMS Excellent, Portsmouth
PO2 8ER

023 9265 4374

NHS / GP Assistance

You may have heard that the NHS, together with the MoD, BLESMA, Blind Veterans UK and Style for Soldiers, has recently launched a veterans trauma network, which has been developed following feedback from veterans, their families and GPs. The network aims to provide specialist care for patients with service-related traumatic injuries and conditions, and responds to a call for both clinical assurance on the advice and excellence of care and a supportive 'safety net' to meet the ongoing health needs of injured military personnel transitioning out of the service and veterans.

Located in ten major trauma centres across England (Plymouth, Oxford, London (three centres), Birmingham, Nottingham, Liverpool, Leeds and Middlesbrough), the network acts as a regional hub for veteran care, linking with NHS veterans' mental health services, national centres of expertise and key service charities to provide a complete package of care.

Patients referred to the service have a personalised treatment plan developed and provided by a specialist team of military and civilian experts in trauma. As part of this, the needs of families and carers are also considered.

Referrals to the network can be made via a GP to: england.veteranstraumanetwork@nhs.net<mailto:england.veteranstraumanetwork@nhs.net> or via BLESMA, which is the umbrella charity for the Veterans Trauma Network (email at bsoprosthetics@blesma.org<mailto:bsoprosthetics@blesma.org> or telephone at 0208 548 7080). Blind Veterans UK and Style for Soldiers can also assist in referring veterans to the network.

Early use of the network is already highlighting better care and health outcomes for patients, as shown in this video<http://bit.ly/2hH5mk5>.

A recent Radio 4 programme included an interview with Shehan Hettiaratchy, Clinical Lead for the Veterans Trauma Network.

For further information on the service or referrals, please email: bsoprosthetics@blesma.org<mailto:bsoprosthetics@blesma.org> or england.veteranstraumanetwork@nhs.net<mailto:england.veteranstraumanetwork@nhs.net>.

Officers' Association Scotland
Officers' Association Scotland provides employment and career transition services for serving and former officers and relief of distress among former regular or reserve officers and their dependants. Applicants must be resident in Scotland at the time of their initial application or have been members of a Scottish Regiment.

http://www.oascotland.org.uk

New Haig House
Logie Green Road
Edinburgh
EH7 4HR

0131 550 1575 / 1581

Officers' Association

Officers' Association is dedicated exclusively to supporting officers, ex-officers and their dependants. Including provision of employment services, financial and welfare support.

http://www.officersassociation.org.uk

info@officersassociation.org.uk

Mountbarrow House
6-20 Elizabeth Street
London
SW1W 9RB

020 7808 4160

On Course Foundation

OCF provides long-term benefits for wounded, injured and sick servicemen and women and former service personnel through the medium of golf. It provides golf familiarisation, skills and employment training, and facilitates work experience placements and full-time employment opportunities.

http://www.oncoursefoundation.com

info@oncoursefoundation.com

28 Falstaff House
Bardolph Road
Richmond
TW9 2LH

020 8334 2010

Outside the Wire (Matthew Project)

Outside the Wire provides a bespoke alcohol and drug service offering confidential advice and support. The service is available to current and ex-HM Forces personnel, reservists and their families across Norfolk and Suffolk.

andy.wicks@matthewproject.org

nicky.jones@matthewproject.org

http://www.matthewproject.org/the-junction/outside-the-wire

enquiry@matthewproject.org

Nedeham House
St Stephens Road
Norwich
NR1 3QU

Poppy Factory, The

The country's leading employment charity for veterans with health conditions or impairments. The Poppy Factory provides bespoke opportunities and ongoing employment support for hundreds of disabled veterans around the country, helping to restore their financial independence through sustainable and rewarding work.

http://www.poppyfactory.org

Administrator@poppyfactory.org

20 Petersham Road
Richmond
TW10 6UR

020 8940 3305

COURAGE AFTER THE BATTLE

Poppy Scotland (Earl Haig Fund Scotland)
Money raised from the Scottish Poppy Appeal and Poppyscotland's year-round fundraising enables them to deliver support to members of the Armed Forces community in Scotland by providing tailored funding and assistance. The charity also funds services in advice, employment, housing, mental health, mobility and respite.

http://www.poppyscotland.org.uk

New Haig House
Logie Green Road
Edinburgh
EH7 4HR

PTSD Resolution
PTSD Resolution helps veterans, reservists and families who are struggling to reintegrate into a normal work and family life because of trauma suffered prior to and during service in the UK Armed Forces.

http://www.ptsdresolution.org

contact@ptsdresolution.org

7 Cromwell Mews
Burgess Hill
RG15 8QF

0300 302 0551

RAF Benevolent Fund
The RAF's leading welfare charity, providing practical, financial and personal lifetime support to all members of the RAF family, whether serving or veterans, and their families.

http://www.rafbf.org

mail@rafbf.org.uk

67 Portland Place
London
W1B 1AR

020 7580 8343

RAF Bomb Disposal Association

RAF Bomb Disposal Association is dedicated to the men and women who render safe unexploded ordnance, to foster and maintain friendship.

http://www.rafbdassociation.com/

Fell View
Armathwaite
Carlisle
CA4 9TA

01772 792697

RAF Central Fund
Sitting within the heart of the Royal Air Force, the RAF Central Fund, originally founded by serving RAF personnel, is dedicated to providing support to enhance the sense of well-being, morale and community cohesion for those serving in the RAF today and into the future.

http://www.rafcf.org.uk/

mail@rafcf.org.uk

SO2 Service Funds, HQ Air command
Hurricane Block
Ground Floor, RAF High Wycombe
HP14 4UE

01494 569068

RAF Families Federation

RAF Families Federation represents the views and concerns of RAF personnel and their families to those who can make a difference, for example senior RAF and MoD staff and Ministers. The RAF FF is outside the chain of command and can promise an independent and confidential service.

http://www.raf-ff.org.uk

enquiries@raf-ff.org.uk

13-15 St Georges Road
Wittering
Peterborough
PE8 6DL

01780 781650

RAF Widows Association

RAF Widows Association gives emotional support and practical help to Service widows.

https://www.rafbf.org/raf-widows

info@rafwidowsassociation.org.uk

12 Park Crescent
London
W1B 1PH

0870 5143 901

Recruit for Spouses

Recruit for spouses is the social enterprise which has helped hundreds of military spouses find employment.

http://www.recruitforspouses.co.uk/

enquiries@recruitforspouses.co.uk

Hartham Park
Corsham
SN13 0RP

0333 2020 996

RFEA – The Forces Employment Charity
Part of the Career Transition Partnership. To help men and women of all ranks leaving the Armed Forces to find and remain in employment throughout their working lives.

http://www.rfea.org.uk

Mountbarrow House
6-20 Elizabeth Street
London
SW1W 9RB

Riverside Care & Support
Riverside Veterans Services are committed to supporting veterans facing homelessness and our services are developed and driven by staff who have served in the Armed Forces. Key to these housing services is the support provided around employment, training, health & well-being and resettling veterans into mainstream permanent housing. Referral to the supported housing services is via SPACES.

https://www.riverside.org.uk/care-and-support/veterans/

spaces@riverside.org.uk

The Welfare Dept.
Military Correction Training Centre
Berechurch Hall Road, Colchester

CO2 9NU

01748 833797

Row 2 Recovery

Row 2 Recovery are based in Henley-on-Thames. Row2Recovery is a charity which supports Military Para-Rowing (MP-R) throughout the country.

http://www.row2recovery.com

Christina@commonbarn.com

Common Barn
Remenham Hill
Henley-on-Thames
RG9 3ES

Royal Air Forces Association (RAFA)
Providing friendship, help and support for the whole RAF family. Incorporating RAF Families Federation representing the concerns of RAF personnel.

http://www.rafa.org.uk

RAF Association Headquarters
Atlas House
41 Wembley Road, Leicester
LE3 1UT

0800 0182 361

Royal Artillery Centre for Personal Development
Royal Artillery Centre for Personal Development provide nationally recognised civilian qualifications to Service personnel and the wider defence community including veterans and dependants.

http://www.racpd.org.uk

info@racpd.org.uk

RA Barracks
Larkhill
Salisbury
SP4 8QT

Royal British Legion Industries

A not-for-profit charity providing accommodation, employment and support services to Armed Forces individuals and families, particularly those who have experienced injury or sickness.

http://www.rbli.co.uk

enquiries@rbli.co.uk

Hall Road
Aylesford
ME20 7NL

Royal British Legion Scotland
Royal British Legion Scotland helps ex-services men and women of all ages across Scotland to adapt to civilian life by providing community, friendship and practical advice, whether they left military service yesterday or 50 plus years ago.

http://www.legionscotland.org.uk

info@legionscotland.org.uk

New Haig House
Logie Green Road
Edinburgh
EH7 4HR

Royal Commonwealth Ex-Services League
Royal Commonwealth Ex-Services League to help Commonwealth ex-service men and women now in need.

http://www.commonwealthveterans.org.uk

Haig House
199 Borough High Street
London
SE1 1AA

020 3207 2413

Royal Fleet Auxiliary Association

Royal Fleet Auxiliary Association aims to further the efficiency of the Service and caring for its community.

http://www.rfa-association.org.uk/

deputy.chairman@rfa-association.org

3-4 Station House
Bellington
Hexham
NE48 2DG
07919 253417

Royal Hospital Chelsea
Royal Hospital Chelsea is there to provide veterans with the care, support, and comradeship they need in order that they can grow old with dignity.

Contact Information

http://www.chelsea-pensioners.co.uk/

info@chelseapensioners.org.uk

Royal Hospital Road
London
SW3 4SR

0207 881 5200

Royal Marines Association, The
Royal Marines Association maintains and promotes esprit de corps and comradeship amongst all Royal Marines, past and present.

http://www.royalmarinesassociation.org.uk

chiefexec@rma.org.uk

Central Office Building
Building 32
Whale Island, Portsmouth
PO2 8ER

Royal Naval Association
Royal Naval Association was established to further the efficiency and well-being of the Service, preserve its traditions and encourage recruiting. MOU with RN for serving RN / RM / RNR / RFA / QARRNS.

http://www.royal-naval-association.co.uk

admin@royalnavalassoc.com

Room 209
Semaphore Tower
PP70 HM Naval Base, Portsmouth
PO1 3LT

023 9272 3747

COURAGE AFTER THE BATTLE

Royal Naval Benevolent Trust
The RNBT was established under Royal Charter in 1922 to help those who are serving or have served as Warrant Officers and below in the Royal Navy or Royal Marines, and their dependants, in times of need and distress; the collective term for the RNBT's beneficiaries is The RNBT Family.

http://www.rnbt.org.uk

rnbt@rnbt.org.uk

Castaway House
311 Twyford Avenue
Portsmouth
PO2 8RN

02392 690112

Royal Navy and Royal Marines Charity
Single focus charity for the Naval Service. Provides major grants to serving units and to naval charities. Key areas are (Serving – Dependants, Amenities, Sport and Prizes, Through-life care–Benevolence).

http://www.rnrmc.org.uk

theteam@rnrmc.org.uk

Building 29
HMS Excellent
Whale Island, Portsmouth
PO2 8ER

Royal Navy Officers Charity
Royal Navy Officers Charity offer financial assistance to serving and retired RN and RM Officers in distress.

http://www.arno.org.uk

RNOC@Arno.org.uk

70 Porchester Terrace
London
W2 3TP

0207 402 5231

Sailors' Children's Society
Children's charity supporting Royal or Merchant Navy and Fishing Fleet families in severe financial hardship.

http://www.sailorschildren.org.uk

info@sailorschildren.org.uk

Newland
Cottingham Road
Hull
HU6 7RJ

01482 342331

Samaritans
Samaritans provides completely confidential emotional support face-to-face and via phone, email and text message, around the clock every day of the year. Operators are trained to support people in emotional distress and vulnerable situations, such as those faced by veterans, reservists and service families; mental health issues; relationship breakdown; financial difficulties and suicidal thoughts.

http://www.samaritans.org/

reception@Samaritans.org

The Upper Mill
Kingston Road

Ewell
KT17 2AF
020 8394 8300

Sandhurst Trust
The Sandhurst Trust is the charity of the Royal Military Academy, Sandhurst. It promotes the Sandhurst brand of leadership and helps to preserve the heritage and traditions of Sandhurst. It supports the officer cadets and staff at Sandhurst and the wider Army serving and retired officer community through partnership with the Officers' Association.

https://www.sandhursttrust.org/

director@sandhursttrust.org

Old College
The Royal Military Academy
Sandhurst, Camberley
GU15 4PQ

01276 412000

Sapper Support
Sapper Support is a 24:7 PTSD helpline staffed solely by veterans and 999 staff, giving veterans and their families instant access through a 24:7 helpline to support from trained veteran volunteers.

http://www.sappersupport.com

timevers@btinternet.com

5 Charles Street
Gomersal
BD19 4QF

07852 994222

Scottish Veterans' Residences

Scottish Veterans' Residences provide supported independent living accommodation for ex-service people and ex-Merchant mariners who are homeless or in need.

http://www.svronline.org

info@svronline.org

53 Canongate
Edinburgh
EH8 8BS

0131 556 0091

Scotty's Little Soldiers

Scotty's Little Soldiers provide relief from the effects of bereavement to young people up to and including the age of 18 who have suffered the loss of a parent whilst serving with the Armed Forces of the Crown.

http://www.scottyslittlesoldiers.co.uk

hello@scottyslittlesoldiers.co.uk

Unit 21 Bergen Way
King's Lynn
PE30 2JG

08000 928 571

Seafarers UK
Seafarers UK is a charity that provides grants to other front line charities working right across the maritime sector, supporting charities that help seafarers or ex-seafarers from the Royal Navy, Royal Marines, Merchant Navy or fishing fleets. We also give grants to maritime youth groups and charities that help seafarers' families, including widows and children.

http://www.seafarers-uk.org

contact@seafarers-uk.org

8 Hatherley Street
London
SW1P 2QT

0207 932 5972

Services Sound and Vision Corporation
The Services Sound & Vision Corporation exists to inform, entertain and connect Britain's Armed Forces around the world.

http://www.ssvc.com

WelfareMedia@ssvc.com

Chalfont Grove
Narcot Lane
Gerrards Cross
SL9 8TN

01494 878239

SHAID/St Peters Court
SHAID/St Peters Court's a purpose is to house ex-service personnel who have found themselves homeless. However, in most cases you will find that the individual has become homeless because of a situation or area in their life that has become negative. The support offered while living here is hoped to address this and give the individual the opportunity to turn themselves around within the security of being housed, understood and listened to.

http://www.shaid.org.uk

stpeters@shaid.org.uk

COURAGE AFTER THE BATTLE

St Peters Court
Front Street
Sacristan
DH7 6FB

01913719813

Shelter, The National Charity for Homeless People
Shelter helps millions of people every year struggling with bad housing or homelessness through our advice, support and legal services. And we campaign to make sure that, one day, no one will have to turn to us for help.

http://england.shelter.org.uk

info@shelter.org.uk

Shelter
88 Old Street
London
EC1V 9HU

Skill Force Development
SkillForce offers employment opportunities to ex-service personnel, supporting their transition back into civilian life. Successful candidates train as instructors in the awards which are aimed at 6-14 year-olds and devised to help promote character, resilience and confidence. SkillForce works to support veterans and has been trialling a veteran to veteran mentoring service for those who are finding the transition from a service career difficult, and who may also have come into contact with the judicial system.

http://www.skillforce.org

Edwinstowe House
High Street, Edwinstowe
NG21 9PR

01623 827 651

COURAGE AFTER THE BATTLE

South Atlantic Medal Association 1982
Association of service personnel who took part in the Falklands campaign.

http://www.sama82.org.uk

secretary@sama82.org.uk

Unit 25 Torfaen Business Centre
Panteg Way
New Inn, Pontypool
NP4 0LS

01495 741592

South West Scotland RNR
South West Scotland RNR help wounded combatants to recover from injuries and their experiences by providing week-long adventure holidays in Dumfries & Galloway.

http://www.southwestscotlandrnr.org.uk/

admin@southwestscotlandrnr.org.uk

The End House
Carsethorn
DG2 8DS

Special Boat Service Association
To relieve members or their dependants who are in need by virtue of financial hardship, injury or sickness.

secretary@association1664.com

Secretary SBSA
PO Box 1014
Hamworthy
BH15 4YT

SSAFA
SSAFA provides lifelong support to anyone who is currently serving or has ever served in the Royal Navy, British Army or Royal Air Force and their families.

http://www.ssafa.org.uk

info@ssafa.org.uk

4 St Dunstan's Hill
London
EC3R 8AD

020 7403 8783

Stand Easy (Productions)
Stand Easy works towards the recovery of wounded, injured or sick veterans through the use of drama activities.

http://www.standeasyproductions.org/

alanc658@aol.com

6 High St
Pittenweem
KY10 2LA

01333 278 853

Step Together
Step Together helps people in need of intensive support across the UK to take positive action to change their lives and the lives of others through volunteering. Outreach workers provide tailored one-to-one support to help individuals into volunteering placements that match their needs and interests, and help them develop the personal and practical skills required to build a more positive future.

http://www.step-together.org.uk

enquiry@step-together.org.uk

5 Russell Town Avenue
Bristol
BS5 9LT

0117 955 9042

Stoll

Stoll, formerly known as the 'Sir Oswald Stoll Foundation', provides housing and rehabilitative support to vulnerable and disabled ex-service personnel, including those who have been homeless.

http://www.stoll.org.uk/

info@stoll.org.uk

Sir Oswald Stoll Foundation
446 Fulham Road
London
SW6 1DT

020 7385 2110

STUBS

Assist the most seriously wounded with rehabilitation and social reintegration.

http://www.stubs.org.uk/

craig.vassie@stubs.org.uk

The Clare Foundation
Wycombe Road
High Wycombe
HP14 4BF

01494 811 500

Support Our Paras, The Parachute Regiment Charity
The relief of need, hardship and distress amongst past and present members of The Parachute Regiment and their dependents:

https://supportourparas.org/

plansdir@supportourparas.org

Director - plansdir@supportourparas.org

Secretary - secretary@supportourparas.org

Welfare - rwo@parawelfare.org

RHQ PARA
Merville Barracks
Colchester
CO2 7UT

01206 817074

Supporting Wounded Veterans (Skiing with Heroes)
Supporting Wounded Veterans (formally Skiing with Heroes) is a charity that helps wounded veterans get back into civilian life and employment.

http://www.supportingwoundedveterans.com/

info@supportingwoundedveterans.com

38 Connaught Square
London
W2 2HL

07909 090291

COURAGE AFTER THE BATTLE

Surf Action

Surf Action promote and protect the physical and mental health and welfare of those who have been wounded whilst serving in the Armed Forces and civilian emergency services by introducing them to surfing and other peer group activities. To assist veterans in adjusting to civilian life, including those challenged by mental and physical problems, and improving their quality of life.

http://www.surfaction.co.uk/

info@surfaction.co.uk

Unit 11
Long Rock Industrial Estate
Long Rock, Penzance
TR20 8HX

01736 365645

Taxi Charity for Military Veterans

The Objects of The London Taxi Benevolent Association for War Disabled are as follows:

http://www.taxicharity.org/

info@taxicharity.org

88 Grasvenor Avenue
Barnet
EN5 2DB

07860 850102

The Buchanan Trust

The Buchanan Trust provides support and assistance for those that have served in the UK's armed forces who are in need of assistance or interested in a career in agriculture. The Trust provide short- to medium-term accommodation in self-contained flats and cottages on our rural estate near Ledbury for veterans and their families whilst they decide on careers in the rural or construction sectors.

http://www.buchanan-trust.org.uk/index.html

info@buchanan-trust.org.uk

Rylstone
Hoarwithy
Hereford
HR2 6QP

07866508797

The Calvert Trust
The Calvert Trust enables people with disabilities, together with their families and friends, to achieve their potential through the challenge of outdoor adventure in the countryside.

http://www.calvert-trust.org.uk/

http://www.calvert-trust.org.uk/unite

Calvert Trust Exmoor:
Wistlandpound, Kentisbury
Barnstaple, North Devon
EX31 4SJ
Exmoor:

01598 763221

exmoor@calvert-trust.org.uk

Calvert Trust Kielder:
Kielder Water & Forest Park
Hexham

Northumberland
NE48 1BS
Kielder:

01434 250232

enquiries@calvert-kielder.com

Lake District Calvert Trust:
Little Crosthwaite
Keswick
Cumbria
CA12 4QD
Lake District:

017687 72255

enquiries@lakedistrict.calvert-trust.org.uk

The Ely Centre
The Ely Centre is a Registered Charity specialising in the provision of multi-disciplinary support services for security force personnel, civilians and their families, who have experienced bereavement and injury as a result of the "Troubles in Fermanagh and Tyrone."

http://www.elycentre.com/

info@elycentre.co.uk

52 & 60 Forthill Street
Enniskillen
BT74 6AJ

028 6632 0977

The Fellowship of the Services

The Fellowship of the Services is a brotherhood of ex-servicemen drawn from all ranks of HM Forces – an undying spirit of comradeship.

http://www.thefellowshipoftheservices.co.uk

fosregoff@talktalk.net

The Fellowship of the Services
Thornbank House
Mountenoy Road, Rotherham
S60 2AG

0191 4661265

The Gwennili Trust

The Gwennili Trust provides offshore sailing to disabled ex-service personnel and their dependants and disabled other people of all ages and disabilities.

http://www.gwennili.org.uk

admin@gwennili.org.uk

Wingham House
Winchester Road
Bishop's Waltham
SO32 1BZ

The League of Remembrance

The League of Remembrance provide enduring, practical support to widows and dependants of those who served with the UK Armed Forces, to veterans of the UK Armed Forces, and to retired nurses (either military or civilian). To act as an enduring memorial to those who died in the service of their country through the voluntary work carried out by our beneficiaries, who are formally known as Remembrance Workers.

http://www.leagueofremembrance.org.uk/

info@leagueofremembrance.com

142 Buckingham Palace Road
London
SW1W 9TR

020 7881 0987

The Not Forgotten Association
The Not Forgotten Association provides leisure and recreation for wounded serving and ex-service men and women with disabilities

http://www.nfassociation.org

info@nfassociation.org

4th Floor
2 Grosvenor Gardens
London
SW1W 0DH

020 7730 2400

The Radley Foundation (Armed Forces Fund)
The Radley Foundation (Armed Forces Fund) fund the education of sons and daughters of Forces personnel of all ranks killed or wounded while serving their country. Radley College has a long history of helping families affected by death and injury in warfare.

http://www.radley.org.uk/The-Radley-Foundation

colin.dudgeon@radley.org.uk

Radley College
Abingdon

OX14 2HR

01235 543000

The Ripple Pond
The Ripple Pond enables a self-help support network for the adult family members of physically or emotionally injured service personnel, veterans and reservists.

http://theripplepond.org/

director@theripplepond.org

Mandora House
Louise Margaret Road
Aldershot
GU11 2PW

01252 913021

The Royal British Legion
The Royal British Legion, caring and campaigning for the serving and ex-service community.

http://www.britishlegion.org.uk

info@britishlegion.org.uk

199 Borough High Street
London
SE1 1AA

02032072100

The Royal Marines Charity
The Royal Marines Charity are a single, unified and integrated charity for

the Royal Marines extended Corps family.

http://www.rmctf.org.uk

adminasst@rmctf.org.uk

Normandy Building
HMS Excellent
Whale Island, Portsmouth
PO2 8ER

01392 346 424

The Royal Navy & Royal Marines Children's Fund
The Royal Navy & Royal Marines Children's Fund are dedicated to supporting children in need whose parents work, or have worked, for the Naval Service

http://www.rnrmchildrensfund.org.uk

rnchildren@btconnect.com

Castaway House
311 Twyford Avenue
Portsmouth
PO2 8RN

The Royal Navy Royal Marines Widows' Association
The Royal Navy Royal Marines Widows' Association are a special group of volunteers, recently formed to try and offer a much needed service of friendship, support and comfort.

http://www.rnrmwidowsassociation.org

rnrmwidowsassociation@hotmail.com

Conference of Naval Associations (CONA)

COURAGE AFTER THE BATTLE

Room 209 Semaphore Tower (PP70)
HM Naval Base, Portsmouth
PO1 3LT

023 92654374

The Royal Star & Garter Homes

The Royal Star & Garter Homes provides nursing and therapeutic care at two residential care homes for ex-service personnel with physical disabilities and dementia.

http://www.starandgarter.org

general.enquiries@starandgarter.org

15 Castle Mews
Hampton
TW12 2NP

The Veterans Contact Point
The Veterans Contact Point's vision aim to be there for those who have served in any of the UK Armed Forces (veterans) for one day's service or more, their families and dependents, who experience adverse issues and conditions, discrimination, or disadvantage during transition from military service, through resettlement, and in civilian life.

    The Veterans Contact Point (VCP) is a local military charity supporting veterans and their families in Warwickshire, Coventry & Solihull. The VCP started as a veteran to veteran run information, referral and peer support centre in 2011 to improve the access to support and information for serving and former members of the UK Armed Forces.

http://www.veteranscontactpoint.co.uk/

contactus@veteranscontactpoint.co.uk

Bentley Road

Nuneaton
CV11 5LR

02476 343793

The Warrior Programme
The Warrior Programme is a personal motivation and training programme. The course teaches individuals how to take control of their life, and how to increase confidence, motivation and focus, enabling participants to create a healthy, independent and balanced life style. The programme is particularly suitable for ex-service and serving personnel in transition post operations.

http://www.warriorprogramme.org.uk

enquiries@warriorprogramme.org.uk

1 Thorpe Close
London
W10 5XL

0808 801 0898

The White Ensign Association
The White Ensign Association inform and provide guidance to all serving and former members of the Royal Navy, Royal Marines and Reserves on financial matters including resettlement and employment.

http://www.whiteensign.co.uk

office@whiteensign.co.uk

HMS Belfast
Tooley Street
London
SE1 2JH

020 7407 8658

Tickets for Troops

Tickets For Troops was set up in 2009 to provide all serving members of the Armed Forces and those medically discharged since 2001 with free tickets for major sporting events, theatre performances, music concerts and cultural attractions. Over the last five years, the charity has been donated over 500,000 tickets which have been made available to their 140,000 registered members.

http://www.ticketsfortroops.org.uk

info@ticketsfortroops.org.uk

6 Lower Grosvenor Place
London
SW1W 0EN

0207 932 0808

Tom Harrison House

Tom Harrison House is a Liverpool-based addiction recovery centre for military veterans, reservists, emergency services personnel, and their families. The abstinence-based, 12-week recovery programme provides support via a bespoke model which aims to treat addiction within the context of those who have a history of military service – with emphasis placed on the role of co-occurring trauma, safety, confidentiality, and camaraderie, as well as reintegration into "civilian" communities.

The project is framed as a community of veterans who possess shared experiences, perspectives, resources and potential blocks to recovery, and who also share the ability to overcome their issues through a highly structured and intensive programme, and with the mutual support of the group. We work to help our veteran clients to make strides toward improving their mental, physical and emotional health, and to regain the sense of community and camaraderie that they had previously experienced during their active service.

http://www.tomharrisonhouse.org.uk/

info@tomharrisonhouse.org.uk

Fern Lea
Oak Hill Park
Liverpool
L13 4BP

0151 909 8481

Troop Aid
Troop Aid aims to Relieve Serving Personnel Of The Armed Forces, Injured In Situations Of Armed Conflict, In Particular But Not Exclusively In Afghanistan Who Are In Need By Reason Of Distress, Injury, Sickness, Disability Or Other Disadvantage, Through Such Charitable Means As The Trustees Think Fit

http://www.troopaid.info

troopaid@icloud.com

56 Rowlands Crescent
Solihull
B91 2JE

0121 711 7215

Turn to Starboard
Turn to Starboard uses sailing courses to support those affected by military operations.

http://www.turntostarboard.co.uk/

shaun@turntostarboard.co.uk

71 College Way
Gloweth
Truro
TR1 3RX

01326 314262

Veterans Aid
Caring for homeless veterans.

http://www.veterans-aid.net

info@veterans-aid.net

40 Buckingham Palace Road
Victoria
London
SW1W 0RE

0207 8282468

Veterans at Ease
Veterans at Ease aim to increase the mental health fitness levels by delivering 1:1 specialist psychotherapy to serving members of the Armed Forces, veterans and their immediate family members.

http://www.veteransatease.org

admin@veteransatease.org

Alington House
4 North Bailey
Durham
DH1 3ET

07584056181

Veterans In Action
VIA help veterans who have suffered the effects of war or who have found the transition to civilian life difficult.

http://www.veteransinaction.org.uk

info@veteransinaction.org.uk

The Old Grain Store
Redenham Park
Andover
SP11 9AQ

01264 771658

Veterans in Communities
Veterans In Communities (VIC) is an ex-services charity based in Rossendale, East Lancashire. VIC was established in September 2012 to support serving, ex-service personnel, their families and members of the uniformed services who have experienced difficulties with transitioning back into the community on leaving the services.

http://www.veteransincommunities.org

info@veteransincommunities.org

Veterans In Communities
12 Bury Road
Haslingden
BB4 5PL

01706 833180

Veterans' Gateway
What is the Veterans' Gateway?

In November 2016, the Ministry of Defence announced £2 million of funding from the Armed Forces Covenant Fund for a one-stop service to better support British Armed Forces veterans in need. The service responds to calls from veterans' charities and groups for help in navigating the wide range of services and organisations set up to support those who have served in the Forces.

The service will be the first point of contact for veterans and their families to access information, advice and support on a range of issues including healthcare, housing, and employment. It will allow information and services from partners to be accessed from one place and all enquiries will be followed up to ensure that veterans receive the right support.

The Veterans' Gateway will provide website, online chat, phone line and text message services available to any veteran, from anywhere in the world, 24 hours a day. Veterans can access face-to-face support through the Veterans' Gateway network of partners and organisations across the UK and overseas.

More than 2,000 charitable groups currently offer help to veterans, but they can prove difficult to navigate. By having a first point of contact, the Veterans' Gateway team will be able to quickly work out which of the partners is best placed to help with the information, advice and support required.

A consortium of military charities including The Royal British Legion, Poppyscotland, SSAFA, and Combat Stress, and service provider Connect Assist is managing the contact centre. A wider group of referral partners from military and other charity sectors have currently signed up to be a part of the Veterans' Gateway. This means that the service will offer advice and support on a broad range of issues and from a multitude of providers.

www.veteransgateway.org.uk

Phone: 0808 802 1212

Veterans Outreach Support
Veterans Outreach Support provides welcoming and relaxed places where UK veterans and family members can come for confidential social or psychological support, or simply to meet for a chat and a cuppa. Former members of British Armed Forces and Reserves, the Royal Fleet Auxiliary and the Merchant Navy are all welcome. Drop-in centres are normally open once a month: follow the link to their website for more details.

http://www.vosuk.org

admin@vosuk.org

The Royal Maritime Club
75-80 Queen Street
Portsmouth
PO1 3HS

02392 731 767

Veterans Scotland
Veterans Scotland is concerned with enhancing the welfare and well-being of the veterans community in Scotland by encouraging cooperation and coordination between the ex-service charities in Scotland; engaging where appropriate with the UK and Scottish governments on matters relating to veterans affairs and acting as a point of contact for government and other agencies for all matters relating to veterans policy.

http://www.veteransscotland.co.uk

info@veteransscotland.org.uk

New Haig House
Logie Green Road
Edinburgh
EH7 4HR

0131 550 1569

Veterans' Foundation
The Veterans' Foundation gives grants to organisations that support serving and former members of the armed forces, and their dependents, who are in need.

enquiries@veteransfoundation.org.uk

5 South Charlotte Street
Edinburgh
EH2 4AN

COURAGE AFTER THE BATTLE

07878 349394

Veterans UK helpline

Veterans Aid
http://veterans-aid.net (Info@veterans-aid.net)

Veterans Council
https://www.veteranscouncil.org.uk

Veterans in a crisis (Urgent Help)
https://www.gov.uk/government/publications/urgent-help-for-veterans-in-a-crisis

Veterans Employment Transition Support Programme –
https://www.veteranemployment.co.uk/

Veterans UK, Ministry of Defence , Norcross, Thornton Cleveleys, FY5 3WP

Email veterans-uk@mod.uk

A guide to the Veterans Welfare Service
https://www.gov.uk/government/publications/a-guide-to-the-veterans-welfare-service

https://www.gov.uk/government/publications/a-guide-to-veterans-services

Walking With The Wounded
Walking With The Wounded supports veterans with physical, mental or social injuries on their journey to reintegrate back into society, regain their independence and secure sustainable employment.

http://walkingwiththewounded.org.uk

info@wwtw.org.uk

Stody Hall Barns
Stody
Melton Constable
NR24 2ED

01263 863900

War Widows Association of GB
War Widows Association of GB is a group wishing to improve the conditions of War Widows and their dependants, petitioning for improvements in pensions, benefits and other issues.

http://www.warwidows.org.uk/

info@warwidows.org.uk

199 Borough High Street
London
SE1 1AA

0845 2412 189

Welfare Support Organisations

Royal Navy and Royal Marines Welfare
https://wwwroyalnavy.mod.uk/welfare/resurces/welfare-support/welfare-team

Army Welfare Services
https://www.army.mod.uk/welfare-support/welfare-support.aspx

Specific Information can be found at
https://army.mod.uk/welfare-support/23199.aspx

RAF - SAAFA Support
https://www.saafa.org.uk/how-we-help/health-and-social-work/social-work-services-in-the-uk/

Wings for Warriors

Wings for Warriors aims to facilitate the transition of veterans affected by injury or illness into sustainable careers in aviation.

http://www.wings4warriors.org.uk

info@wings4warriors.org.uk

42 Admirals House
Gisors Road
Southsea
PO4 8GX

07760 154074

Winston's Wish

Winston's Wish is a leading childhood bereavement charity in the UK. We support families when someone important has died and have been working with bereaved children and their families since 1992. Winston's Wish offers specialist support to children, young people and families who have been bereaved through the military. This work is funded by the service charity Help for Heroes.

http://www.winstonswish.org.uk/

info@winstonswish.org.uk

3rd Floor
Cheltenham House
Clarence Street, CheltenhamGL50 3JR

01242 515157

X-Forces

X-Forces supports ex-forces and their families to start-up businesses across the UK by start-up loans, mentoring, training and support. X-Forces work directly with various military charities to deliver enterprise training through business planning programmes to the military community. These programmes help those who are interested in setting up their own business reach out for the tools and knowledge they require.

http://www.x-forces.com

info@x-forces.com

Mountbarrow House
6-20 Elizabeth Street
London
SW1W 9RB

0800 307 7545

BIBLIOGRAPHY

3D bespoke Prosthetics – www.teamunlimbited.org

3 Commando Brigade in the Falklands – No Picnic- Julian Thompson

10 Surprising Connections Between Veterans Day and Blindness – www.Perkins.org

10 things no one tells you before you lose a limb, by a Royal Marine – Mark Time

7,000 Soldiers Left to Rot on Our Streets – www.veteransassociationuk.co.uk

A Better Deal for Military Amputees – Andrew Murrison MD MP – www.Gov.UK

A guide to the Joint Casualty and Compassionate Centre - https://www.gov.uk/government/publications/a-guide-to-the-joint-casualty-and-compassionate-centre

A Heavy Reckoning – Emily Mayhew – Welcome Collection / Profile Books

A History of Prosthetics and Amputation Surgery – www.Prosthetics.Org.Uk

A Wallasey First The Guide Dogs For The Blind Association - http://www.historyofwallasey.co.uk/wallasey/Guide_Dogs_For_The_Blind/index.html

AA and the Armed Services Leaflet – Alcoholics Anonymous

Aftershock – Matthew Green – Portobello Books

Al Sweady Inquiry (Summary) www.Gov.UK

All Wales Military Prosthetics Working Group – Improved Prosthetic Services for Military Veterans – www.Gov.UK

Armed Forces Act 2011 – www.Gov.uk

Armed Forces and Reserve Forces Compensation Scheme Order (AFCS) 2011 in Force from 6 April 2015 to 30 May 2016 – www.Gov.uk

Armed Forces Compensation Scheme – House of Commons Briefing Paper March 2017

Armed Forces Compensation Scheme Biannual Statistics 6 April to 30 September 2016 (Published 2 June 2016) – Ministry of Defence

Armed Forces Compensation Scheme Biannual Statistics 6 April to 30 September 2016 (Published 8 December 2016) – Ministry of Defence

Armed Forces Compensation Scheme Consultation Document 2013

Armed Forces Compensation Scheme The Facts – www.actiononhearingloss.org.uk

Armed Forces Compensation Scheme What You Need to Know – www.Gov.uk

Armed Forces Covenant - https://www.gov.uk/government/uploads/system/uploads/attachment_data/file/578212/20161215-The-Armed-Forces-Covenant.pdf

Army Elite Sports Programme - http://armysportcontrolboard.org/army_elite/army_elite_sport_launch.html

Battle Back Programme - https://www.gov.uk/guidance/the-battle-back-programme

Battlefield Casualty Aide Memoire Army Code 71638 – www.Gov.uk

Blast Force - The Invisible War on the Brain - Caroline Alexander - January 2015
http://www.nationalgeographic.com/healing-soldiers/blast-force.html

BLESMA Amputation Explained - https://blesma.org/about-us/

BLESMA NHS Limb Service and Prosthetic information - https://blesma.org/about-us/

BLESMA Phantom Limb Pain - https://blesma.org/about-us/

BLESMA Stump Care - https://blesma.org/about-us/

Bloody Sunday Enquiry – The Rt Hon Lord Saville of Newdigate

British Army captain Dave Henson looking to honour his fallen colleagues on the road to Rio Paralympics - http://www.telegraph.co.uk/sport/olympics/paralympic-sport/11946046/British-Army-captain-Dave-Henson-looking-to-honour-his-fallen-colleagues-on-the-road-to-Rio-Paralympics.html

Build Force Mentor Pack – www.buildforce.co.uk

Business in The Community _Capitalising on Military Talent WWW.BITC.org

Care of the Combat Amputee Progressive Management –
US Military Department of Defence, US Army, Borden Institute, Surgeon General

COURAGE AFTER THE BATTLE

Civvy Futures – www.Civvyfutures.Org

Combat Stress - http://www.combatstress.org.uk/

D-Day – Minute by Minute – Jonathan Mayo – Short Books 2014

Deaths in the UK Regular Armed Forces: Annual Summary and Trends Over Time 1 January 2006 to December 2015 - Ministry of Defence

Defence Medical Research Services Rehabilitation Presentation – Michael Arnell

Doctor For Friend or Foe – Rick Jolly – Conway Books

Domestic Abuse – Getting help – www.Gov.UK

Domestic Abuse and the Public/Private Divide in the British Military – www.lse.ac.uk

Domestic Abuse Case Study (Army) – www.Gov.UK

Domestic Abuse Case Study (Foreign and Commonwealth) – www.Gov.UK

Domestic Abuse Case Study (RAF) – www.Gov.UK

Domestic Abuse Case Study (RN-RM) – www.Gov.UK

Domestic Abuse Common Concerns – www.Gov.UK

Domestic Abuse World Wide – www.Gov.UK

Elite Military Athletes – Help for Heroes – www.helpforheroes.org

Employment Guidance - https://www.ctp.org.uk/futurehorizons
(One of the many companies out there to assist you in finding employment)

Evolution of Prosthetics – Jay Patel University of Rhode Island
Treatment Protocol for High Velocity / High Energy Gunshot Injury to the Face - https://www.ncbi.nlm.nih.gov/pmc/articles/PMC3348750/

Ex-Service Men and Women Entering Criminal Justice System – www.Gov.uk

Financial Advice on what you will be faced with once leaving - https://www.moneyforce.org.uk/
(One of the many companies out there to assist you in finding your way through the plethora of bills and financial requirements of civvy street)

Future horizons - https://www.ctp.org.uk/futurehorizons

Gordon Taylor War Surgeon and Historian - Royal College of Surgeons 1974 Vol 5

Handbook for Civilian Support Services on Domestic Abuse – www.Gov.UK

Headley Court – www.thednrc.org.uk

High Cost of Healthcare for UK Military Amputees – www.Imperial.ac.uk

Honourable Warriors – Richard Streatfeild – Pen and Sword

Horse thinking – http://www.horsethinking.co.uk/

Horseback UK - http://www.horseback.org.uk/

House of Commons Briefing Paper – Statutory Homelessness in England March 2017 – www.Gov.UK

House of Commons Paper on Social Care and Military Compensation – Hansard 25 March 2015 Vol 594 - https://hansard.parliament.uk/Commons/2015-03-25/debates/150325101000003/SocialCareAndMilitaryCompensation

How Common is Domestic Abuse – www.womansaid.org.uk

International Paralympic Committee – Explanatory notes to Paralympic Classification – Paralympic Winter Sports – www.paralympic.org (classification@paralympic.org)

International Paralympic Committee – Explanatory notes to Paralympic Classification – Paralympic Summer Sports – www.paralympic.org (classification@paralympic.org)

Joint Service Housing Advice Office (JSHAO) - RC-AWS-JSHAO-0Mailbox@mod.uk

Libya and Mali Operations transatlantic Lessons Learned www.Gov.UK

Life Force – Hull and East Riding – A practical Guide for Working With Military Veterans

Literary Review – UK Veterans and homelessness – http://www.britishlegion.org.uk

Liverpool Veterans HQ - http://www.liverpoolveterans.co.uk/

Long Term Responses to Treatment in UK Veterans to Military Related PTSD – www.bmjopen.bmj.com

Management of Major Limb Injuries – Vijay Langer - The Scientific World Journal January 2014

Mark Ormrod - http://www.markormrod.com/about-mark/

Marmaduke Sheild. Treatment of the Main Nerves in Amputations. - The Lancet. 1916; 188: 342–343

Marmaduke Sheild. Some Practical Observations on the Injuries of War. - The Lancet. 1916; 188: 1003–1005 -

Marmaduke Sheild - Letters of reply (p309) - The Lancet August 26 1916

Military Amputees to get Bionic Leg – WWW.Gov.UK

Moneyforce (Financial advice website) - https://www.moneyforce.org.uk/

National Statistics Notice – Deaths in the UK Regular Armed Forces 2013 – www.Gov.uk

Merseycare NHS trust – PTSD (Supporting You) www.merseycare.nhs.uk

New Hope for Soldiers Disfigured in War - Discovery Magazine Science for the Curious
http://discovermagazine.com/2014/sept/11-face-of-hope

On Afghanistan's Plains - Barry Alexander - CreateSpace Independent Publishing

Operations In Afghanistan 4th report Session 2010-12 Vol 1 & 2 www.Gov.UK

Operations in Libya 9th report session 2010-12 Vol 1 & 2 www.Gov.UK

Our Community Our Covenant (Aug 2016) - http://www.fim-trust.org/wp-content/uploads/2016/08/Our-Community-Our-Covenant-Report-30.08.16.pdf

Painting The Sand – Kim Hughes GC – Simon Schuster

Paralympics Offers Life After Trauma for Wounded Veterans - https://www.theguardian.com/sport/2012/aug/23/paralympians-british-military-rehabilitation

Pension Trends 2005 (Chapter 1 Pensions Legislation: An Overview) – Office for National Statistics / Palgrave Macmillan

Post-Traumatic Stress Disorder – Key facts – www.rcpsych.ac.uk
Post Traumatic Stress – Support For you – Mersey Care NHS trust /

COURAGE AFTER THE BATTLE

CivvyFutures – www.merseycare.nhs.uk / www.civvyfutures.org

PTSD Recovery to Overcome the Pain and Start Living Again – David Walker

Recovery Centre Services - http://www.army.mod.uk/welfare-support/23815.aspx

Rough Sleeping – www.crisis.org.uk

Row to Recovery – Sam Peters - Vision Sports Publishing

Royal Army Medical Corps Archives (First World War)

March 1915 volume 24-3
New pattern stretcher

Apparatus for unloading of sick from hospital ships etc

September 1915 volume 25-3
Chair stretcher

January 2016 volume 26-1
The treatment of concussion blindness

February 1916 volume 26-2
The Bradshaw lecture on wounds in war

May 1916 volume 26-5
The treatment of gunshot injuries of the jaw

Contributions to the study of shell shock being an account of certain cases treated by hypnosis

June 1916 volume 26-6
Contributions of the study of shell shock (iii) being an account of certain disorders of cutaneous sensibility

COURAGE AFTER THE BATTLE

July 2016 volume 27-1
Malingering – examination of the upper extremities

August 2016 volume 27-2
The rate of mortality in the British armed forces 100 years ago

Severe tetanoid spasm limited to the wounded limb

October 1916 volume 27-4
Treatment of wounds in war by magnesium sulphate

November 1916 volume 27-5
A note upon the employment of blood transfusion in war surgery

Hearing in the army

May 1917 volume 28-5
Shell shock and its treatment by cerebrospinal galvanism

Mechano-therapy at the Croydon war hospital

August 1917 volume 29-2
Shell shock, stammering and other affections of voice and speech

December 1917 volume 29-6
Adaptation of the Miller-James stretcher carrier for trench work

March 1918 volume 30-3
Improvised amputation shield

May 1918 volume 30-5
The technique of amputation, particularly the treatment of nerves

August 1918 volume 31-2
Recent developments in Royal Army Medical Corps front line education

Royal Army Medical Corps Archives (Second World War)

September 1940 volume 75-3
Practical Hints on the Treatment of War Injuries in Forward Areas

July 1941 volume 77-1
Burns in Wartime

Treatment of Burns in Wartime

June 1943 volume 80-6
Army Medical Services in Action

December 1944 volume 83-5
Infection in War Wounds

January 1945 volume 84-1
Effects of Heat in Iraq

February 1945 volume 84-2
Psychiatric Aspects of Rehabilitation

May 1945 volume 84-5
Medical Aspects of Air Landing Operations in the East

October 1945 volume 85-4
Notes on Air Evacuation

December 1945 volume 85-6
Surgical Advances During the War

Royal Army Medical Corps Archives (Korea - June 50–July 53)

December 1950 volume 95-6
History of the Royal Army Medical College

February 1951 volume 96-2
The Promotion and Maintenance of Mental Health in the Military Community

March 1951 volume 96-3
The Investigation of Load-Carrying in the Army

Soldiers' Loads

October 1951 volume 97-4
Impressions on the Use of "Antabuse" in the Treatment of Alcoholism in the Army

Service leavers guide - https://www.gov.uk/government/publications/service-leavers-pack

Shell shock at Queen Square: Lewis Yealland 100 years on – Oxford University Press
https://www.ncbi.nlm.nih.gov/pmc/articles/PMC3673538/

'Shell Shock'—The 100-Year Mystery May Now Be Solved – Caroline Alexander – June 2016
http://news.nationalgeographic.com/2016/06/blast-shock-tbi-ptsd-ied-shell-shock-world-war-one/

Sixth Sense Michael (Iddy) Iddon - WWW.Gov.UK

Solicitors Regulatory Authority- v-Philip Joseph Shiner - Solicitors Disciplinary Tribunal

SPACES - https://www.riverside.org.uk/care-and-support/veterans/spaces/

SSAFA – New frontline vets in need - www.ssafa.org.uk

Standing Tall – Andy Reid - John Blake Publishing

Stories From the War Hospital – Richard Wilcocks – Meerkat Publications Ltd

Support for Single Homeless People in England Annual Review 2015 – www.Homelesslink.org

Support for Single Homeless People in England Annual Review 2016 – www.Homelesslink.org

Synopsis of Causation – Acute and Chronic Soft Tissue Injury of the Lower Limb – www.Gov.UK

Synopsis of Causation – Compartment Syndrome – www.Gov.UK

Synopsis of Causation – Schizophrenia – www.Gov.UK

Synopsis of Causation –Personality Disorder – www.Gov.UK

Tackling Homelessness and Exclusion – Understanding Complex Lives – Joseph Roundtree Foundation

Talking Sense – Deaf Blind War Veterans – www.sense.org.uk

The Impact of Domestic Abuse on Children and Young People – www.womansaid.ork.uk

The Last Ambush – Aspects of mental health in the British Armed Forces - ForcesWatch

The Medical History of the First World War - Major General Sir William Grant Macpherson KCMG, CB (1858 - October 1927).

The Mental Health of the UK Armed Forces Where Fact Meets Fiction – www.ncbi.nlm.nih.gov

The Mental Health of Serving and Ex-Service personnel – Forces in Mind Trust (FiMT)

The Nature and Impact of Domestic Abuse – www.womansaid.org.uk

The Needs of Ex-Service Personnel in the Criminal Justice System: A rapid Assessment – Ministry of Justice 2014

The Poor Bastards Club – SSG Paul Mehlos -

The Veterans Transition Review – Lord Ashcroft KCMG PC

Treatment of the Main Nerves in Amputation – The British Medical Journal August 26th 1916 Page 309

Treatment of Wounds – A historical review - https://www.ncbi.nlm.nih.gov/pmc/articles/PMC2706344/

Treatment Protocol for High Velocity / High Energy Gunshot Injury to the Face - https://www.ncbi.nlm.nih.gov/pmc/articles/PMC3348750/

UK Armed Forces Charities – An Overview and analysis – Directory of Social Change in Conjunction with COBSEO, Forces in Mind Trust (FiMT) and National Lottery

Urgent help for veterans in a crisis - https://www.gov.uk/government/publications/urgent-help-for-veterans-in-a-crisis

Various articles on related matter which have been acknowledged where used - The Daily Mail Newspaper http://www.dailymail.co.uk/home/index.html

Various articles on related matter which have been acknowledged where used - The Guardian Newspaper https://www.theguardian.com/uk

Various articles on related matter which have been acknowledged where used - The Independent Newspaper http://www.independent.co.uk/

Various articles on related matter which have been acknowledged where used - The Telegraph Newspaper http://www.telegraph.co.uk/

Veterans Access to Work – Deloitte LLP / FiMT

Veterans UK helpline, Veterans UK, Ministry of Defence, Norcross, Thornton Cleveleys, FY5 3WP

COURAGE AFTER THE BATTLE

Email veterans-uk@mod.uk

Veterans Employment Transition Support Programme - https://www.veteranemployment.co.uk/

War Widows Association – http://www.warwidows.org.uk/

War Wounds – Edited by Ashley Ekins / Elizabeth Stewart – Excise Publishing (Australia)

We Were Warriors: One Soldier's Story of Brutal Combat - Johnny Mercer - Sidgwick & Jackson

What are the Consequences of Deployment to Iraq and Afghanistan on the Mental Health of UK Armed Forces? A Cohort Study – The Lancet Vol 375 May 2010

What Causes Homelessness? – www.england-shelter.org.uk

What Explains Post Traumatic Stress Disorder (PTSD) in UK service Personnel: Deployment of Something Else – Cambridge University Press - Psychological Medicine

WORLD WAR I: 100 YEARS LATER - Faces of War
Caroline Alexander - http://www.smithsonianmag.com/history/faces-of-war-145799854/

WORLD WAR I: 100 YEARS LATER – Shell Shock
Caroline Alexander - http://www.smithsonianmag.com/history/the-shock-of-war-55376701/

WORLD WAR I: 100 YEARS LATER - The Shock of War– Caroline Alexander – September 2010
http://www.smithsonianmag.com/history/the-shock-of-war-55376701/

Overseas Military Sites

America

https://obamawhitehouse.archives.gov/blog/2013/09/25/blackstone-group-hosts-inaugural-veterans-hiring-summit

https://www.va.gov/

Canada

http://www.veterans.gc.ca/eng

http://truepatriotlove.com/